DAWN

A Complete Account
of the Most Important Day
in Human History

Nisan 18, AD 30

Mark Miller

good turn
PUBLISHING

DAWN

*A Complete Account of the Most Important
Day in Human History: Nisan 18, AD 30*

Good Turn Publishing
www.goodturnpublishing.com

Good Turn Publishing books may be purchased in bulk at
special discounts. All inquiries should be addressed to
inquiry@goodturnpublishing.com.

Feedback to the publisher or author should be addressed to
feedback@goodturnpublishing.com.

ISBN 13 TP: 978-0-9794393-1-5
ISBN 13 eBook: 978-0-9794393-2-2

Published January 2023

Cover photo credit: Vivian Vedder. Used by permission.
Tomb illustration credit: Amy Avery Smith; © Good Turn
    Publishing.

To my wife Valeta

Friend and fellow traveler
On the Emmaus Road

"And God said,
Let there be Light."
Gen 1:3

"In Him was life,
And the life was the Light of men.
The Light shines in the darkness,
And the darkness did not comprehend it."
John 1:2-3

The Light shines still.
Always has, always will.

CONTENTS

THE CHARACTERS - A BRIEF SKETCH

The story of the resurrection involves quite a few key characters, whose names may or may not be familiar to you. Even for readers who are familiar with the written accounts, keeping track of the individuals can be challenging because of name duplication (several Jameses and several Marys, for example), and multiple appellations given to single individuals.

So, here is a list of the names of the historical characters connected to the resurrection, with brief descriptions. A more detailed look at each person is provided in Part Three. The names in the following list are used consistently throughout the resurrection accounts in this book to uniquely identify each one and thus minimize confusion. For example, Peter (who was also known as Simon) is consistently identified as Peter to avoid confusion with Simon the Zealot.

The Family

1. *Jesus* likely needs no introduction. He was the long-awaited Messiah, born in Bethlehem but raised in Nazareth. His parents were Joseph the carpenter and Mother Mary.

2. *Mother Mary* was the mother of Jesus. She is identified throughout the book as "Mother Mary" solely to avoid using the longer phrase—"Mary, the mother of Jesus." Her husband Joseph was deceased by the time of these events.

3. *Clopas,* a brother of Joseph the carpenter, and thus uncle to Jesus, was a follower of Jesus. Clopas was married to a woman named Mary.

4. *Mary Clopas* was Clopas' wife and also a follower of Jesus. Clopas and Mary were parents of James the Younger, the lesser-known of the two disciples named James.

5. *Salome,* Mother Mary's sister and thus Jesus' aunt, was the wife of Zebedee, and mother of the disciples James Zebedee

and John.

6. *Zebedee* was the husband of Salome and father of the disciples James Zebedee and John.

7. *James bar Joseph* was the son of Joseph the Carpenter and Mother Mary, and was the brother of Jesus.[1] He is identified as "bar Joseph" to distinguish him from the other Jameses in the story.

The Disciples

8. *John* was one of the twelve disciples, and the only one of the Twelve present at Jesus' death. He was the son of Zebedee and Salome, and brother to James Zebedee.

9. *Peter* was the most prominent of the twelve disciples who, along with John, witnessed the trial and condemnation of Jesus.

10. Nine of the original twelve disciples—namely, *Andrew* (Peter's brother), *James Zebedee* (or, *the older James*; John's brother), *Philip, Nathanael, Matthew, Thomas, James the Younger* (son of Clopas and Mary), *Thaddaeus, and Simon the Zealot*—fled to Bethany after Jesus' arrest.

Other Followers of Jesus

11. *Lazarus* lived in Bethany (near Jerusalem) with his two adult sisters. Lazarus had died and been raised from death by Jesus not long before Jesus' crucifixion.

12. *Martha* was the sister of Lazarus and Mary (Magdalene).

13. *Mary Magdalene* was the first person to meet the risen Jesus, and is the same person as Mary of Bethany, the sister of Martha and Lazarus. Identifying these two Marys as the same individual is somewhat controversial, yet, in this author's opinion, fully justified. (A full explanation follows in Part Three.)

---

[1] To be precise, Jesus and James were half-brothers because Jesus was not descended physically from Joseph. However, throughout this book James will be referred to simply as the brother of Jesus to better capture their relationship in this close-knit family.

14. *Joanna* was another follower of Jesus. She was a woman of wealth and position, the wife of Chuza, who was the steward of Herod Antipas,[2] tetrarch (that is, ruler) of Galilee and Perea.

15. *Susanna* was, like Joanna, a woman of means who followed Jesus in Galilee.

16. *Joseph of Arimathea* was the man who buried Jesus.

17. *Nicodemus* assisted Joseph of Arimathea in the preparation and interment of Jesus' body.

18. *Mark,* also known as John Mark, was a young man who lived at the large house of the upper room (the location of Jesus' Last Supper) with his mother.

19. *Mariam* was the mother of Mark and matriarch of the upper room house.[3]

The Enemies of Jesus

20. *Judas,* one of the original twelve disciples, had betrayed Jesus to his enemies and was gone before this account opens.

21. *Annas* was a former high priest, deposed by the Romans in AD 6, yet still exercising considerable influence behind the scenes.

22. *Caiaphas*, the Jewish high priest, was the primary advocate for killing Jesus.

23. *Herod Antipas* was the Roman appointed ruler of Galilee and Perea.

24. *Pontius Pilate* was the Roman appointed ruler of Judea who sentenced Jesus to death by crucifixion.

---

[2] Herod Antipas was the son of Herod I, (sometimes called Herod the Great), the cruel and despotic king of Palestine who infamously slaughtered the children of Bethlehem. Herod I died about 1 BC.

[3] Mariam's name is transliterated from Greek. It is the same name in Greek as the other Marys, but is not anglicized here to avoid having one more Mary to contend with.

MAPS

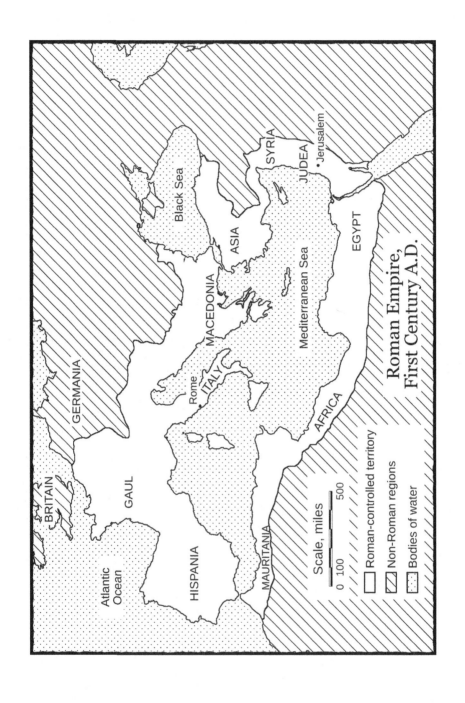

**Roman Empire,
First Century A.D.**

Scale, miles

0   100   500

☐ Roman-controlled territory

▨ Non-Roman regions

⸭ Bodies of water

BRITAIN

GERMANIA

GAUL

Atlantic
Ocean

HISPANIA

MAURITANIA

AFRICA

Rome

ITALY

MACEDONIA

ASIA

Black Sea

Mediterranean Sea

SYRIA

JUDEA

•Jerusalem

EGYPT

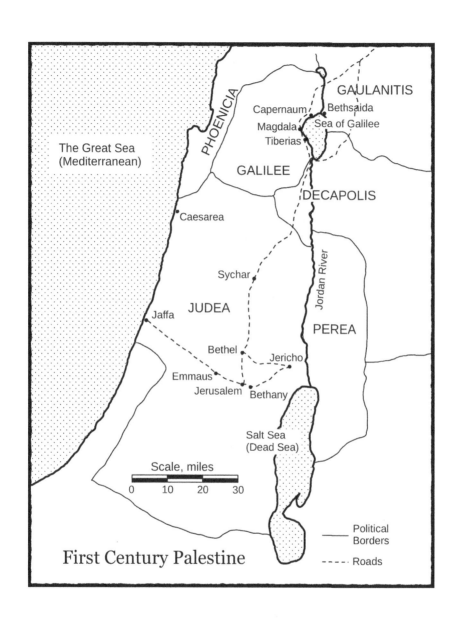

First Century Palestine

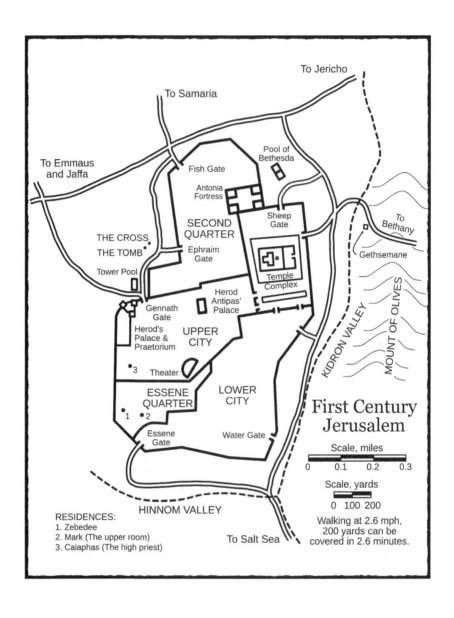

First Century Jerusalem

PREFACE

Some years ago, shortly after I converted from agnosticism to Christianity, a fellow insisted to me that Jesus was not crucified on a Friday as is traditionally accepted, but rather on a Thursday, and that this detail was of great importance.

His argument was based on Jesus' prophecy in Matthew 12:40 that "...the Son of Man will be three days and three nights in the heart of the earth." (The "Son of Man" is a phrase Jesus applied to himself, and "heart of the earth" is another way of saying "the grave.")

While I recognized that it would be easier (in light of that verse) to justify a view of Thursday rather than Friday for the time of Jesus' death, I didn't personally feel that this distinction was of any great significance. At the time, it was sufficient to me to believe that Jesus had been crucified and resurrected; the fact that the traditional day accepted for this event didn't seem to align perfectly with a given verse was a minor detail I could, perhaps, wrestle with later.

Thus, I placed that question in a mental "shoebox," alongside other shoeboxed mysteries, on a mental shelf to be examined again later, time and interest permitting.[4]

About the same time—and unconnected to that conversation—I developed a desire to combine the four primary accounts of the resurrection event (from the gospel writers Matthew, Mark, Luke, and John) into a single, integrated, sequential account. That desire was stimulated by two observations: first, that the resurrection of Jesus is a matter of preeminent foundational importance to the entire fabric of Christianity and thus to every Christian, and second, that the four accounts read very differently.

This latter observation did not cause me any great consternation, as I understood that the accounts came from

---

[4] Hat tip to my friend Allan Reitz for the shoebox metaphor.

different observers and would reflect not just different points of view and different intended audiences, but also different opinions about which details were important.

Nevertheless, I felt that with an hour or two of work, I could "cut and paste" verses to produce an integrated account for my own satisfaction and enjoyment—ultimately, to paint a better picture for myself of that world-shaking event. In hindsight, I was naïve about the complexity of the task.

It has taken years to get to this project, and when I finally began in earnest, I first searched to see if someone else had already done the work and hopefully saved me a couple of hours, but without success. Now, having tackled the challenge, I've found that it was not a trivial task; rather, it became a piece of detective work with many elements.

To reasonably order the verses, I had to consider the physical layout and topography of Jerusalem and its environs; the laws, culture, customs, and feasts of the Jews; and a number of verses and sources outside of the primary four gospel records. In the process, the chronology of events of the week preceding the resurrection became very important, even to determine on which day of the week Jesus was crucified. (Remember, my intention initially was only to examine the resurrection, so the crucifixion was outside the scope of the project.)

And as this project grew from a personal study into this book, its value became more apparent to me. There emerged a genuine beauty in the way God brought all the pieces together of the actual event. Old Testament and New Testament prophecies came together in fulfillment.

Further, the personalities of the characters and their relationships came into focus. The emotions they must have felt became evident, enabling me to appreciate the events more vicariously and personally. For me, the resurrection transformed from a black-and-white news article to living color, and I hope this book will help you see the same colors.

But as for the particular day that Jesus died, well, it still isn't crucial to Christian faith or doctrine, but should you want to know in advance, I believe it was a Wednesday, in the year AD

30, at 3:00 p.m. Very significantly, it occurred on the day of the Jewish calendar called Nisan 14, otherwise known as the day of preparation for the Passover feast.

Significantly too, it was 40 years to the *very day* before the Roman general Titus surrounded the city of Jerusalem with 60,000 soldiers to destroy it.

ACKNOWLEDGEMENTS

One of the most significant resources for this book was John Wenham's book, *Easter Enigma* (Wipf & Stock, 1992). It provided a number of important insights, especially his thoughts on the relationships between some of the key people involved, and their movements around the city of Jerusalem. While I came to different conclusions on the chronology of several events, nevertheless I would highly recommend this book to anyone interested in further reading.

Although The Unified Account (Part Two of the book) is my own interpretation, compilation and translation of Scripture verses to create an integrated narrative of the events surrounding and including the resurrection, yet the construction of this material was guided and influenced by numerous non-paraphrased English translations to which I am indebted. Other inputs included various Greek language tools and commentaries. Therefore, the resulting Unified Account is my own work, as are any mistakes therein. However, I feel enormous gratitude to the many, many people who contributed directly or indirectly to the creation of these and other resources. I should say also that Part Two is, by nature, somewhat speculative and is not being proposed as a substitute for the original scriptural texts.

Also I wish to heartily thank my editor Bonnie Smith for proofreading the manuscript and providing many helpful comments. I take responsibility for any remaining errors.

Lastly, I wish to thank God, who conceived the plan of redemption long before its fulfillment. In him, as Paul wrote, we "live and move and have our being," and I thank him for putting in my heart the desire to combine the resurrection accounts into one.

INTRODUCTION

The resurrection of Jesus Christ: it either happened, or it didn't. If it did, it is the most important day in all of human history by a large margin. If it is true, the resurrection is also the most important day in *your* life as well, regardless of who you are, regardless of your awareness of it or your beliefs.

If it didn't happen, then it's just a sad hoax.

If it did not happen, I doubt you ever would have heard the names of Jesus, Peter, Paul, or any of the other various persons associated with the accounts recorded in the book we call the New Testament (NT). These names are common in the Western world only because they were recorded in the NT, and the NT exists only because of the resurrection. If the resurrection had not happened, the merry band of Jesus fans would have gone back to their vocational pursuits and the story of Jesus' crucifixion would have been lost to history. None of these names would have persisted.

There were others in first-century Judea who made messianic claims about themselves, then died, and we know nothing about them, save their names. Like Judas of Galilee. (Not the Judas who betrayed Jesus; that Judas was from Judea.) Or like Theudas. Both of these men gathered followers and died, and their followers were dispersed. But wait—how do we happen to know their names? Because they are recorded in the 5th chapter of the book of Acts in the NT. But for the resurrection of Jesus, even their names might not be known.

The Romans were not restrained in the area of capital punishment. Crucifixion was commonly applied for the worst offenders and especially, for insurrectionists. As it happened, they had a plenteous supply of both, and so they crucified large numbers of individuals over the centuries of empire. Yet despite so many people being crucified, very few names of the executed are known today. And exactly one crucified person's remains have been discovered—those of Jehohanan, whose bones were found in an ossuary inscribed with his name in Jerusalem in 1968. He, like Jesus, was also crucified in the first century. If Jehohanan had followers, they left no records. Fortunately for us, though, Jehohanan's bones, and particularly the nail through his foot bones, have given us some insight into the details of a crucifixion that are not covered in ancient textual sources.

So, is the resurrection an actual historical event or a hoax? There are already numerous books available that examine this question, so that question is not explored here—although I will say in passing that the principle objection to the resurrection is that it is *supernatural*, and I think it foolish to disregard something with so much attestation for that reason alone.

If you wish to research in depth the question of the resurrection's historicity, I would recommend journalist Lee Strobel's book, *A Case for Christ*. In this present book, however, the resurrection is taken to be a reality.

It is relevant nonetheless, that those who discount the historicity of the resurrection have sometimes pointed to the divergence of the four accounts in the first four books of the NT and asserted that they cannot be reconciled—that is, brought together without conflicts. This is not the case; these four accounts are completely "reconciled" (I prefer *unified*) here in this book, with a detailed explanation provided.

This book has three main divisions, or parts. Part One is titled "Dawn," an eponym from the book's title. This version of the account is fleshed out, as I envision it, with dialogue and additional details as historically accurate as my research and conjecture have been able to shape it. It is, if you will, a "colorized" or more three-dimensional version as I imagine it might have happened. Someone might describe it as "historical fiction," but I feel such a descriptor is misleading, as "Dawn" adheres completely to the historical foundation, and all added color is as true to the situations, culture, and norms as possible. I have deliberately avoided Hollywood-esque distortions; you will find no mention here of climate change, for example, and no sizzling romances, alas.

Part Two is the Unified Account of the resurrection—my

original goal that morphed into the larger book. In it, all the biblical verses related to the resurrection are merged, with a handful of additional words to smooth transitions. This version has no "color" added to the story, and all commentary is contained in footnotes.

Part Three is the Explanation of the Unified Account. Here, the details, reasoning, and sources behind the entire book are laid out in all their granularity. Despite the level of detail, this part of the book contains too much interesting material to relegate it to an appendix.

Finally, the Epilogue discusses why the resurrection is so important to every individual and to Christians in particular.

DAWN

Anno Domini 30

PART ONE

DAWN - THE STORY

DAWN

Introduction to Part One

Dawn. Daybreak. Sunrise. Every dawn is the start of a new day. But over 2,000 years ago, one particular dawn was so much more—it was the start of a new epoch for humanity, for every man, woman, and child who has ever lived, or ever will. Before that day, mankind lived in nearly complete spiritual darkness, given only glimmers of hope for something better, delivered in enigmatic passages by ancient Jewish prophets. They had spoken of a Promised One, a Messiah, to arise from the lineage of King David, who would set people free from the darkness of their souls.

The prophet Isaiah prophesied of him some 700 years before his birth:

> "The people who walk in darkness will see a great light;
> Those who live in a dark land, the light will shine on them."

And so it was that, after three years of walking with him, the disciples of Jesus came to recognize him as that prophesied great light—that is, the promised Messiah.

Yet dark forces arose against Jesus, and from an unexpected source: Jewish religious leaders, motivated by envy and greed, conspired to seek his death. Knowing they lacked the authority to legally effect an execution, they enlisted the power of the mighty Roman Empire by claiming Jesus was guilty of sedition. A brutal scourging followed, and a gruesome death, with Jesus nailed naked and bloody on a cross. An overwhelming darkness.

The spiritual darkness arrayed against the light was mirrored by the physical darkness covering the land, plunging it into night at noon, and continuing three hours until Jesus died.

Today, it seems hard to imagine the darkness felt by his followers, upon seeing him expire on the cross, or hearing the news shortly thereafter. It wasn't just that they had left everything to follow him; it was that he meant *everything* to them. He was holiness, peace, and joy. He was light and life. All of their hope was in him. He was their connection to God; every word he spoke was the Word of God, and he had been cut off from the earth. Insofar as they could see, darkness had triumphed, the Light had been extinguished forever and with it, all hope.

The physical darkness ended after Jesus passed away, and the sun shone again. But the darkness pressing upon his followers continued unrelenting, day after day.

Then came dawn, on Nisan 18, the first day of the week. As the sun broke over the Mount of Olives east of Jerusalem, five women found his tomb to be empty. Their first reaction was emotional anguish because they believed his body had been stolen, his remains desecrated.

Within the hour, however, all five of the women had met Jesus, *alive*, and their world turned right-side up again. The Light was back: stronger, and victorious over darkness and death. They were forever changed.

Dawn, the 18th of Nisan. The day when morning light broke the darkness forever. The moment when eternal life was first offered, freely, from nail-scarred hands. The most important day in human history by a large margin.

This is the story of that event. Join me as we travel back in time to another place far removed from the present era, but no less real.

Prologue to Part One: The Backstory

For as much as the twelve disciples of Jesus the rabbi had been attracted to him, they had also been equally perplexed by him. For nearly three years while he led them through the region of Galilee, Jesus had stretched their minds with his teaching, amazed them with his supernatural power, drawn their hearts with his love and compassion, and delighted them as he outwitted his opponents. And yet—he was a great enigma.

While Jesus had never claimed to be a prophet, he often spoke prophetically. He had never, to them, *directly* claimed to be the Messiah, but his character and miraculous works were so *messianic*. One thing was clear: he had come from God, for no one could have done the works Jesus did unless God was with him. But exactly who was he, and why had he come from God?

From their earliest days with Jesus, the Twelve had considered that Jesus might be the Messiah. Over time, that conjecture had turned into conviction. Yet in some important ways, he didn't fit their assumptions of what the Messiah—The One predicted by Moses and the Prophets—would look like. Their paradigm of the Messiah was at such variance with their experience of Jesus; he didn't remotely fit the popular Jewish concept of a conquering, political, priestly king. He obviously had no aspirations for political power. And although Jesus showed great respect for Jewish Scriptures, he did not hesitate to sharply criticize religious leaders. Regarding the hated Romans, from whom the Messiah was expected to deliver the nation, Jesus had virtually nothing to say. In fact, he had even healed the servant of a Roman officer!

In addition, he frequently spoke in parables and made cryptic statements. He once said, "Beware of the leaven of the Pharisees," at a time when they were short on bread. Sometimes, he explained himself privately to his disciples, but other times he left them unsure whether he was speaking literally or parabolically—and they were reluctant to ask him too many questions.

In the weeks leading up to the Passover, Jesus' statements had become more difficult to fathom than before, and he spoke repeatedly about his upcoming suffering and death, which raised troubling questions in their minds: How could the Messiah possibly die if his reign was supposed to be eternal, or, in the very least, before accomplishing his purpose of restoring Israel? That is, of course, if he truly had been speaking of his death. For when he had said, "Destroy this temple and in three days I will raise it up" (Jn 2:19), was he speaking figuratively of his own dying, of a literal destruction of the temple, or of something else entirely?

Less than a week before his arrest, Jesus had been hailed as a king by the people of Jerusalem as he entered the city on a colt. What an exciting time that was for the Twelve, as the people of the city seemed to capture the same vision of Jesus that the disciples held! But, immediately after, everything quickly turned sour.

In a perplexing move, Jesus provoked the already hostile Jewish leaders by driving the money-changers[5] out of the temple complex. And then, to a public crowd, he prophesied of his upcoming death. It was all troubling, but the disciples held out the hope that Jesus would somehow triumph, as he always had before when facing his adversaries, violent storms, incurable diseases, or demonized individuals. All he had needed to do was say a word, and all would be well.

But he never gave that word. When he had led his disciples to the garden of Gethsemane the previous night, and the traitor Judas had arrived with soldiers and the Jewish leaders, he

---

[5] The money-changers were profiteers that worked under the approval of the temple priests. The priests only accepted the half-shekel temple tax in the form of Tyrian shekels, rather than Roman coinage which was of lower silver content. The money-changers profited well from the exchange. Annual temple taxes have been estimated at about $150,000,000 USD equivalent.

assented to arrest and even rebuked Peter for offering armed resistance.

Among his last words in the garden were, "If you are looking for me, then let these men go" (Jn 18:8 NIV)—thus protecting his own followers, while willingly—*willingly*—submitting to arrest. It shouldn't have—couldn't have—ended this way. Every long-cherished idea of what the Messiah would do vanished in that moment. With Jesus in custody, the disciples fled in fear for their lives. The date was Nisan 14.

The road on which they ran away from Jerusalem led to Bethany, about two miles east of the city, and the eleven disciples headed that way under the light of a nearly full moon. Meanwhile, the arresting party led Jesus by torchlight down the hillside of the Mount of Olives and through the city gate located south of the temple complex into the city. Peter and John had second thoughts, reversed direction and followed the arresting party from a distance into the city, while the remaining nine disciples continued to Bethany—to the relative safety of their friends Lazarus and his sisters—Martha and Mary Magdalene.

The fears of the disciples were not irrational. The Jewish priests had, for some time, been maneuvering to execute Jesus. Lazarus also had become a target of the priests—since a miracle experienced by Lazarus influenced some Jews to begin following Jesus (Jn 12:10-11). If Lazarus was at risk, certainly the disciples and other associates of Jesus were in danger of being swept up in an extermination campaign.

Compounding their troubles, the disciples and followers of Jesus were physically separated from each other. Judas was gone, having betrayed them all. Peter and John were in Jerusalem, but their whereabouts and safety were unknown. The nine disciples were holed up at Lazarus' home in Bethany, but they were not beyond the reach of Jerusalem authorities. Some of the disciples had relatives who were in Jerusalem for the Passover. Communication between Jerusalem and Bethany was slow by today's standards. Although important news traveled quickly on well-oiled grapevines, it went by foot. And on Sabbaths, neither travelers nor news could reach Bethany, as

Bethany was beyond the "Sabbath day's journey" travel restriction of Jewish law—a limit of 2,000 cubits (or 1,000 yards).

In the early morning hours, Jesus was put on trial six times: first by the former high priest Annas, followed by the current high priest Caiaphas, the Sanhedrin,[6] Pilate, Herod Antipas, and Pilate a second time. None of these authorities found sufficient evidence for condemning Jesus to death. Even so, the hatred of the Jewish leaders toward him was so vitriolic that it overcame all Jewish and Roman legal and judicial restraints and forced Pilate to condemn him. It was a state-sanctioned lynching, through which Jesus was sentenced to die by crucifixion.

Peter, having denied knowing Jesus three times, and hearing that Jesus had been condemned, was emotionally shattered. He left to find refuge at the home of the upper room; this was the same home in which the disciples had shared their last supper with Jesus. The home belonged to a family with a son in his teens by the name of Mark, and who thought highly of Peter. It was located a city block away from the Jerusalem home of Zebedee, John's father.

Mark had known of Jesus' arrest, as he had been present when Jesus was seized in the garden of Gethsemane. When Peter arrived at his home to request sanctuary, Mark learned from Peter the news that Jesus had been condemned, and that John was following Jesus to see the outcome. Thus informed, Mark took the news immediately down the block to the home of Jesus' uncle Zebedee. In the home were Zebedee, his wife Salome, and extended family, including Mother Mary, Clopas and his wife Mary Clopas, and others, including children.

Mother Mary, her sister Salome, and her sister-in-law Mary Clopas immediately left the house and walked northward

---

[6] The Sanhedrin Council was essentially a senate combined with a supreme court. It was the governing body of Judea, although under the ultimate control and oversight of Rome. It governed both civic and religious affairs, which for the Jews were interwoven.

through the city streets to find Jesus and John.

They found John—and joined him along with other followers of Jesus who had heard about his arrest. They followed Jesus, the Roman soldiers, and the unruly mob from the Praetorium, where Pilate had issued the death sentence, out through the Gennath Gate to Golgotha. Golgotha was the name of the site used by the Romans for crucifixions. It was on a small rise, only a short distance outside the city wall, and about 800 cubits (400 yards) from the Praetorium. On quiet days, the cries of the condemned being nailed to crosses could be heard in the Praetorium. This particular day, however, was the preparation day for Passover, so the city bustled with activity, masking sounds from Golgotha.

As with all public executions, this one had drawn onlookers: the idle, the curious, the morbidly fascinated, and people connected to the condemned through friendship, family, or even animosity. The crowd on this day was particularly large for two reasons: the city was packed with feast-goers and Jesus was renowned throughout the land and popular among the common people.

The records state that Jesus was crucified at the third hour, i.e., around 9 a.m. At noon, the sky darkened and remained dark until Jesus died, around 3 p.m.

We begin the story at Lazarus' home in Bethany just one hour before Jesus dies on the cross.

Death at Mid-Afternoon

Bethany: A Comfortable Home about Two Miles East of Jerusalem
Nisan 14, AD 30, the Eighth Hour (Nearing 2 p.m.)

Though it was mid-afternoon, a deep and frightening darkness enveloped the entire land. Martha, standing in the courtyard outside of her home, was barely able to discern a man coming down the road, leading a donkey and a lamb. She quickly strode to the door, stepped inside the house, and closed the door behind her. She addressed her brother Lazarus, who was holding an oil lamp, together with the nine disciples of Jesus in the room.

"Our neighbor Shua is coming!" she blurted, with a mixture of concern and urgency.

"May he bring us good news," said Lazarus. The disciples instantly rose and quickly moved to an adjacent room, where they would be able to hear the news that Shua was bringing, without being seen.

Martha scurried to remove evidence of the other occupants as Lazarus began pacing back and forth.

As expected, there came a knock on the door. Lazarus quickly opened it with the lamp in his other hand.

"Shua," greeted Lazarus, "We have awaited you with such hope. Do you bring good news? Please come inside."

Shua continued to stand at the door, framed in the yellow glow of the lamp. He frowned and slowly shook his head in the negative.

"I'm sorry," said Shua, "It was the only thing people were talking about in the city. Your friend Jesus—I know he was a good man—our priests and leaders persuaded Pilate this morning that he must be killed. Pilate had him cruelly whipped, and he hangs on a cross as we speak. I'm so sorry."

Inside, the disciples silently glanced at each other, eyes wide.

Martha hugged her midsection and began to cry.

Shua started turning to go, then turned back, "Oh, and there were two other men crucified with Jesus. I was hoping to find out their names, but with the darkness..." Shua glanced up at the sky, "...such an ominous sign. So I was eager to purchase our Pesach lamb and get home quickly." Looking at the grief evident on Lazarus' face, Shua added, "I hate the Romans. May our Lord deliver us from them."

"Thank you for coming, Shua. You are a good friend," said Lazarus as Shua departed. Lazarus slowly turned to his sister.

Simon the Zealot whispered loudly, "Crucified!"

Thaddeus added, "With two others—Peter and John!"

The nine disciples returned to the entrance room, where Lazarus and Martha were in a hug of grief.

"What do we do now?" asked Matthew.

The disciples turned and looked at James Zebedee, the oldest among them.

"What else can we do right now but wait and pray?" replied James.

Lazarus addressed James, "I also asked another neighbor, Shimeath, to inquire after Jesus. And our sister Mary should be bringing us further news. Let's not abandon all hope."

"Hope," echoed Nathanael reflexively as a prayer, as a question, and with a note of despair.

Jerusalem: The Temple
The Eighth and a Half Hour (about 2:30 p.m.)

The daily afternoon sacrifice had just finished being offered on the enormous stone altar. Caiaphas and his father-in-law Annas stood side-by-side and adjacent to the raised platform of the altar, observing the great crowd as it slowly dispersed.

Caiaphas said, "I thought this darkness might keep some people away from the afternoon sacrifice, but attendance is equal to or greater than usual."

"It certainly has many very frightened," observed Annas. "But, where would they go for comfort and courage? To the temple, of course. I expect the offerings to be unaffected."

"Of course," returned Caiaphas. "Although, my comfort comes from knowing that the Galilean is on a cross. He was an elusive adversary. And I will give him this much praise—he was a clever schemer."

"It's good for you that one of his own led you to him," said Annas, a bit reproachfully.

Caiaphas didn't appreciate the obvious insult, implying that he never would have arrested Jesus without inside assistance. Even so, he ignored the barb and said, "It's good for the whole nation that the Galilean has no magic that enables him to come down off a cross."

Pressing his insult, Annas responded: "The nation owes a debt to Judas Iscariot. He redeemed himself by his action."

Though Caiaphas was annoyed, that was the end of the discussion. There were pressing exigencies and much to be done by both men over the next half hour in preparation for the great Passover offering ceremony.

Jerusalem: The Praetorium[7]
Approaching the Ninth Hour (about 3 p.m.)

Darkness had fallen over the entire land about midday. The disk of the sun was barely visible in the cloudless sky, and the illumination coming from it was less than from a full moon; even the constellations were visible. A palpable nervousness had grown among the soldiers, attendants, and slaves in Herod's Palace-fortress, headquarters of the Roman governor of the province of Judea, Pontius Pilate. The streets of the city, normally boisterous with families and pilgrims on this preparation day before the Passover feast, were noticeably subdued. With a sense of trepidation, women hustled their children to their homes or quarters, and men on the way to temple with animals for the Pesach sacrifice whispered among themselves as to the meaning of the darkness.

---

[7] This was the courtyard, or common hall, of Herod's Palace. It was within the largest residence in Jerusalem, used by the governor Pontius Pilate for temporary stays in the city during the major feasts.

Pilate stood silent and expressionless on top of the wide wall surrounding Herod's Palace, one hand on the carved sandstone railing, the other on the pommel of the pugio at his belt. On each side of him stood a fully armed soldier, in constant attendance to the governor.

Silently, Gallus, one of Pilate's counselors, approached him but stopped at a respectful distance. After a moment, Gallus spoke up:

"Have you ever seen a sky like this one?"

Pilate turned to see who was addressing him. Turning back and looking upward, Pilate simply said, "No."

"I've seen an eclipse before, but this is no eclipse," continued Gallus. "It's too dark and has lasted about three hours. Everyone is unnerved by it."

When Pilate did not respond, Gallus added with a wry smile, "Perhaps the gods are angry."

Pilate turned towards Gallus. "And which god would that be, Gallus? The god of the Jews? One of Rome's gods? Or one from the Greeks, or a barbarian god? If there are gods, I'm sure I have as little influence on them as I have on the sky, so I worry about neither."

"Indeed. But if some god is angry over the mob scene from this morning, I can understand that," said Gallus, "It was an ugly business."

"It was," said Pilate. He paused for a moment. "These Jews are impossible to govern. This morning was an example. First, the Pharisees—they are damn religious fanatics. They've got laws for everything; I swear, they must have a law for which sandal to put on first! And you can't control them with intimidation or money."

Pilate spat. "And the Sadducees? They're greedy bastards that feign religion but worship gold. Sometimes you can work with them. But here's the thing: Normally you can't find three Jews that agree on anything except hating Romans."

"But this morning was different," Pilate observed, "they all seemed in agreement against that Galilean."

Pilate turned and started for the stairs down to the Praetorium pavement. Gallus joined him.

"Do you think this fellow was truly any threat?" inquired Gallus.

"To Rome?" returned Pilate rhetorically. "Not at all. There was no rebellion in his eyes. Reports about his followers said that they were an odd mix: old, young, more women than men, and almost none of them carried weapons. His supporters were no army of zealots. To me, he seemed more like a philosopher or teacher type."

"But he called himself a king," Gallus said.

"Yes, but king of what? The Jews? The same crowd that screamed for his execution this morning? Better to be king of a hive of bees! If this Jesus wanted to be king of them, I am sorry for him. The only threat he posed was to the Sanhedrin. They were jealous because of his popularity with the people. You could see the envy in their faces."

"I think it was also about money," Gallus replied.

Pilate raised an eyebrow. "How so?"

Gallus said, "I heard that two days ago Jesus cleared the money-changers out of the temple with a whip."

"Eh," retorted Pilate, with half a laugh. "That was not reported to me. That would explain the vehemence of the chief priests— they relish that temple revenue. You know about the bloody riot that happened when we took the temple treasury money to fund the aqueduct to the city."

"It left a big impression on me," said Gallus, "to hear that the priests would rather keep their gold and let their own people thirst for water."

"But about this morning," continued Gallus, "I'm curious why you offered the Jews a choice between Barabbas and Jesus."

"That was an unfortunate miscalculation on my part," confessed Pilate. "I underestimated the number of conspirators the Sanhedrin had brought in to pack the crowd. And I overestimated the number of followers of Jesus in the crowd, though there were some."

"You didn't have many options once they claimed that Jesus was opposing Caesar," sympathized Gallus.

Pilate stopped walking and faced his counselor with a frown. "I had none that I could see," said Pilate. "Tiberius has received some negative reports about my administration here, but he has no idea how intransigent this backwater nation is, or how difficult it is to maintain peace here. Believe me, Gallus, I would rather spend this week seaside at our Caesarea headquarters than be here monitoring the temple for signs of sedition!"

"Certainly," said Gallus. "What now?"

Pilate said, "They forced my hand this morning, and I resent it. They know it, too, so they must have calculated that the political coin they were spending was worth destroying this man. I doubt that; there will be a price to be paid for this morning's ugliness."

"For forcing an execution?" asked Gallus.

"No," said Pilate, "but for thinking they can force their will on Rome's governor."

He paused. "Nevertheless, it gives me no pleasure to execute an innocent man. This Jesus might have done something useful with his life, had he lived."

Golgotha: A Hill outside the Walls of Jerusalem
The Ninth Hour (3 p.m.)

Three crosses, each bearing a crucified man, stood on the hill called Golgotha. Near to the cross, in the middle, stood Jesus' relatives: his Mother Mary, his aunts Salome and Mary Clopas, and his cousin John, who was also one of the twelve disciples. At a respectful distance stood friends and followers of Jesus, including Mary Magdalene, Joanna and her friend Susanna, and others. Also in the crowd were two members of the Sanhedrin Council, Joseph of Arimathea and Nicodemus.

Joseph was a rich and prominent member of the Council, from the Jewish city of Arimathea. He was a good and righteous man, an observant Jew, who had not consented to the Council's plan and action against Jesus. While waiting for the fulfillment of God's promises in the Scriptures, Joseph had become a disciple of Jesus, but a covert one, for fear of the Jews.

Jesus said softly, "It is finished!" Only those closest to the cross heard it. John wondered what it meant. He had been hoping, against all hope, that somehow God would intervene, that Jesus would come down off the cross.

Then, astonishingly, Jesus cried with a loud voice, loud enough for all of the onlookers to hear: "Father, I commit my spirit into your hands!" Then he gave up his spirit and breathed his last.

Sosia, the centurion who was keeping guard over Jesus (and standing right in front of him) saw how he breathed his last, as though in triumph. He praised God, saying, "Surely this man was innocent!" Sosia had watched over dozens of crucifixions, and every man had been unconscious well before the time of death from slow asphyxiation, but not this man. Suddenly, the earth shook, and the rocks were split, and the centurion and his fellow soldiers became very frightened and said, "Truly this was the Son of God!"

Jerusalem: The Praetorium
The Ninth Hour (3 p.m.)

Pilate and Gallus both turned to begin walking farther across the courtyard. Just then, they heard a shout in the distance.

"That sounds like it came from Golgotha," remarked Gallus.

"Maybe a friend of one of the condemned," said Pilate, "...no man would have any voice left after six hours on a cross."

A moment later, there was a rumbling sound, and the ground shook.

"Earthquake!" exclaimed Gallus. Both men bent their knees instinctively to retain their balance. The shaking lasted only a few seconds, and both men slowly straightened up.

Pilate shrugged his shoulders with a smile, "Perhaps the gods are angry."

Jerusalem: The Temple Mount
The Ninth Hour (3 p.m.)

In the darkness, illumined by hastily arranged torches, everything stood ready for the Passover ceremony within the court of the priests, situated immediately in front of the grand temple. All twenty-four courses of priests stood ready to assist in the duties associated with sacrificing tens of thousands of animals.

The great altar, directly in front of the temple, was built entirely of uncut stones, and covered with whitewash. The base was forty-eight feet square, and over ten feet high. A long ramp ended at the top of the base on the south side. On top of the base was the altar platform, thirty-six feet square and rising three feet above the base, thus providing for a six foot wide pathway on all sides, three feet below the platform, for priests to circuit as they performed their duties. At the four corners atop the platform were four "horns," hollow rectangular projections that rose another foot and a half above the platform. The total height to the top of the horns was fifteen feet.

The first of three divisions of Jewish men with their sacrificial lambs had been admitted into the great court, and the massive doors of the Nicanor Gate to the court were shut.

These heads of households stood in defined rows, each holding the rope collar that was around the neck of their sacrifice, each man with a sharp knife sheathed at his waist. The men filled the area all around the temple, within the walls defining the court, except where only the priests were permitted: that is, immediately around the altar and between the altar and the temple. Two rows of priests extended across the court, up to the middle of the eastern side of the altar. One row held silver bowls; the other row held gold bowls.

Caiaphas stood on the elevated walkway that circumscribed the stone altar, in the center of the eastern side; Annas stood an arms-length to his side. Although Annas would provide a couple of prayers, this event belonged to Caiaphas, as he wore the vestments and the ephod[8] of the high priest. Ordinarily, Caiaphas basked in the glory of this moment, when he was the

---

[8] Ephod: a richly embroidered, apron-like vestment having two shoulder straps and to which was attached the breastplate, with its twelve precious stones

most important man, on the most important stage, on the most important day in worldwide Judaism. But this day was different.

Caiaphas furrowed his brow. "When will this darkness end?" he wondered. He had no concern for what the darkness may have portended—he was too much of a Sadducee for that kind of superstition—but he was very concerned about the uneasiness of the crowd before him.

Behind him, the upper portion of the sanctuary, that stunning gem of their ancient religion, was not even visible in the blackness. On the steps of the sanctuary stood rows of priests and Levites. Before him, the court was packed with orderly rows of dimly lit worshippers. From his elevated position, he could sense the nervousness of the crowd, and he was greatly concerned there could be a stampede of the worshippers if panic took hold. It had happened before in the days of Hillel, when a single old man was crushed. That year was remembered as the "Passover of the Crushed," and Caiaphas was determined that no such event should attach itself to his occupancy of the supreme office.

Caiaphas muttered under his breath, "I will have no man's blood on my hands today." He resolved to prevent any disaster from happening now.

"Shalom, brethren!" Caiaphas sang out, as he lifted his hands towards the crowd. "Praise the Lord!"

At that moment, the earthquake struck. Annas and Caiaphas both leaned in towards the altar platform to avoid falling off the elevated walkway. Caiaphas felt panic engulf his stomach as he brought both hands down to stabilize himself on the platform's edge behind him. Fortunately, the shaking was brief.

Inside the sanctuary, devoid of all priests because of the ceremony, the tall, thick veil—which separated the Holy of Holies from the holy place—ripped in two from top to bottom, with a deafening roar.

Caiaphas heard the sound, but his attention remained on the crowd. He could see that the lines were distorting, the crowd was losing all focus, and panic was rising.

"Brethren, listen to me!" Caiaphas screamed over the rising

murmur of the people. "Ah...God has just *blessed* us, ah...blessed us, with this extraordinary sign from heaven! ..." The murmur only grew louder.

Amazingly, serendipitously, the sun came back in the time it took for Caiaphas to slowly exhale, and he now stood in the new shadow formed by the 100-cubits-tall temple with the sunshine from the west. The temple's four polished marble columns and entablature[9] again shone bright white in the reflected sunlight, with its gilded facade mirroring the temple's environs in breathtaking beauty. The crowd froze in stunned silence.

"As I said," continued the chief priest, "God has done an extraordinary—a supernatural—thing today. A thing you will remember all your lives—a thing you will tell your children and your grandchildren. Yes, God has given us a sign—a miracle from his own hand—testifying by the shaking of the earth and the glory of the sun at this special moment, of his great pleasure in our nation, the priesthood (Caiaphas waved his hand towards the priests), and of you, the obedient, who are here this day to remember the Passover and to sacrifice according to the sacred command given by Moses. Praise the Lord!"

The crowd broke into spontaneous praise and worship. Many of them had tears in their eyes.

Subsequent to that unscripted introduction, Caiaphas gave a hand-sign to the priests who were holding silver trumpets, and they sounded three blasts to initiate the Passover ceremony. Immediately, ranks of Levites between the altar and the sanctuary began leading everyone in a responsive hymn of praise based on the psalms.

"Praise the Lord!" sang the Levites.

"Praise the Lord!" sang back the worshipping crowd.

"Praise him, O servants of the Lord!" sang the Levites.

"Praise the Lord!" responded the crowd.

As the hymn commenced, the great sacrifice started. The two rows of priests holding the silver and gold bowls turned towards

---

[9] Entablature: the upper construction of a temple between the tops of the columns and the eaves

the worshippers facing them and held the bowls under the necks of their lambs. In a brief moment, the worshippers slit the necks of their lambs, and the blood gushed out into the bowls. When the blood slowed to a trickle, the men with the slain lambs picked up their sacrifices and carried them to the butchering tables, north of the altar, for evisceration and skinning. As they did, a new line of men with live lambs stepped forward to take their places adjacent to the priests with the bowls.

While the line-changes were happening, the priests passed the blood-filled bowls up the line toward the altar, while passing empty bowls back down the line. At the altar, two priests (one handling the silver bowls, and the other the gold bowls) tossed the blood at the base of the altar with quick motions.

And so continued the most efficient sacrificial slaughtering operation in the history of humanity. There were still two more divisions of men to go, and many thousands of animals to be slain.

Caiaphas watched the proceedings with relief and satisfaction. The priests were splendid in black-and-white vestments, the sky was clear, and the river of bright crimson blood from the sacrifices brought a euphoria to the gathering. The chief priest smiled.

Annas stepped toward Caiaphas and said, "'God has blessed us with an extraordinary sign from heaven.'—that was clever, Caiaphas, very good."

Caiaphas kept smiling as he thought, "This *has* been a good day: a near disaster averted in the ceremony, the Nazarene is gone, and you pay me an uncharacteristic compliment. A very good day indeed."

The Crucifixion Site

When all of the crowds at Golgotha saw what had happened, they began to slowly leave, beating their breasts. But many of his devoted followers, including many women, remained standing there, looking on from a distance—people who had followed and ministered to Jesus when he was in Galilee and who had traveled with him to Jerusalem from Galilee. Among them were Mary Magdalene, Mary Clopas (the mother of James the Younger and Joseph), and Salome, the wife of Zebedee and mother of disciples James and John.

Jesus' Mother Mary was wailing in grief. The other family members were also sobbing. John looked up at the cross and whispered through his tears, "Jesus, this cannot be." Salome and Mary Clopas clung to Mother Mary. Mary Clopas turned and saw her good friends Mary Magdalene, Joanna, and Susanna at a distance. She then turned to Salome and John, "I must speak with Mary Magdalene. I will join you at the house before nightfall."

They nodded.

Mary Clopas approached Mary Magdalene. "Oh Mary," they said in unison as they embraced and wept together. Mary Clopas then hugged the others in the little group.

Joanna said, "Susanna and I need to return to Antipas' Palace. Let me know if there is anything we can do. Let me know if there is any news of the disciples."

Mary Magdalene said, "We will stay and see what is done with his body. We will talk again soon." Joanna and Susanna hugged and kissed the two Marys, and began a slow walk to Herod Antipas' Palace. The two Marys turned and walked towards the cross.

Joseph of Arimathea and Nicodemus had stood for hours watching the crucifixion, each with a pair of attendants beside him. Nicodemus was known in the Council as having sympathies for Jesus, but Joseph had been a secret follower of Jesus, for fear of the Council's opinion. Now the two men looked at each other silently, tears streaking both faces. Finally, Joseph felt it was time to voice his convictions: "This Jesus was the One spoken of by Moses and the Prophets, the One we have been waiting for."

Nicodemus closed his eyes briefly, nodded, and acknowledged, "He was."

Following another pause, Joseph said, "The Romans will throw his body in a common grave, like a criminal. I must try to prevent this final indignity."

"What do you intend? We have very little time before sundown and the High Sabbath begins," asked Nicodemus.

"In the garden near here is my new family tomb, recently carved from the rock. No other body has been placed in it," said Joseph. "We can lay his body there. The Agora market is closed, but I will obtain the burial cloths."

"And I will procure spices and help you prepare the body," said Nicodemus. He then turned to his attendants and said, "Let's go," and headed into the city.

Joseph turned to one of his attendants. "I need to request the body from Pilate," he said, "so go to the first street in the Essene quarter, find Zephath the cloth merchant, and purchase for me a set of burial cloths." Then he tapped the man on his chest with his finger, and added, "And get the best he has. The very best."

Jerusalem: The Praetorium

In Jerusalem, the Jews, concerned because it was preparation day for the Passover, and not wanting the bodies to remain on the cross into the Passover Sabbath (especially since that Sabbath was a high holy day), came to Pilate with a request.

Their spokesman, a Sanhedrist, asked Pilate, "As you know, Most Honorable Governor Pilate, at sundown begins our most holy day of Passover Sabbath rest. It would be an unholy and unclean thing to allow the bodies of those three crucified men to remain unburied on the Sabbath. Therefore, we respectfully request that their legs might be broken to hasten death, and that they might be taken away before the sun sets."

Pilate gave his assent, "I will take care of it."

Pilate therefore called Sylvius, his centurion, and gave him orders to dispatch the crucified men and remove them before sundown. Sylvius in turn called two soldiers, relayed the orders, and sent them to Golgotha.

As the soldiers went through the Gennath Gate, they passed Joseph and his attendant Micah traveling in the opposite direction.

So the soldiers came from Pilate to Golgotha, and after reporting to the centurion Sosia, they took a heavy hammer and broke the legs of the two men who were crucified with Jesus. When they came to Jesus, however, they saw that he was already dead and therefore did not break his legs. But one of the soldiers pierced his side with a spear, and immediately blood and water came out.

John cringed as he watched this happen, and felt sick. Much later, John understood that these things came to pass to fulfill the prophecy in Scripture: "Not one of his bones will be broken" (Ps 34:20) and "They will look on him whom they pierced" (Ze 12:10).

The two men whose legs had been broken were now incapable of pushing themselves up to gasp for breath, and they died quickly. Sosia spoke to the two soldiers who had come from the Praetorium, "Take word to Sylvius that all of the condemned men are dead."

Golgotha: By the Foot of the Cross

John felt a great urge to get Mother Mary back to the home of his parents, Salome and Zebedee, in the southwest corner of Jerusalem.

John turned to Salome, "Mother, we need to take Mother Mary home now." Salome nodded and, holding Mother Mary's arm, began to guide her in the direction of the Zebedee home, as John took her other arm.

Mary Magdalene had been standing with Mary Clopas a few feet behind the others out of respect for Jesus' mother. But Mary Magdalene's heart also ached with grief, and even though Jesus was now dead, she wanted to be nearer, to say goodbye. As Mother Mary, Salome, and John moved away, Mary Clopas stepped to where they had been, dropped to her knees, bent her face to the ground, and wept.

Mary Magdalene stepped towards the very foot of the cross. She dropped to her knees, then leaned forward and grasped his bloody left foot, suspended less than two cubits off the ground.

Then she slowly bowed forward and placed her forehead against his foot.

Her whole body began to shake, with great sobs, with such pain she hadn't known existed. Her tears dropped onto his foot and mixed with his blood. After several minutes, when she became aware of this, she took the small alabastron that was hanging around her neck, unsealed it, and poured a little spikenard ointment onto each of his feet.

Then Mary took her hair and wiped his feet one last time.

Burial before Sundown

Bethany: Lazarus' Home
The Ninth Hour (3 p.m.)

Martha returned to her vigil in the courtyard of their home, looking up the road that descended from the Mount of Olives and from Jerusalem just beyond. About an hour after Shua's news, she felt the earth shake.

Lazarus came out from the house and put an arm over her shoulder. "Did you feel that, Martha?" he asked, knowing that she must have felt it.

"What do you think is happening?" asked Martha.

"I do not know," answered Lazarus, "but I know this: No more than two weeks ago, I was dead and in a tomb. For four days I was dead. Then Jesus called me, and I came to life again and walked out of there. That has never been recorded before, not with Moses, Elijah, or any prophet. He is the Messiah. We know it.

"Shua said the Pharisees and chief priests used the sword of Rome to crucify him. And on this holy day! The earthquake, the darkness, too, I think are signs from God. I can believe that even the earth itself is angry.

"Remember, Martha, God will have the final word." At that moment, the sky brightened.

Martha said, looking up, "I hope that is a good sign. Mary and the others must be there at the cross. I wish we were with them."

Lazarus said, "I will continue watching for Shimeath, so that you can finish Passover preparations for our guests. I will slaughter the lamb after we've heard from our neighbor."

Martha turned and re-entered the house. She asked James Zebedee, "Would you ask one of the disciples to set the wood for a fire for me, for the Pesach lamb, while I prepare the herbs?"

James looked pained. "Martha, we ate Passover with Jesus at the start of this day. Besides, I have no appetite for anything."

Martha looked at the others. "I couldn't eat either," said one. "Me either," said another. The rest nodded in agreement.

25

Simon the Zealot said sorrowfully, "Without Jesus, we're still in Egypt."

"So it will be," said Martha, "for the first time ever in this house, there will be no Passover. God will understand."

Martha returned to Lazarus outside. "No one wants to eat the Passover," she said.

"I understand," said Lazarus. "Neither do I."

From Golgotha to the Praetorium in Jerusalem
Nisan 14, Between the Ninth and Tenth Hours (3 to 4 p.m.)

As the crowd dispersed from the public executions and returned to their Passover preparations, the sky began to lighten, and sunlight returned. Joseph of Arimathea, accompanied by his remaining attendant Micah, made his way from the place called Golgotha outside the city wall, through the Gennath Gate to one of the main entrances to Herod's Palace. Joseph was an older man and moved deliberately, but the walk was a short one, about a quarter of a Roman mile.

His attendant asked, "Do you think Pilate will grant us the body?"

Joseph answered, "We will know soon."

They reached the entrance. Guarding the door were two Roman soldiers. Joseph straightened up and spoke to one, "Hello. I would like to speak with the Governor."

"Name and purpose?" the soldier asked.

"Joseph of Arimathea. I wish to request custody of the body of one of the men crucified today, to provide a proper burial."

The soldier turned to the door and banged the bronze knocker twice. In a moment, the door opened and a servant's face appeared. The soldier repeated the information, and the door closed again.

So Joseph waited. After a number of minutes, Joseph and Micah sat down on the sandstone wall alongside the steps to the door. Just as they did, the door opened again, and there was the same servant, accompanied by a third soldier.

The servant said, "The Governor will see you now."

Jerusalem: Zebedee's Second Home, in the Essene (SW)
Quarter
Between the Ninth and Tenth Hours (3 to 4 p.m.)

In the absence of the women, Zebedee and Clopas were doing their best to prepare the Passover meal for the extended family guests staying in Zebedee's house.

Earlier in the day, before the shops closed at noon, Zebedee had gone to the city market and purchased a Passover lamb out of duty to his religion and his guests, but his heart hadn't been in it; instead, his mind had been preoccupied with anguish for his nephew Jesus and concern for his sons John and James.

Zebedee thought about his conversation with the merchant, as he had stood choosing one of the animals:

"Did you hear about the rabbi, Jesus?" the merchant had said.

"Hear what?"

"What happened this morning. The chief priests betrayed him to the Romans. Pilate scourged him—whipped him to a bloody mess—and he hangs on a cross now."

"I heard of the crucifixion."

"Yeah, and here's what makes me mad. You see my son Eli there?" he had said, while pointing to a boy working behind him. "He was crippled in one leg. Walked with a terrible limp. Well, Jesus healed him; he runs everywhere now. In my opinion, Caiaphas is an idiot, and a fraud too—you know the Romans made him chief priest, not God. Anyway, so, I hear about Jesus being on the cross, and I can't leave my shop—it's the busiest day of the year for me—so I tell Eli to run up to Golgotha and see what's going on with Jesus. He goes, sees Jesus and how bloody He is, and throws up right there. Now he's going to have nightmares—and Eli is used to seeing blood."

Zebedee had said nothing, but pointed to one animal and handed his payment to the merchant.

The merchant had handed him the rope leash, and noticed Zebedee standing motionless, staring at the lamb.

"What's the matter? This lamb is *unblemished!* You will find no fault with it," the merchant had said, defensively.

"Nor did they find any with Jesus," Zebedee had said softly.

"Jesus, oh, yeah, so...I think this Jesus was maybe the greatest rabbi ever. We won't see another like him in my lifetime. What do you think?"

Zebedee, still staring at the lamb, said, "He is my nephew."

A knock at the door broke into Zebedee's thoughts of the merchant. He walked to the door, taking a deep breath before opening it. There stood Mother Mary, with Salome holding one arm and John on the opposite side holding her hand. He was relieved to see John, but one look at Mother Mary told him that Jesus was gone.

"Mary, dear Mary," Zebedee said.

The three of them came into the house, and Zebedee gave Mary a tender hug, then left the two women to comfort one another. He turned to his son John and gave him a strong hug.

"I'm glad you are here, John. I was worried about you," said Zebedee.

"Jesus was everything to me, Father; I don't know what I will do now."

"I don't know what to say, John. We all loved him dearly."

Zebedee took John's head in both hands, and with eyes closed, touched his forehead to John's for a long moment.

Finally, Zebedee spoke, "Do you know where James is?"

"Mary Magdalene told me that James and the other eight disciples are in Bethany with Lazarus and Martha, or at least they were when she left the house early this morning. She's been at the cross all day with us, but I think they will probably stay in Bethany for a few days. Also, Mary Clopas is with Mary Magdalene, and she said she would be back before nightfall."

Clopas was relieved to hear that his wife would be returning soon.

Zebedee said, "Eight disciples, plus you, James, and Peter makes eleven. Who is missing?"

"Judas Iscariot," answered John, "he was the one who led them to us." "I see," acknowledged Zebedee. "I can't say I am surprised."

Jerusalem: The Praetorium

Joseph and Micah arose, stepped past the guard at the door, and entered the Palace complex. They were led to a large room with a door facing the Praetorium. Entering the room with the soldier who had led them, they saw Pilate seated at a table, looking at some documents. On either side of Pilate was a soldier standing. He looked up and studied Joseph's face and attire for a moment.

"Greetings, Joseph. So you want to bury one of the executed prisoners. Which one?"

"Yes, Governor. Jesus the Nazarene," replied Joseph.

Pilate said, "I recall seeing your face in the crowd this morning. Are you family?"

"No," answered Joseph.

"What then is your relationship to the deceased?"

"He was a man that I, eh, greatly admired," said Joseph.

Pilate slowly nodded. "You don't seem to have much company among your fellow Sanhedrists in that opinion."

"No, sir," responded Joseph.

Pilate sighed, and said, "I'm sorry about all this, Joseph." He then spoke to the soldier at Joseph's side, "Summon Sylvius."

A moment later the soldier returned with the centurion. Pilate inquired, "Sylvius, is the condemned man Jesus dead yet?"

"He is," Sylvius confirmed. "I have just received word that all three crucified men are dead."

"Then I am releasing the body of Jesus to this man for burial," Pilate spoke, nodding towards Joseph. "Communicate that promptly to the execution detail before they dispose of the bodies."

"Sir," Sylvius acknowledged as he saluted and turned to go, signaling Joseph and the soldier with him to follow.

Joseph politely bowed his head towards Pilate and said, "Thank you, Governor." Pilate gave a slight nod in return and watched Joseph leave.

Once outside the governor's office, Sylvius called for another soldier and spoke to the two soldiers now standing with Joseph, "Accompany this man to Golgotha, and inform Sosia of the order of the Prefect to release the body of Jesus to this man for burial."

The two soldiers saluted and left the Palace together with Joseph and his attendant.

Jerusalem: Golgotha, outside the City Walls

At Golgotha, Sosia had instructed his squad of soldiers to begin removing the bodies for disposal in accordance with the earlier order received from Pilate. Out of respect for the two women mourning at the cross in the middle, they moved first to the cross on the left and began their work. The soldiers were noisy and boisterous, relieved that the sky had brightened and anticipating relief from work and the coming evening meal.

The presence of the soldiers nearby made the two Marys uncomfortable, so they arose from their mourning and removed themselves to a suitable distance to monitor what would happen to the body of their Lord.

As Joseph, Micah his attendant, and the two soldiers with him arrived at Golgotha, the four men found the execution detail already taking down the body of one of the other men crucified alongside Jesus. The two soldiers that had come with Joseph spoke to Sosia the centurion, and Sosia handed the soldiers a forked crowbar and hammer. The two soldiers returned to Joseph and handed him the tools.

Joseph first handed the hammer to Micah and then jammed the crowbar between the heel of Jesus' foot and the square wooden plaque under the head of the nail holding the foot. It pained Joseph that he was causing additional damage to remove the body, but there was no other way.

Joseph spoke to Micah, "Hit the bar near his foot."

Micah proceeded to do that, and after several blows, the foot with the embedded nail was free of the upright stipes.[10] Joseph and Micah walked to the other side of the cross and repeated the effort until the other foot was also free of the stipes.

Now the body hung entirely by the arms from the horizontal

---

[10] The vertical portion of a cross, left permanently anchored in the ground for repeated executions

patibulum.[11] The two soldiers with Joseph returned to the execution detail; they had just removed the first body from its cross. They picked up two short wooden steps and returned to Joseph with them.

One of the soldiers positioned a step behind the cross, stood on it, and removed the peg that locked the horizontal patibulum to the vertical stipes. After he stepped down, the soldier then positioned the two steps under the two ends of the patibulum.

Recognizing that Joseph was too aged to lift half the combined weight of the body plus the patibulum and that his attendant was too young, the two soldiers mounted the steps. Together they lifted the patibulum up from the notch at the top of the stipes and brought it down with the body, to the front of the cross. They walked it forward a few steps and then backed up towards the stipes while lowering the beam, thus laying out the body of Jesus, face upwards.

Joseph and Micah returned to the task of removing Jesus from the wood of the crossbeam. His hands had been nailed through the wrist bones, but with the patibulum on the ground, there was no room to swing the hammer. Joseph realized that if they put the crowbar under the head of the nail and simply pried upward, they would badly damage the hand or arm. The soldier nearest Joseph, seeing the perplexity of the two men, stepped forward, placed the head of the hammer alongside the wrist, and made a prying motion with his free hand. Then Micah took the hammer and held it on the wood while Joseph leveraged the nails out with the crowbar, working against the head of the hammer as a fulcrum.

This done, the body was free of the cross, but not from the four nails embedded in it. Joseph's second attendant, having returned from the marketplace with the burial cloths, set them down on a nearby rock and joined the two men. Working carefully with the hammer and using the patibulum as a support, the three men drove the nails out of the bones. As they finished, Micah noticed three men walking towards them and

---

[11] The horizontal wooden beam of a cross, sometimes carried by the condemned to the crucifixion site

31

said, "Here comes Nicodemus," and all three men straightened and turned their attention to the approaching party.

Nicodemus came towards Golgotha with his two attendants, each of whom carried a bag over his shoulder. While approaching, Nicodemus spoke to his companions, "Good. I see Joseph was able to obtain the body from the governor."

As they reached the top of the rise by the cross, Nicodemus spoke first, "Joseph. I was able to procure spices—myrrh and aloes, 100 pounds.[12]" Joseph's attendants looked at each other with raised eyebrows, recognizing that this must have cost a king's ransom.

Joseph, wearied from the exertion of his recent task, looked down at Jesus' body. It was a bloody mess and completely naked. His face was puffy and distorted from blunt blows. His forehead was punctured in many places, and his hair was matted with the blood that had flowed from those punctures. Joseph looked at the bloody nail holes and an open spear wound below the right breast.

Yet despite those marks of violence, the most arresting sight was the pattern of bloody lacerations and welts on the skin—hundreds and hundreds of them; many were so deep that pieces of skin hung loose and the muscles underneath could be seen. Joseph had seen men scourged before but never with such demonic viciousness. There was not one place on the body, except the soles of the feet, where Joseph could have placed his hand on wholly intact skin.

Joseph turned to Nicodemus, "That is good, Nicodemus. My tomb is nearby; let's remove his body to the garden there to prepare it." Nicodemus nodded.

Jerusalem: to the Garden Tomb
About Half Past the Tenth Hour (4:30 p.m.)

Mary Magdalene and Mary Clopas had watched Joseph and Nicodemus remove the body initially with surprise, which quickly changed into deep gratitude. They did not know either

---

[12] Roman pounds; equal to about 75 English pounds

Joseph or Nicodemus, but they recognized them as men of stature by their appearance, probably Sanhedrists.

"They are going to bury his body!" Mary Clopas whispered to Mary Magdalene.

Mary Magdalene nodded. "I am so relieved he won't be thrown into a ditch with criminals."

Joseph signaled to the attendants, and the four men lifted the body—two of them holding the arms, and the other two holding the legs at the knees. Joseph picked up the burial cloths and led the group to the tomb, followed by the four attendants with the body and Nicodemus in the rear.

Mary Magdalene and Mary Clopas intended to follow discretely, but because they were also concerned about losing sight of the burial party, they trailed not far behind Nicodemus.

Sosia watched them go. His soldiers were now working on removing the third man from his cross. As Jesus' small burial procession moved out of sight, Sosia remarked again, "That was an innocent man." Although a few soldiers heard him, none offered any reaction.

The burial party walked in silence from Golgotha. The four young attendants were uneasy carrying such a mutilated corpse, so they did their best to avert their eyes from the man they were carrying. Mercifully for all, the transport took little time.

"Here, set him here," said Joseph, pointing to a low stone ledge that served as a bench for the garden.

As they did so, Joseph spoke to Micah, "Quickly, run to the Towers Pool and bring back some water for washing."

Micah frowned. "And with what should I carry it?"

Joseph responded, "You are right. Here, take these"—Joseph handed him a few strips of linen—"and just get them well-moistened. We have no time for proper washing anyway." Micah immediately ran off to the pool.

Joseph spoke to the remaining three attendants: "Unroll the cloths on the ground here so they are ready." The men proceeded to the task, while the two Marys sat down a short distance away to watch.

Bethany: Lazarus' Home
Near the Eleventh Hour (5 p.m.)

Lazarus and Martha saw him at the same instant and chorused, "Shimeath!" as their neighbor appeared on the road from Jerusalem, carrying the sacrificed Passover lamb wrapped in sheepskin on his shoulder. They waited until he was closer, then walked about a field's length out to meet him.

Concern and expectancy filled their faces, and Shimeath's face displayed heavy sorrow.

"I'm sorry, Lazarus, Martha," Shimeath said, while nodding towards each in turn. "Jesus is dead; the chief priests and Pilate killed him, on a cross. He died just before the sky brightened again. Many of the common people are angry, and some are saying that the priests have betrayed our nation to the Romans."

"We heard earlier there were two others crucified with him," prompted Lazarus.

"That's right," said Shimeath, "two thieves who deserved it. You know how the feasts attract not only the righteous but also the unrighteous into the city. But Jesus did nothing wrong, except make the priests jealous."

"Yes," agreed Lazarus.

"I'm very sorry to bring you such terrible news, and on a feast day—a day that should be for rejoicing. Forgive me, Lazarus. We are living in fearful days."

"Shimeath, have a blessed Passover meal with your family," said Lazarus.

"Thank you," returned Shimeath, "I pray for the peace of God and his blessing on your house. Such a shame, such a crime. Jesus was a good man, a mighty prophet."

Shimeath turned and continued to his home.

Lazarus, with tears streaming down his face, embraced Martha as she cried on his shoulder.

Jerusalem: The Temple Complex
The Eleventh to the Twelfth Hour (5 to 6 p.m.)

The last of the third division of worshippers were collecting their sacrificed and butchered lambs from the priests working at the marble tables, who had prepared the animals for roasting by gutting and skinning them. Each man took his Passover lamb, wrapped in its own skin, and slung it over his shoulders before filing out of the court of the priests and returning to his family.

Two more significant religious duties remained for the priests: the offering of incense and the trimming of wicks in the sanctuary. These daily routines normally followed the afternoon offering, except on Passover, when they followed the great offering.

A young priest named Ahuzam had been chosen by lot to trim the wicks of the lamps in the holy place, another by the name of Uzzi had been chosen to prepare the small altar of incense before the Holy of Holies, and an older priest named Jehoada had been chosen for the once-of-a-lifetime honor of offering the incense inside the temple. No priest was permitted to offer incense twice in his life, unless there were insufficient numbers of priests for the task.

The temple courts were largely empty now except for ranks of priests and Levites, inasmuch as most of the common people were with their relatives for their family celebrations of Passover prior to consuming the meal.

The floor of the court was more than ankle-deep in blood. Caiaphas and Annas ascended the dozen steps leading to the sanctuary's entrance, passing between the rows of priests ranged across the steps, and leaving bloody footprints behind them on the white stones. Uzzi, Jehoada, Ahuzam, and a few attending priests stood waiting barefoot in the pool of blood just below the steps.

When Caiaphas gave the signal, Uzzi and Ahuzam ascended the steps to the holy edifice, carrying consecrated gold vessels. They walked past the four marble columns, two on each side, and through the massive, open golden doors, around the southern edge of the great curtain, and into the holy place. There they paused.

It was a vast room with a very high ceiling, illumined only by oil lamps. The golden lampstand on their left glowed from the seven lamps upon it. Uzzi's eyes drank in the beautiful and sacred view of the holy lights. As he started forward, he turned his head to the right to view the table with the twelve sacred loaves of shewbread.

Then he froze in fear.

As he had turned his head, something had caught his eye. Something was very wrong. He slowly turned his gaze back toward the incense altar, his destination directly in front of him, then quickly dropped his gaze to the floor.

Forty cubits away, the veil shielding the Holy of Holies was sheared from top to bottom, and stood partially open! Uzzi's heart raced, and his hands started trembling. "What should I do?" he frantically thought.

He knew that only the high priest was allowed into the Holy of Holies, and only once a year on the Day of Atonement. He knew it wasn't his place to even gaze into it. He also knew the story of Uzzah, who had died before the Lord when he had carelessly touched the ark of the covenant. Fear urged him to run from the sanctuary, but he also had a most sacred task to perform, and the fear of failing that task constrained him to stay.

Uzzi prayed fervently, "Lord God, have mercy on me. Lord, have mercy." Perspiring heavily, with his heart pounding in his ears, he walked slowly forward with his eyes set to see only a few feet in front of him. Reaching the small table called the altar of incense, he set his gold vessel on the floor, then scooped the leftover cinders and burnt incense into his two hands and deposited them in the vessel. He repeated this several times until the altar was cleared and ready for Jehoada to offer the incense.

He leaned over the vessel, rubbing his hands to remove the ashes on them, but it was in vain—the ashes only smeared in his sweaty palms. He straightened, leaving his container of ashes in place as required, and strode briskly to Ahuzam, who was waiting for him.

The two men exchanged no words—it wasn't necessary. Ahuzam had felt the same panic, and the two men looked at each other with wide eyes. The young Ahuzam had been at a complete loss about what to do about the situation, but having just seen

Uzzi proceed with the rituals, he now followed Uzzi's example.

Ahuzam walked forward one-half the length of the inner court and made a precision left turn to face the lampstand. He ascended the three steps and stood level with the seven-branched golden stand. All seven lamps were still burning. He carefully trimmed five of the seven wicks with trembling hands, taking care to not extinguish them in the process. Two of the lamps he extinguished and left untrimmed for later. From a flagon of fresh olive oil, he filled all seven lamps, then set his flagon beside the lampstand, and returned to join Uzzi near the entrance.

Both men exited the sanctuary.

There was a certain cadence in the way priests walked, and every movement in the temple ceremonies was carefully choreographed and rehearsed. Yet, Ahuzam was panicked and broke pace with Uzzi in order to rush the news to the high priest. The loss of decorum was immediately evident to everyone watching, and Caiaphas wondered if Ahuzam had lost his mind or if the sanctuary had been profaned. Something was amiss.

Ahuzam franticly sputtered something unintelligible to Caiaphas, who grabbed Uzzi's vestments with both hands and drew him up close. The high priest wanted to strike him with a backhand but refrained because of the audience.

"Stop!" hissed Caiaphas. "What madness has come over you?"

"It's torn! It's torn!" gasped Ahuzam.

"Torn? What is?" asked Caiaphas.

"The inner curtain! It's ripped in half from top to bottom!"

Caiaphas paused and thought, "How could that be? The curtain is a hand-breadth thick and forty cubits tall.[13] How could this be true?" However, the fear in Ahuzam's eyes, and in the face of Uzzi—who had just joined them—testified that his words were true.

"Just—be still. Did you prepare the lamps?"

"Yes," said Ahuzam, feeling a mite calmer.

"And the incense altar?" Caiaphas asked, looking at Uzzi.

---

[13] Forty cubits equals sixty feet

"Yes," said Uzzi.

"Alright, alright," said Caiaphas, gathering his thoughts. He turned to the others.

Annas interrupted loudly, "It must be some minor damage from the earthquake. We will get some skilled workers to conduct repairs as soon as possible. Continue with the incense."

"Yes, continue worship," said Caiaphas, also off-script.

Uzzi and Ahuzam regained their composure, and Jehoada and his two assistants began a metered descent down the stairs, stepping into the blood-filled court. They walked to the bottom of the ramp leading to the large altar of burnt offering, and began their ascent—their bloody bare feet kept from slipping by the salt that had been sprinkled there.

The three men reached the altar platform at the southern side. Sitting upon it were a gold bowl of incense and a small charcoal fire of fig wood. One attendant picked up the gold bowl and emptied the holy incense mixture into the golden censer he carried with him. Using a hand-shovel, the other attendant scooped hot coals from the fire into a silver vessel that he carried. Turning, the three men retraced their steps down the ramp and up the steps to the sanctuary.

Upon reaching the top of the steps, Jehoada sounded the Magrephah.[14] At the sound, ranks of Levites began singing and all the priests began to worship. Ahuzam and Uzzi joined the other three, and together, all five men entered the temple.

The priests stood inside the sanctuary; all five, unsettled by the torn veil, kept their eyes directed downward at the beautiful tiled floor in front of them. On cue, Ahuzam and Uzzi strode forward, collected the vessels they had previously left, and returned, exited the sanctuary, and stood alone at the top of the steps at the center; Annas and Caiaphas had withdrawn to each side in front of the giant pillars.

Inside the holy place, Jehoada and his assistants strode forward until their eyes caught sight of the small incense altar.

---

[14] A device of which little is known, but much speculated. It may have been a percussion instrument, like a gong, or a pipe instrument.

The first attendant carefully arranged the burning coals taken from the great altar onto the top of the altar of incense. The second attendant set his censer beside the altar; both attendants then slowly exited the sanctuary. As they did so, Jehoada picked up the censer and stood before the altar, waiting for the command.

After Jehoada's two assistants had rejoined Ahuzam and Uzzi, Caiaphas gave the signal for the singing and worship to cease.

Then, with a booming voice, Caiaphas announced, "The time of incense has come!" Immediately, all the priests raised their hands and commenced praying silently. Within the sanctuary, Jehoada took the censer and carefully spread the incense on top of the hot coals, creating an instant, fragrant, rising cloud of smoke.

Jehoada had waited for this moment all his life, believing it would be the highest honor and greatest experience he would ever have. He had relished the stories of other priests who had been chosen for the task, as they described having felt the powerful presence of God during the ritual. Instead, he felt nothing but fear and a concern over what the torn veil might signify. He took the censer and slowly retreated from the cloud of rising smoke.

Outside, Jehoada took his place in the middle of the line at the top of the stairs, flanked by his two attendants. Outside of them stood Ahuzam and Uzzi. Caiaphas and Annas stood at opposite ends of the line.

Caiaphas gave two more signals; at the first, all the priests brought their arms down to their sides. At the second signal, the priests began to pray in unison as the incense burned. It was a lengthy supplication for blessing upon the nation, ending with these words:

> And may it please you to bless your people Israel at all times, and at every hour with your peace. May we and all your people Israel be remembered and written before you in the book of life, with blessing and peace and support. Blessed be you, Lord God, who blesses your people Israel with peace.

At this point, Ahuzam turned and entered the sanctuary for a second time with his vessels. The strong scent of incense filled his nostrils as he approached the lampstand again. He trimmed the two wicks that had been extinguished and then relit them from the other lamps. Despite what Annas had said, Ahuzam was nervous and eager to exit the sanctuary.

Once outside, Ahuzam took his place again with the other priests. Now that all the ministry within the sanctuary was completed, all the non-officiating priests raised their arms and joined their hands with intertwined fingers.

Jehoada took one step forward and gave the ancient blessing:

> Lord bless you, and keep you; Lord make his face shine upon you, and be gracious to you; Lord lift up His countenance upon you, and give you peace.

In response, the Levites, other priests, and remaining people proclaimed, "Blessed be the Lord God, the God of Israel, from everlasting to everlasting."

Immediately, priests standing on both sides of the marble table on the north side of the great altar blew their silver trumpets, and a choir of Levites began singing the closing psalm. Since it was the fourth day of the week,[15] the 94th psalm was sung, in three parts. The Levites sang:

> The LORD is a God who avenges. O God who avenges, shine forth! Rise up, Judge of the earth; pay back to the proud what they deserve. How long, LORD, will the wicked, how long will the wicked be jubilant? They pour out arrogant words; all the evildoers are full of boasting. They crush your people, LORD; they oppress your inheritance. They slay the widow and the foreigner; they murder the fatherless. They say, "The LORD does not see; the God of Jacob takes no notice."

The trumpeter-priests gave three blasts of their trumpets, then

---

[15] On our calendar, a Wednesday

the Levites continued:

> Take notice, you senseless ones among the people; you fools, when will you become wise? Does he who fashioned the ear not hear? Does he who formed the eye not see? Does he who disciplines nations not punish? Does he who teaches mankind lack knowledge? The LORD knows all human plans; he knows that they are futile. Blessed is the one you discipline, LORD, the one you teach from your law; you grant them relief from days of trouble, till a pit is dug for the wicked. For the LORD will not reject his people; he will never forsake his inheritance. Judgment will again be founded on righteousness, and all the upright in heart will follow it.

The priests gave three more trumpet blasts; the Levites then finished the psalm:

> Who will rise up for me against the wicked? Who will take a stand for me against evildoers? Unless the LORD had given me help, I would soon have dwelt in the silence of death. When I said, "My foot is slipping," your unfailing love, LORD, supported me. When anxiety was great within me, your consolation brought me joy. Can a corrupt throne be allied with you—a throne that brings on misery by its decrees? The wicked band together against the righteous and condemn the innocent to death. But the LORD has become my fortress, and my God the rock in whom I take refuge. He will repay them for their sins and destroy them for their wickedness; the LORD our God will destroy them.[16]

The priests finished with a final three trumpet blasts, upon which everyone bowed low and worshipped.

As the Levites filed out, Caiaphas and Annas exchanged a long glance: Both knew the torn veil was a curious and disturbing problem—not just as a practical matter of making repairs, but

---

[16] Ps 94, English Standard Version.

also for its potential to generate crazy theories among the people.

But it would have to wait. The chief priests needed to shed their special vestments, change into daily priestly clothing, and lead Passover meals in their own homes.

The floor of the court of the priests, beautifully tiled in geometric patterns with a variety of colored stone from many parts of the Roman Empire, was still submerged under a sea of crimson. The priests with the precious bowls of the blood offerings, their hands and feet covered with blood, began collecting the bowls for cleaning and storage. Two priests worked together to remove the stone plugs at the base of the altar and release the pool of blood. A small army of priests fanned out across the court to wash and scrub everything. All hands were present—all twenty-four courses of the priesthood served the temple on this day.

In front of the altar, the great pool of blood began to drain down through two funnels at the junction of the court and altar. Now mixed with water from the washing work, the blood and water continued down into a masterfully carved stone drainage system beneath the court.

The steady stream of lambs' blood mixed with water ran through the drainage system and dumped into the Kidron valley between Jerusalem and the Mount of Olives. At first, the blood of the tens of thousands of sacrificed animals and the cleansing water gushed out of the port in the temple wall as a powerful torrent.

From there, it flowed southward in the dry riverbed, alongside the "Lower City," where the poor people lived, and into the King's Garden. There it fertilized the soil, as it had done for hundreds of years prior.

Israel had been without a king for 615 years. Nevertheless, the garden was still maintained by the priests, in anticipation of the day when a redeemer-king, the Messiah, would arrive to sit on the throne and walk through the garden once again.

Jerusalem: Joseph's Tomb, outside the City Walls
Approaching Twilight

In the garden that contained Joseph's tomb, Nicodemus and Joseph rolled Jesus' body onto its side and tried to brush off sand and small pebbles that were stuck to his back, without much success. Coagulating blood and serum from his speared side were slowly dripping off the bench onto the ground. They removed a few large splinters from his upper back and shoulders, then rolled his body onto its back again.

Thankfully, Micah was already back from the pool. First, Nicodemus closed the eyes fully with his thumbs. Then, Joseph daubed his face a bit with the moist cloth. Nicodemus tried to push his hair to the sides of his forehead, but some remained stuck there from the congealed blood. They wiped his body from head to foot using the moistened cloth strips, while quoting the traditional Scriptures, providing the best impromptu washing they could manage under the circumstances.

Nicodemus stood up and said, "We must hurry Joseph." He picked up one of the bags of spices, and with his other hand, reached in and then spread the mixture over half of the long linen shroud, as Joseph continued daubing some of the larger wounds with a dry cloth.

Nicodemus stepped towards the head of the body and grabbed Jesus' hands, lifting them. Joseph stood up and grasped the body at the ankles. Together they lifted his body from the stone bench and moved it to the shroud, a few feet away. They lowered him on top of the spices, with the feet at one end of the cloth.

Joseph took Jesus' arms and overlapped the hands to cover his groin. Nicodemus returned to his spices and shook a large quantity all over the top of Jesus' body, much of which fell off to the sides. Joseph walked to the opposite end and lifted the edge of the shroud.

"Oh, wait," said Nicodemus. He reached to his belt and pulled out a coin purse, opened it, and withdrew two coins. Then he leaned down and put one over each closed eye.

Nicodemus straightened up again and said, "It isn't right,

Joseph."

Joseph looked at the body, so badly wounded and unsatisfactorily washed.

"I know. But it was the best we could do."

"Yes," said Nicodemus, "but I meant that his eyes are closed with coins minted with Pilate's name. Unfortunately I have none that are different."

Joseph replied, "Neither do I, so it is the best we can do. He deserves better."

Joseph walked alongside the body, carrying the end of the shroud over his head and down to his feet, so that the body was enveloped above and below with the single length of herringbone-weave material.

Micah now handed Joseph the square head-cloth, which Joseph and Nicodemus wrapped around the part of the shroud that was covering the head of Jesus. Then Micah handed, one after the other, linen strips to the two Council members, with which they bound the body and secured the other cloths.

Joseph called for Micah and the other attendants, and said, "Pick up Jesus' body and carry it to the tomb opening." While they were hoisting him, Joseph and Nicodemus stooped down and entered the low opening to the tomb. The attendants passed the body through to the two Sanhedrists, and they turned and set his body on a stone shelf, cut into the bedrock, to the right of the opening. After adjusting the position of Jesus' body, they exited the opening.

Mary Magdalene had crept closer and to the left of the opening, so she could see how the body had been laid in the tomb. Having seen the shelf on which he had been laid, she returned to join Mary Clopas.

Joseph went to the side of the large, round stone that set in a track to the side of the tomb opening. He put his shoulder against the stone and strained, but the stone only rocked slightly and didn't roll.

Seeing this, the other men joined him, and together they rolled the stone, closing the tomb.

Joseph and Nicodemus took a few steps away from the door,

then turned and faced it, bowing their heads slightly. The four attendants formed a row behind their superiors and likewise bowed their heads.

Joseph said a simple prayer of commitment, and silence followed. Nicodemus, with tears in his eyes, spoke next, "Joseph, what have we done? We have killed the Lord's Anointed One."

Joseph said, "I fear for our nation."

Nicodemus lifted his face, creased with pain. "Joseph, this is bigger than our nation alone. Isaiah said that he would open the eyes of the blind, and he did."

He continued, "And in the same passage, Isaiah said that he would be the light of the nations. Joseph, I fear for every nation—for all mankind; for we have extinguished the Light of the World!"

Joseph bit his lip, closed his eyes, and lifted his face towards heaven. "Lord, Oh Lord God," he said softly, as the four attendants nervously glanced at each other.

Mary Magdalene and Mary Clopas slipped away and headed for the Gennath Gate to reenter Jerusalem. Both women walked briskly, conscious that the day was declining, and the high holy Sabbath of Passover and Unleavened Bread was about to begin.

As they started south, the women struggled with their emotions.

Mary Clopas said, "They didn't properly wash or anoint the body."

"I know," replied Mary Magdalene, "And we won't be able to wash it later, as the cloths will be completely stuck to his wounds. But we can return with perfumes and give the burial cloths a proper anointing. We must tell Joanna and Susanna."

Mary Clopas had been thinking the same thing. "Mary," she added, "nightfall is almost upon us. You don't have time to return to Bethany, so you will need to stay the night with us at Zebedee's."

"Thank you," Mary Magdalene quietly replied.

Coming through the gate, Herod's Palace with the Praetorium stood prominently to their right, with the outside patio, called

"The Pavement," where they had watched Pilate deliver the death sentence earlier that very morning. It felt like an entire lifetime ago.

Immediately to their left, about 200 cubits[17] away, stood Herod Antipas' Palace. The Palace was Antipas' home, and Joanna's as well, when Antipas was in the city during the feasts. Beyond Antipas' Palace was the southern end of the immense temple complex.

They turned left, eastward towards Antipas' Palace. The upper parapet of the ostentatious building stood illuminated by the last rays of the sun, now setting behind them. Beyond the Palace, the temple mount, with greater size and elevation, dominated their view.

Mary Clopas felt in her very soul the oppressive despotism surrounding them. Behind her were Pilate and the state power of Rome. In front of her was the Palace where, as Joanna had related to them, Herod Antipas had mocked and mistreated Jesus. Visible on the temple mount, just beyond, was the Royal Stoa, where the Sanhedrin had plotted against Jesus and put him on trial. To the left of the Stoa was the gilded temple run by the corrupt high priests who had effected the plot to destroy him.

She spoke to her friend, "There was a time when I viewed the temple with such reverence."

Mary Magdalene concurred, "Nothing will ever look the same."

They were at the Palace and quickly climbed the wide stone steps. At the door, Mary Magdalene lifted and dropped the brass knocker once, twice. Fortunately, the answer was almost immediate, and a guard's face appeared.

"What do you want?" he asked politely.

"We need to speak with Joanna, the steward's wife."

"Wait." The door closed.

Mary Clopas spoke, "I just remembered that the Pesach meal begins this evening! She will be totally engaged with it."

---

[17] 200 cubits equals 100 yards

Mary Magdalene didn't answer but began rocking back and forth impatiently. The wait was not long, and the door opened again. To the relief of both women, their mutual friend Susanna appeared.

"Hi, Mary and Mary," she began. "Joanna cannot break away from managing meal preparation for the many guests. What news do you have?"

Mary Magdalene said rapidly, "The only good news is that two wealthy men—I heard the names Joseph and Nicodemus—took his body off the cross. They didn't move it very far at all, to a rock-cut tomb in a small garden area. I think the men were from the Sanhedrin."

"Yes, that is almost certainly Joseph of Arimathea; he and Nicodemus are members of the Council," said Susanna. "I am relieved that the Romans did not dispose of his body."

"Yes," interjected Mary Clopas, "but the men were not able to wash and anoint his body for burial. They did wrap it with plenty of spices. We won't be able to remove the wrappings or to wash his body, but we can go to the market after Passover, buy the materials for anointing oils, and honor him in that way."

Susanna pondered this information for a moment, then sighed, "I truly want to go with you and participate, and I know Joanna would, too. But we are so fettered with obligations to the Tetrarch and his guests that we can't get away for that long.

"But please do me this favor. When you have the oils prepared, stop by the Palace. We may be able to join you for the anointing at that time.

"And here, please take this..." Susanna said, as she pulled a small cloth purse from her sash and extracted a couple of gold coins.

Mary Clopas put her hands up to block the exchange and said, "Thank you, Susanna, but we will take care of it."

"Please," said Susanna earnestly, "it is my offering to him."

With that, Mary Clopas relented and accepted the money.

"Thank you," continued Susanna. "I don't imagine you have any news of the disciples?"

"No," said Mary Magdalene, "but after Passover I will need to return to Bethany to see my brother and sister, and I think Mary will want to go with me to check on her son James." Mary Clopas nodded in agreement, as she had been worried about her son James the Younger and the others.

"What time do you think you will return here for the anointing?" asked Susanna.

"Mid-afternoon, between the Sabbaths," said the Magdalene.

"God's peace be with you."

"And with you. Shalom."

The two Marys turned and started down the steps to the street, walking in the direction of Zebedee's house, further south into the city. Mary Clopas spoke first.

"This may not sound right, but I don't even feel like it matters if I observe the Passover Sabbath now."

"I think Jesus wants us to," Mary Magdalene responded.

Mary Clopas was struck by her reference to her nephew Jesus in the present tense. She had always felt uncertain about when and whether to refer to a deceased person in the present or past tense.

"In any case, the shops will all be closed," Mary Clopas replied.

"Passover was important to Jesus," said Mary Magdalene. "It reminds us of when the destroying angel passed over the people."

Mary Clopas replied, "Do you think God will pass over the sin of today?"

It was a question not meant to elicit an answer; it was a question that vented from a heart filled with anguish and pain. Further, it was a question, which, although rhetorical on its face, begged for an answer that only God could provide.

And just so, no answer was forthcoming; Mary Magdalene said nothing more but kept her eyes on the street, as the lengthening shadows made it more difficult to see the uneven cobblestones.

So the two women continued walking in silence, side by side, each alone in her grief.

The Longest Night

Peter sat alone in the upper room on the second floor, his shoulders slumped, his eyes red-rimmed and vacant. Mark had brought him the news from Golgotha, and now he knew that his reason for living, his Lord, was dead. Three years prior, he had left everything for Jesus, and his "everything" had just perished.

His thoughts returned to the trial that morning at Caiaphas' house, only two blocks away. Out of fear, he had disowned his best friend. And when the rooster had crowed, and Jesus had turned and looked at him—with sorrow, and yet with love—that gaze had burned into Peter's heart, and the pain of it was unrelenting.

One glance from Jesus, and Peter was undone. In one instant of eye contact, Peter had seen himself for who he truly was, and the shock of that revelation torched his pride, incinerating his lofty opinion of himself.

"If only I had argued for his release, if only I had said something...if only I hadn't been such a coward," Peter said to himself. "If only I hadn't put the sword away when he was arrested. They probably would have killed me there in the garden, but that would have been better.

"It should have been me; it should have been me who died, not him," anguished Peter.

He lifted his eyes from the floor and stared at the low table across the room. It was the table where they had shared their last supper together. As though in a vision, the scene replayed in Peter's mind: There was Jesus in the center, John on his left and leaning against him, Peter on his right.

"Will you die for me, Peter?" Jesus had asked.

It hurt to remember Jesus' words, but Peter couldn't keep them from his mind.

"The truth is, before a rooster crows tonight, you will deny me three times," Jesus had said.

Peter's head tilted backwards, eyes closed. He let out a tremendous cry of anguish. As the cry tapered off to silence, his head came forward again, and he placed his face in his hands and began sobbing.

Downstairs, Mark and his mother Mariam heard Peter's cry. "Oh, the poor man. I pray he will be all right," said Mariam.

"Should I check on him?" asked Mark.

"No, we have no comfort to offer him. He needs to find his own way. But we can pray."

Mariam took Mark's hand, and prayed, "Oh, Lord of Heaven, please have mercy on Peter's soul, and comfort him as only you can. Lord, have mercy on us all."

Bethany: Lazarus' Home

Lazarus and Martha walked slowly back to the house. As they entered, all nine disciples were standing in the room, their eyes intently focused on their hosts. The disciples knew from their faces that the news was going to be painful.

Lazarus decided to lead with the lack of news about Peter and John.

"There's no news about Peter and John, but the two men crucified with Jesus were common thieves, not them."

The disciples said nothing; Peter's brother Andrew closed his eyes briefly in a silent prayer of thanksgiving, and James, John's brother, exhaled with some relief. But the anxiety on their faces remained, and all eyes were fixed upon Lazarus.

"Jesus...has...died." The words came haltingly with a rasp from Lazarus' throat. As he spoke them, the words seemed incongruous, inconceivable, utterly impossible. How could it be that the Messiah—the One who exuded such light and life, whose touch brought healing, whose words brought deliverance, and whose presence brought such joy—was gone?

Lazarus, who only a few days prior had been brought back from the dead by Jesus, still stood at the door. His head sunk to his chest, and tears flowed.

The disciples stood momentarily frozen, the gravity of the news working its way from ears, to minds, to the very center of their souls. Two of them fell to the floor in sitting positions, one holding his head, the other rocking; a couple other disciples fell to slumped kneeling positions, while yet another turned to the wall and started striking it with his fist. Others starting moving around the room aimlessly, while some cried on each other's shoulders.

In Bethany, in the house of Lazarus that night, there was little sleep. Those that did doze for a moment experienced nightmares, only to find upon awakening that a greater nightmare persisted.

Jerusalem: Zebedee's Home

Mary Clopas and Mary Magdalene reached Zebedee's house in southwest Jerusalem as the ram's horn sounded from the temple complex, announcing the beginning of a Sabbath. But this was not the usual weekly Sabbath; it was the High Holy Sabbath of Passover.

Hearing them knock, Zebedee opened the door and greeted Clopas' wife: "Hello, Mary," and then waited for her to introduce her companion.

"Zebedee, I know that you know of Mary Magdalene. She's been with me at the cross all day. I hope it isn't an imposition for you to provide her lodging for the night."

"Yes, of course, and you are welcome here," said Zebedee. "Come in, come in."

The women entered and immediately joined Mother Mary and Salome in their grief, comforting one another by their mutual presence.

Clopas and Zebedee had finished the Passover meal preparation shortly before the arrival of the two Marys, but the house was heavy with grief, and no one could eat; the meal went completely untouched.

Clopas, Zebedee, and John sat together, comforting each other, as men tend to do, by simply sitting together in silence. From time to time, one or another of them would cry silently. Apart from his own grief over Jesus, Zebedee vicariously felt the grief of his son John; so, for a while, he tried to think of something—anything—that he might say that would provide even a mote of comfort to his son. But he could think of nothing, so occasionally he simply placed his hand on top of John's.

After about an hour, John excused himself and went to another room to mourn and pray.

Zebedee arose and began to put away the food that had been prepared. Clopas also rose to assist him, and the two worked together, each lost in his own thoughts and grief.

When they finished, Zebedee turned to his brother-in-law and said, "I think that from the time when my forefathers left Egypt, to today, this is the first Passover without a lamb." Clopas nodded.

Remembering one more task he needed to complete with respect to his guests, Zebedee went to find Mary Magdalene. As Mary was an unexpected guest that evening, Zebedee needed to show her where she could sleep and provide her the customary oil, water, and washcloths. But Mary was too emotionally overwhelmed to wash up, and though she lay down, she didn't sleep—nor did the rest of the house.

It was the night of Passover, and as always on this night, a full moon illumined the earth below. In another room in Zebedee's home, Mother Mary lay down on her mat, looking at the brilliant face of the moon streaming light through her window. From the time she was a child, Mother Mary had loved God and the stories of him learned from her parents and at the synagogue. She recalled that on the very first Passover, in Egypt, it was at midnight with the full moon directly overhead that the destroying angel had gone through Egypt and brought deliverance to her people by striking down the firstborn of the Egyptians.

Then she thought of the words given to her by Anna the prophetess when she and Joseph had brought their infant Jesus to the temple: that Jesus would bring deliverance to Jerusalem.

But tonight in Jerusalem, her son, prophesied to be salvation for Israel and a light to the Gentiles, was the firstborn who had been struck down.

And the moon, so bright, seemed to be mocking her.

Jerusalem: Home of Caiaphas
Nisan 15, before Sunrise

About two blocks away in an opulent, walled compound, the high priest Caiaphas was also having trouble sleeping. Earlier that day, he had followed the crowd to Golgotha and watched with particular satisfaction while the Romans hung the bloodied troublemaker Jesus on a cross. He had smirked as other bystanders had yelled, "Let's see you destroy the temple and rebuild it in three days now!"

"Destroy the temple, indeed," Caiaphas had muttered. "You Nazarene trash won't be turning over any more money-changer tables."

Caiaphas had left Golgotha for the temple complex once he had seen that the crucifixion was well underway; it was the day of preparation, and there were religious ceremonies to conduct. Though he secretly disdained the ceremonies, they were all part of the show, and the show was fabulously lucrative.

Incredibly though, on his way to temple, something strange had happened: The sun had suddenly dimmed. It was dim for about three hours, and Caiaphas had become increasingly unsettled. When the sun had brightened once again, he felt relieved, but his relief had lasted only until Amraphel approached him following the Passover sacrifices.

Amraphel was a member of the Council and generally could be counted upon to be a thorn in Caiaphas' side. He was a Pharisee, which was problematic enough, but even more so, he was a Pharisee of Pharisees, a true believer and extreme stickler for the smallest letter of the Law. The man could be expected to oppose anything Caiaphas wanted to do.

Nevertheless, against Jesus, he had been a useful ally. Amraphel had become angered at Jesus' failure to rebuke his followers for spreading rumors that he was the Messiah, when it was clear to Amraphel from the writings of the prophets that the Messiah would emerge from Judea. He was outraged at Jesus' allusions to himself as Divine and at Jesus' denunciations of the Pharisees.

So there had stood Amraphel, and the conversation had gone like this:

"Caiaphas."

"Amraphel."

"That rebel is dead," reported Amraphel.

"Good," said Caiaphas with a smile, "thank you for letting me know."

"There's something else you might want to know," continued Amraphel. "I stayed at Golgotha because I wanted to see the Romans dispose of his body."

Caiaphas nodded and smiled slightly. It was like Amraphel to be thorough.

Amraphel went on, "But the Romans didn't bury him; instead, Joseph of Arimathea took him off the cross, and he and Nicodemus buried him in Joseph's tomb."

"Oh," uttered Caiaphas, "thank you for that information, Amraphel." Caiaphas pivoted, to return to his duties. It was useful to know that Joseph, another Council member, was a follower of Jesus like Nicodemus was, but less so now that Jesus was dead. Amraphel remained stationary.

"There's something else," said Amraphel. Caiaphas turned back to face him. "Before Jesus was arrested, he told his disciples that he would be killed and would rise from the dead after three days."

"Well, he prophesied truly about his death," responded Caiaphas. "Are you concerned he will rise from the dead?"

Amraphel stated, "I am concerned about two things. One is that there was some kind of spiritual power in that man—obviously not from God, or he wouldn't have spoken against the priesthood established by Moses. The other thing is that his followers might steal his body and say that he did rise from the dead."

On his own, Caiaphas was unconcerned about the reports of Jesus displaying supernatural powers, but he addressed both of Amraphel's concerns.

"The Romans have numerous faults," replied Caiaphas, "but failing to complete executions is not one of them. I've never heard of anyone the Romans have executed, failing to stay dead.

"As for his disciples, I think they are neither so clever nor bold as to attempt such a thing, and besides, we would only have to ask them to produce their leader in order to disprove such a claim. Don't worry about it."

So Caiaphas had spoken then; that was in the afternoon. But the relief of finally ridding himself from the agitator Jesus hadn't lasted long. Word came of rumblings among the people and critical words being spoken against the chief priests and Sanhedrin.

Now, in the middle of the night, Amraphel's concern about the disciples stealing the body became his own. How many followers of Jesus were in the city? Where was the inner circle of them? How many other Sanhedrists or people of position were discreetly loyal to the movement? A major insurrection always begins small, and Jesus' teaching had already attracted considerable crowds.

Even if the temple system could withstand the possible establishment of an opposing political-religious party, Caiaphas' personal position as chief priest might be threatened. In fact, the Romans might just remove Caiaphas if they felt it would be advantageous to maintain peace.

He knew what to do. Caiaphas got up and called down the hallway for a servant. When the servant showed up, Caiaphas instructed him to bring a lamp, a wax tablet, and a stylus.

It was just before dawn.

First Day of Unleavened Bread

Jerusalem: Zebedee's Home
Daybreak

Mary Magdalene sat up on her mat and hugged her knees to her chest. Having not slept, she was happy to see the first glimmers of daylight appearing in the window. It would be better to be up, out of bed, and exhausted than lying down for hours in grief with nothing to do.

Time had lost all regularity. Yesterday morning seemed an eternity ago. Only yesterday, she had been at home in Bethany with her brother, sister, and the nine disciples as guests. Knowing that Jesus had been arrested during the night, she had been anxious to run to Jerusalem and learn what the outcome would be, and to support Jesus in any way that she could. The trials flew by so quickly, but the pain—seeing him so beaten, seeing him nailed to the wood—felt like it continued forever.

In an effort to shed the anguish of that thought, she shook her head and stood up. After pulling on her mantle and straightening her clothes, she rolled up the mat and leaned it into a corner, then headed for the kitchen.

Salome and Zebedee were already in the kitchen, along with a few others. Ordinarily the first meal of the day would be consumed in the late morning, but mindful of everyone missing the Passover Seder, Zebedee had placed hulled grains, nuts, figs, and raisins in bowls, and water in cups for drinking. Salome was busy placing them on the table.

Zebedee saw Mary and motioned to the low table, saying, "Mary, please help yourself."

Although she wasn't especially hungry, Mary responded quietly, "Thank you," and sat down, reclining beside the table. She said a prayer of thanksgiving and, knowing she needed to, forced herself to eat.

Eventually Clopas and his wife Mary came into the kitchen.

Mary Clopas sat next to Mary Magdalene, and Clopas sat next to his wife.

The Magdalene spoke first, "Mary, I am anxious to get to Bethany and see everyone there. I don't know how much the disciples know of what's happened, and Lazarus and Martha worry too much about me. But it's so important that we anoint his body…"

"I know," interrupted Mary Clopas, "and I'm concerned about my young James. We'll go to Bethany tomorrow as soon as we're finished with the work we have to do."

Salome, who was serving the table, joined the conversation. "I'm concerned about my James, too, but I need to stay here with John, who is grieving so deeply, and our guests. I will be eagerly awaiting your report when you return."

At that point, Mother Mary entered the kitchen, and everyone hushed immediately. Her sister Salome hurriedly set down her serving dish and went to comfort her. Likewise, her sister-in-law Mary Clopas rose from the table and joined Salome in providing solace to the mother of Jesus.

Mother Mary loved her family deeply and was thankful they were there for her. But as she stood in Salome's kitchen weeping, the words spoken to her by Simeon, some 33 years prior, that "a sword will pierce even your own soul," echoed in her mind as clearly as the day Joseph and she had brought their baby to the temple to dedicate him to God.

And now, the prophecy was fulfilled.

Caiaphas' House in Jerusalem
Nisan 15, the Passover Sabbath, Early Morning

Caiaphas finished writing on the wax tablet and called a trusted slave, Malchus, instructing him to deliver the message to the half-dozen Council members named in the message greeting. The message was short and pointed, requesting the men to join him immediately for a matter of utmost importance.

The men who assembled that early morning in Caiaphas' courtyard were in a disgruntled mood. This was the High Sabbath after all, and the previous evening's celebrations combined with an early morning summons left them without sufficient sleep. "This had better be important," remarked one named Zichri.

With Malchus standing to the side in a portico, Caiaphas looked them over. They had been chosen for two reasons: First, they were politically astute, in line with Caiaphas, and secondly, they were men he knew to be more religiously observant out of cultural considerations than conviction. Three were chief priests, and three were Pharisees.

"The issue before us is simple. Although we've succeeded in ridding the nation of the Galilean troublemaker," Caiaphas said, "it's come to my attention that there may be a plot in process by his uncivilized followers to steal the body and declare that he rose from the dead."

It was an exaggeration, but in all things political, truth is elastic.

Zichri spoke up, "They might say that, but extreme claims demand extreme evidence. We just say, 'Let's see this Jesus,' and the lie would be evident."

Caiaphas replied, "So it would seem. But, they could say something like, 'He's on his way to Galilee,' and if we go to Galilee, they would say, 'He's on his way to Judea,' and we would never catch up with him."

Zichri argued, "Then simply post some temple guard at the grave for a time. You didn't need to call us here for that."

"Of course I could have done that, but the temple guard is unsuitable for this task," returned Caiaphas. "We need to ask Pilate to post a guard."

The men looked at each other quizzically.

"Why do we need the Romans?" asked one of them. "If our guards can't adequately oversee a dead man's grave, why do we expect that they can guard the temple?" They all laughed, except Caiaphas.

"Do I need to spell it out for you idiots?" yelled the high priest in exasperation.

"There was a lot of support among the rabble for this Nazarene, and there have been strong words voiced on the street against the priests and Council. There will be people coming to the tomb, particularly tomorrow between the Sabbaths, to pay respects to the man who would have destroyed our nation. Do you see how it would look if there were temple guards there? It would make us the focus of their grief and anger.

"But with hated Roman guards present at the tomb, it would remind the fools that he died on a Roman cross, and that should deflect any discontent away from us," explained Caiaphas.

He continued, "Also, think of this. If for some reason this rebellion grows, and we keep the Romans involved from the outset, the Romans will not be able to fault us alone for failure to prevent it. We need to see Pilate now."

The men were sufficiently convinced, but one Pharisee objected that it was the Passover Sabbath.

"So what's more important, the temple and the priesthood, or a minor point of the Law?" Caiaphas countered.

One of them smirked, saying, "Jesus reportedly said it was lawful to pull an ox out of a well on the Sabbath. So, if it's lawful to pull an ox out of a well, then it should be lawful to make sure a corpse stays in a grave on the Sabbath."

Malchus had always considered being the lead slave to the high priest as something of an honor, even though Caiaphas was terribly rude to his staff. But now, as he reached up and touched his right ear, he thought back to two nights earlier, when he had gone to the garden of Gethsemane with the arresting party to apprehend Jesus. They had been expecting violence, yet the only trouble they encountered was when a zealous follower of the Galilean had cut off Malchus' ear with a sword. And then, amazingly, Jesus had put a stop to the attack and actually *reattached* his ear. The very one he was pulling on now! The accusations of insurrection against Jesus seemed so absurd in the light of the miracle he had experienced.

And here these men were, mocking the man they had put to death, the very man who had healed his ear, who had performed a miracle of God. For the first time in his life, Malchus thought, "I would rather serve anybody else, anywhere else. God, set me free from this slavery."

Jerusalem: Herod's Palace
The First Hour (about 7 a.m.)

So it was, on the day after the Passover preparation, that is, on High Holy Sabbath of Passover itself, that the chief priests and the Pharisees ignored the religious dictates of Moses and the Law and went to Pilate.

This was no ordinary occasion, and Pilate recognized that a delegation of Jewish leadership appearing on a Sabbath, violating their own passionately defended laws, meant that there was a serious request in the offing. So Pilate positioned himself on the judgment seat to receive the seven men as an object statement of his position of authority.

Now Caiaphas considered all men to be inferior to himself, and Pilate—a less educated, less cultured, less wealthy *Gentile*— to be more inferior than most, but he knew when to genuflect.

So he began with a formal but stiff bow, and said, "Honorable Governor Pilate, we beg your pardon on this most holy day to bring you a matter of urgency concerning Jesus the Galilean whom you crucified yesterday.

"Sir, we remember that when he was still alive, that deceiver said, 'After three days I will rise again.' Therefore, give orders for the grave to be made secure until the third day; otherwise, his disciples may come and steal his body away and say to the people, 'He has risen from the dead,' and the last deception will be even worse than the first one."

"Yes, that would be a terrible situation, wouldn't it?" asked Pilate. "A group of illiterate Galileans running all over the countryside with a dead man in tow, saying, 'Follow us!'

"Why, I cannot think of any greater threat to Caesar or the temple, than a dead Messiah and all of Judea following him in a funeral procession!" Pilate shouted, standing.

He sat down again, enjoying the moment. "Set your own guard," Pilate commanded.

"Ah, under ordinary circumstances, we would have done that," replied Caiaphas, "but we thought the sight of Roman authority would be more intimidating to his followers."

Pilate sat for a moment staring at them, blinking. He saw what they were up to.

"Oh, yes, his mighty followers. You mean the rag-tag, unarmed, disordered collection of fishermen, women, and children," Pilate corrected. He paused for effect.

"So we have one of two situations here. Either you believe your Jewish guards are completely incompetent, or you want your people to see Rome as the cause of this man's death, rather than the real cause—the jealousy of the men standing before me this morning."

The verbal slap was sweet revenge for yesterday morning, and Pilate sat quietly savoring it and watching the men fidget with nervousness.

"But," Pilate finally said to their relief, "I would be a complete failure as a governor if I allowed a group of Jerusalem's finest armed men to be overpowered by a handful of grieving women. Imagine what they would think in Rome!"

With exaggerated disdain, Pilate ordered, "Take a guard of soldiers, and go make the grave as secure as you know how." Pilate nodded toward his Tribune nearby as a silent command to authorize a squad for the task. The Tribune, in turn, summoned the centurion Petronius and dispatched him and a squad of four soldiers to follow the chief priests.

So they went to the tomb. The priests prepared a seal to affix to the stone. It was a length of cord, one end fixed with molten wax to the round stone covering the tomb entrance, and the other end similarly secured on the stone wall behind it. Petronius and Caiaphas each impressed the lumps of cooling wax with his own signet. Anyone moving the stone would break the seals, each having an impression of Jewish and Roman authority. The penalty thereupon would be death.

Petronius had the squad of soldiers pitch a tent and posted the guard.

Caiaphas returned home from the tomb, muttering expletives against Pilate on the way, yet internally satisfied that he had accomplished his political objective.

Bethany: Lazarus' Home

The disciples began moving slowly on the morning of the Passover Sabbath, drained from a night of grief and mentally foggy from two successive nights with precious little sleep.

Martha had set out an early breakfast of dried fish, unleavened bread, and fresh vegetables for the nine guests. The disciples were appreciative but ate slowly and said little. Each of them was processing feelings and thoughts through a mind muddied by fatigue.

When finished, two of the disciples, perceiving Martha's deep sorrow, assisted her in meal cleanup. Most of the disciples found a place to sit in the courtyard outside, in spots where either trees or the house provided sufficient shade. Their bodily postures bespoke of the weight upon their souls; their minds bounced among thoughts of the past, the present, and an overturned future. Only days ago, the crowds proclaimed Jesus as the Son of David, the King of Israel; now he was gone, and tomorrow was starkly blank.

"May I?" Thaddeus had walked over to Simon the Zealot and was pointing to a spot next to Simon on the stone ledge. Simon simply gestured with an open hand to give assent. Thaddeus sat down.

"Do you think the chief priests and Pharisees will come after us?" Thaddeus asked. "You know that in the days of Herod, he destroyed the followers of anyone who opposed him."

The Zealot's eyes narrowed, "I don't think so, Thaddeus. As evil as they have proven themselves to be, the Council is not Herod. They do not have the power of capital punishment anyway; that's why they used Pilate to destroy Jesus. But more than that, we are viewed by the Pharisees and priests as ignorant peasants. They would think that without Jesus, we would be lost."

"And they would be right," responded Thaddeus.

"They would be right," acknowledged Simon.

Between the Sabbaths

Jerusalem: Zebedee's Home
Nisan 16, before Sunrise

Mary Magdalene sat up on her mat at nautical dawn as she first perceived the eastern sky brightening. In the house it was still too dark to see without a lamp; outside, it was yet too early for the birds to be chirping. The night had been difficult. While sleep had come sporadically and fitfully, enabled only by extreme fatigue, none of it had been deep and restorative. Yet, it was a better night than the last, and she said a prayer of thanksgiving to God for it.

The weight of depression on her soul was crushing. Were it not for her love for others and deep sense of responsibility to them, she might have remained in the room all day. Also, her love for her Lord was calling her to visit the tomb.

From the kitchen came sounds; someone else was up earlier than usual. Mary arose, straightened her tunic, pulled her mantle on over her head, gathered it at the waist with a colorful sash, combed and pinned her hair, and rolled up her sleeping mat. Entering the kitchen, she saw Salome already at work by the light of two oil lamps, grinding flour for the day's bread.

"Salome, God bless you for getting up so early to prepare for the household," Mary Magdalene greeted.

"And God bless you for giving me some company," Salome returned, smiling.

Mary Magdalene offered to assist, and the two women worked on kneading and flattening the unleavened dough. Salome broke away to set some food on the table for the household. It was altogether too early for the first meal of the day, but the women, except for Mother Mary, were leaving for the market this morning. There would be no one to serve the men, and Salome was not about to burden Mother Mary with any domestic chores.

Mary Clopas came into the kitchen, and the three women sat

at the table and shared a light, early breakfast including leftover unleavened bread. They rose immediately afterwards. Salome brought out three woven date-palm bags, one for each.

Zebedee came into the kitchen, rubbing his eyes and a bit unsteady from having just awoken.

"Good, you are up." said his wife. "The bread dough is rolled and cut on the prep table. You will need to heat the oven and bake the bread. If you have any question as to when it is finished baking, ask Mother Mary. No one likes to eat charcoal, dear."

Zebedee rolled his eyes with a hint of a smile, "I was told I could have respect or a wife. So I chose a wife."

Zebedee kissed Salome, and the three women put on their head coverings and sandals and headed for the marketplace to purchase the raw materials for making anointing oils.

The High Sabbath day of Passover was past; today the markets were open, and tomorrow was the weekly Sabbath. Consequently, the women had only this one day to purchase the spices, process them into anointing oils, and anoint the body of Jesus.

Jerusalem: The Agora Market
Early Morning

The walk to the market was a short one, taking them from Zebedee's home in the southwestern "Essene Quarter" with its narrow streets, northward through the affluent Upper City with its walled residential compounds. The women made the trip in about a quarter hour. The morning was still cool when the women arrived.

It was certainly the finest market in town, arguably the finest in the eastern Mediterranean, with the upscale shops aligned north to south on the street facing Herod's Palace. Despite being early, the shops were already open, and there was a fair amount of traffic, mostly from the Jewish visitors from outside of Judea. Salome, being more familiar with Jerusalem than the other women, directed her companions to the best merchant for spices.

Salome placed an order for three spices and a few logs of rose petals.

The shopkeeper recognized the request as typical for burial preparation.

"Is this for a family member who has passed?" he inquired.

"It is," replied Salome succinctly, without satisfying the man's curiosity by giving a name.

"My condolences," the man said, as he moved to gather the spices.

A young woman who had just stepped into the shop spoke to Salome, "My condolences also for your loss. I just came from a tomb myself, of that rabbi Jesus whom the Romans murdered two days ago. Many are going to see where he was buried, and many are grieving. There must be a hundred people there already."

"Oh. Well. Thank you," murmured Salome, greatly surprised. She paid the shopkeeper and distributed the bundles of spices among the women for their bags. The stunned women exited the shop.

Bethany: Lazarus' Home

For those in Lazarus' home, the day prior—seemingly so long ago—had been a day of intense grief, a day of trying to grapple emotionally with the indescribable tragedy that had befallen them. This morning that grief had become mixed with deep depression and feelings of uncertainty.

"I think we should try to find Peter and John today," said James the Younger.

"I'm not sure that's a good idea," cautioned Thaddeus. "We only have one place for all of us to stay in the city, and Judas may have told the priests about it. Or, someone might recognize us and alert the priests or elders."

"Assuming we don't overstay our welcome, we should remain here and wait," said the older James. "Peter and John would know where we are."

Lazarus, having just entered the room, responded warmly, "Of course, you are all welcome here. As long as you need."

James Zebedee continued, "Thank you, Lazarus. ...And there is another important consideration. Remember how Jesus said that after three days, he would rise from the dead?"

Everyone's attention riveted on James.

"Of course," said Andrew. "We discussed it among ourselves at the time."

"And what did Jesus mean by that?" Philip asked seriously. It was an honest question.

"Philip is right. We don't know what that meant," said Matthew. "Did he say that figuratively or literally? Was he really speaking of his physical death? And even if so, did he also mean a physical rising, or rather that his spirit would rise after three days and return to God?"

"Right, Matthew, Jesus never explained it," answered James, "but I think it would be wise to wait here three days, if that's acceptable to Lazarus. Maybe we will receive more direction then."

Lazarus spoke up, "We should not forget that less than two weeks ago Jesus raised me from the dead, and I was dead four days."

Thaddeus retorted, "Yes, but it was Jesus who raised you from the dead. Who do we know who can raise Jesus from the dead? Can you?"

There was a moment of uncomfortable silence. Lazarus simply bowed his head and closed his eyes. The older James frowned at the impertinence of Thaddeus.

The Zealot, sitting next to Thaddeus, leaned over and whispered, "Honor our host, man."

Thaddeus expressed his embarrassment, "I'm sorry, Lazarus. I didn't mean to be so sharp with you."

"But you are right," said Lazarus graciously, looking up at Thaddeus. "I don't know anyone who can raise Jesus."

Jerusalem: The Upper City

Immediately after leaving the shop, the women stopped on the street and huddled to discuss this news.

"What can we do now?" whispered Mary Clopas. "There will be an even larger crowd by this afternoon, which is the earliest time we could get there with the anointing oils. We need to do this privately."

"If we went at dawn tomorrow, we could do the anointing before anyone else would be there," said Mary Magdalene.

Salome replied, "Tomorrow is Sabbath."

"Oh, I forgot what day it was," said Mary Magdalene, closing her eyes briefly. "So, we will need to go the first day of the week. Let's do this: First, we need to notify Joanna and Susanna of the change of plans. Then, we will prepare the spices. After that, Mary and I will go to Bethany for the Sabbath, and at dawn after Sabbath, we will go to the tomb."

The women agreed and commenced walking towards the Palace of Herod Antipas. Upon arrival, Joanna and Susanna were notified of the change in timing of the anointing. Both were pleased that an early morning plan to honor their Lord would certainly make it possible for them to participate.

And so, the women's plans were fully crystallized. As early as possible on the morning after Sabbath, Mary Clopas and Mary Magdalene would travel from Bethany to Zebedee's home and pick up Salome and the anointing oils, after which they would travel to the Palace to pick up Joanna and Susanna. Then all five women would walk to the tomb and anoint Jesus' body.

Satisfied with this plan of action, Salome and the two Marys continued their circuit back to Zebedee's home.

Yet their plan was doomed to failure. Not one of the women had considered the difficulty of moving the massive stone from the entrance to the tomb, and there would be no one available to provide assistance at that early hour. But that was actually the least of their problems. For the women did not know that five Roman soldiers stood guard at the tomb, which was sealed shut with a wax insignia designating the authority of Rome. The guards risked execution if they allowed anyone to disturb the seal or the body.

This much was certain: No one was going to open that tomb. The women had set themselves upon a fool's errand.

Jerusalem: Zebedee's Home
The Second Hour (8 a.m.)

The three women arrived at Zebedee's house, slightly comforted by having something useful to do. Salome separated from her shopping companions to sit alongside Mother Mary and hold her hand.

Mary Clopas and Mary Magdalene went to the kitchen with the spices, diced them, and crushed them using stone mortars and pestles. The spices were fresh and yielded their oils well, but the extraction method for the oil of each spice was slightly different and time-consuming, and the yields were small. After several hours, their total output was only a few ounces of oil. But it was enough.

Salome provided three alabaster vials, into which the women carefully spooned the precious oils. When each vial was full, it was stoppered with a wax plug and left with Salome for safekeeping.

Jerusalem to Bethany

It was now past midday. Mary Magdalene and Mary Clopas prepared themselves for the trip to Bethany, about 3 miles away from Zebedee's home in southwest Jerusalem. Clopas decided to accompany his wife and Mary Magdalene on the journey, not only for protection but also because he was anxious to see his son James the Younger. All three donned head coverings and sandals. Clopas took a staff, and the women took woven baskets with fruit that Zebedee insisted on sending with them.

Because the streets were much busier than on non-feast days, the three of them took a less-traveled but slightly longer route. Passing south through the city wall at the nearby Essene Gate, they turned immediately left and took the footpath that followed the city wall on the outside of it, going due east about a half mile, then turning north for about three-quarters of a mile until they picked up the road to Bethany.

From Jerusalem, the road climbed up the Mount of Olives.

Partway up the Mount, having reached the walled garden of Gethsemane, Mary Magdalene stopped and announced to Clopas and Mary, "Here is where they arrested him."

She turned and looked back down the hill, across the Kidron valley, to the massive temple mount opposite them. The temple itself faced them directly, its grand white stone pillars and parapet rising high above the entire city. Smoke from votive and freewill offerings ascended in front of the temple, although the altar was obscured by a lower wall. Clopas and Mary turned and joined Mary Magdalene in looking at the temple.

"They didn't recognize the Messiah," stated Mary Clopas quietly.

Clopas said, "And they don't comprehend the Law or the Prophets, even though they sit in Moses' seat."

"Pride was the reason," answered Mary Magdalene, who then turned and continued up the Mount. Clopas and his wife followed. They reached the top of the ridge and began the long descent to Bethany.

Bethany: Lazarus' home
Afternoon

Lazarus and Martha were overjoyed to see their sister Mary Magdalene standing at the door along with Clopas and his wife Mary. The greetings were full of warmth and love but were greatly subdued as the atmosphere was leaden with grief.

Clopas and Mary hugged their son James the Younger and gave the older James the message of love sent by his parents Zebedee and Salome. They also shared with Andrew the news that his brother Peter was staying at the upper room, although no one seemed to know why. Andrew thought it might be that Peter thought it a better place to hide from the Jewish authorities, since Caiaphas knew the Zebedee family.

When they were all settled, Mary Magdalene described to Lazarus, Martha, and the disciples what she and Mary Clopas had seen when Jesus was removed from the cross and interred in the tomb. They were all gratified to know that despite the humiliating death he had suffered, at least his burial was honorable.

Lazarus said to his sister, "We have all worried about you and missed you so much. Now I hope you will be staying put here for a while."

"No, we can't do that," Mary replied. "The burial was hasty, and his body wasn't anointed with perfuming oils. Earlier today we bought the spices and prepared the oils. On the morning after the Sabbath we must return very early to do this work before crowds gather. We heard that there were many people at his grave today, paying their respects."

"I understand," said Lazarus, "and wish I could accompany you. I would like to see where he is buried and offer prayers myself."

Mary replied, "The tomb is just outside the Gennath Gate on the path to Golgotha. It is the only one near there with a round stone sealing it. We will be leaving tomorrow, probably before anyone else is up."

Lazarus stood up straight, walked over to his sister, and kissed her on the forehead. "God bless you for doing this, Mary. I am proud of you." Then he turned to Clopas and his wife Mary, "And God bless you two also, for doing my friend Jesus this honor."

Weekly Sabbath

Jerusalem: Joseph's Tomb, Outside the City Walls
Nisan 17

On the weekly Sabbath, another day of rest, many Jewish mourners visited the tomb of Jesus, although fewer than the day before. Periodically a Gentile would stop by. The mourners would say a prayer, and most left a pebble on the growing pile beside a stone bench in the garden. The mourners would have preferred to place their "stones of remembrance" closer to the golel, the round stone that covered the tomb entrance, but the soldiers prevented it.

It was now mid-morning. Two Roman soldiers by the names of Lurio and Scaurus stood guard by the tomb, holding spears vertically, with butt ends resting on the ground. Two more soldiers rested in the shade of the garden as they waited for their rotation.

"I have to say, Lurio, that I never thought I would travel this far from Italia, just to guard the tomb of a dead Galilean," said Scaurus.

"Well, it won't get you a triumphal procession in Rome, that's for certain," Lurio responded. "But, don't be discouraged, Scaurus. I would applaud you. You're doing a damn good job," Lurio chuckled.

"Yeah, if only there was recognition for this kind of valor," Scaurus said sarcastically. "What I don't understand, though, is why anyone might want to steal a commoner's corpse. I mean, this guy wasn't buried with any riches or anything."

"It doesn't make sense to me either, but neither does Judea. My opinion is, if some Jews want to steal a Jewish body, why not let them? To me, it's a Jewish matter, not a Roman one."

"Hey, Scaurus," hollered Albinus, one of the Romans lounging in the shade, "if anybody's coming to steal a corpse, then you'd better look lively, man, or they might haul your ass off by mistake!"

The remark brought howls of laughter from the soldiers, including Scaurus.

The women who were planning to visit the tomb on the following day were resting according to the commandment. Longer prayers than usual were being said by Joanna and Susanna in Herod Antipas' Palace. In Zebedee's house, Salome still spent most of her time sitting with Mother Mary, but she took time by herself for her weekly Sabbath devotions, which included extra prayer time this day, as she poured out her grieving heart before God.

Bethany: Lazarus' home

In Bethany, Mary Magdalene and Mary Clopas were anxious about getting back to Jerusalem, yet they appreciated the required time of rest and the comforting company of family and friends.

Lazarus saw Martha sitting by herself, so he came and sat beside his sister.

"Martha, how are you?" he asked.

"As you would expect," returned Martha, "my soul is just overwhelmed. Two weeks ago, I was mourning your death. But that turned into a fountain of joy when Jesus called you forth from the tomb. And now, I am mourning Jesus. My joy is gone, my lamp extinguished."

"Remember what Jesus told you when I was in the tomb?" asked Lazarus.

Martha smiled faintly, as she recited the words: "I am the resurrection and the life; he who believes in me, even though he dies, will live."

Lazarus looked at her. "And you told him that you believed it."

Martha replied, "Yes, I did. And I said I believed he was the Messiah."

Tears welled up in her eyes. "But the Messiah was supposed to remain forever," she said despondently, "and he is gone."

Lazarus patted her hand, "I know, Martha, I know. I feel right now like a boat completely adrift on the sea. But we should try to do as the psalmist wrote, 'From the rising of the sun, to the going down of the same, the name of the Lord is to be praised.' So we should try to praise him, even though our sun has gone down."

He kissed his sister on the side of the head, then arose and walked into the courtyard. In the courtyard he found Clopas standing by himself, looking out at the landscape where the land and road descended to the ancient city of Jericho. Lazarus knew little about Clopas and, indeed, greatly desired a moment of solitude for himself, yet he felt compelled as a host to engage his guest.

"Greetings, Clopas," Lazarus began. "I hope I am not interrupting deep thoughts."

"Oh, no," said Clopas. "I was just thinking about a business obligation that has come at a bad time. You know, Jesus was my nephew, and his mother is my sister-in-law, so I need to be with the family during this time of mourning. Yet I own a family farm in Emmaus, worked by tenant farmers, and the barley is ready for harvest now. Harvest waits for no man. I think I will travel there tomorrow to see if everything has been made ready, and return to Jerusalem the day after."

Clopas sighed. "My work, it seems so unimportant after my nephew's death. But the taxes are high, and if we lose a crop, we could lose the farm."

"May God speed your journey and bless your steps," said Lazarus. "I'm glad you and Mary have come to stay with us, even for a day. You both are always welcome here. A relative of Jesus is a friend to me."

On the other side of the courtyard, the disciples sat together in a cloud of depression. However, the feelings of total confusion they had yesterday were giving way to thoughts of the immediate future.

Nathanael spoke to Matthew, "Matthew, have you given any thought to what you are going to do now?"

It was a question each had been asking internally, but now it was on the table. Some harsh realizations had begun to percolate through their minds, and the ordinarily quiet Matthew now voiced them all:

"Well, Nathanael, without Jesus, we have no financial support. People who have supported the work gave because of Jesus, not because of us disciples. Without Jesus, we have no message for the people. His was the wisdom; our message was just to point to him. Without Jesus, there can be no ministry of power. When we healed people, it was because he told us to do it. Without Jesus, we aren't "the Twelve" any longer—in truth, only eleven now. We are no longer the hand-picked men being trained by the Messiah; we are nothing.

Matthew's statement stung; they knew it was true.

"Now, I don't want to proclaim bad news," continued Matthew, "and I love you all. These three years together have meant everything to me. He meant everything to me. But he's gone. And the nine of us sitting here are just nine homeless, unemployed Galileans."

After a moment of silence, Nathanael asked again, "So, what are you going to do now?"

Matthew answered, "After three years on the road, I don't feel like the small towns of Galilee are really my home anymore. The sun and the stars feel closer than Galilee.

"I can't go back to tax collecting either. Jesus never condemned me for tax collecting, but after being with him, I saw the greed that had motivated me as a tax collector. I'm not the same person anymore."

Nathanael asked again, softly, "So what are you going to do?"

"Well," Matthew replied, "I think there would be more work in the larger cities. Jerusalem is out because of the chief priests; I never want to see another one of them. So the coastal cities— Joppa, Caesarea, maybe even Tyre—I will probably go to one of them."

Nathanael pressed again, "...and do what?"

Matthew answered, "Whatever work I can find. Maybe I'll find work as part of a boat crew."

The Zealot popped his head up, "What, you, a tax-collector-turned-sailor? What do you know about sailing?"

"Well, I've spent a lot of time on the Sea of Galilee over the last few years," countered Matthew.

"Yeah, sitting on the cushion, a-trembling and a-shaking!" ribbed Philip. Everyone but Matthew was chuckling now.

"Easy, now," began Nathanael, in mock seriousness, "the boats in Joppa may have need of some extra ballast."

"Hey..." protested Matthew.

Thaddeus piled on and said, "Mr. Seasick himself at your service! Now where is that bilge bucket? I'm going to be sick!" Thaddeus added some retching noises for effect.

The Zealot added, "Yeah, remember the storm when Matthew was greener than the water?"

James the Younger then spoke up, "That was the storm Jesus stopped with a word."

Instantly, the banter and levity ceased; silence fell over the group.

It was only broken by one comment from James Zebedee, who said softly, "I will never forget that."

The Sabbath Ends

Jerusalem: The Temple Mount
Nisan 17, Approaching Twilight

Three members of the Sanhedrin stood waiting in the Gentile's courtyard of the temple complex, as a joyous, boisterous crowd began to gather in front of them. Each Sanhedrist held a large woven basket with a sickle set within it. Attendants to the Sanhedrists held torches to counter the gathering dusk. The occasion was the harvesting of the sheaves of first fruits, the preparatory part of an offering of the "first fruits" of the earth—the first grain harvest of the year.

When the appointed time came—that is, when the Hazzan sounded the trumpet on the temple wall, signifying that Nisan 17 had ended and Nisan 18 had begun—three priests began leading the crowd in singing psalms and celebratory songs. At that point, the Sanhedrists turned and led the happy crowd, singing as they went, down the stairway to the Sheep Gate of the temple complex, across the Kidron valley, and up the hillside of the Mount of Olives. They paused at the edge a particular small field, designated and marked out for their purpose, located not far from the garden of Gethsemane.

The Sabbath of Passover was over. *Yom HaBikkurim,*[18] the day of first fruits had begun.

In the field was the objective of the three elders of the council: three clumps of barley, still standing, each tied separately, in preparation for this moment.

Zichri was the lead Sanhedrist. He step towards the center sheaf, as the other two Sanhedrists stepped simultaneously towards their respective sheaves. All three turned and faced the crowd and waited until the song being led by the rabbis was finished.

---

[18] *HaBikkurim* is derived from the same root word as *firstborn;* the two words sound nearly identical.

With a nod from Zichri, the Sanhedrists set their baskets alongside their sheaves, grabbed their sickles from the baskets, and stood upright again.

Zichri cleared his throat and asked the crowd with a loud voice, "Has the sun gone down?"

"Yes!" responded the crowd.

Thereupon, all three Sanhedrists held the blades of their sickles aloft. Zichri asked the crowd, "With these sickles?"

"Yes!" responded the crowd again.

The Sanhedrists pointed their sickles at their baskets in unison, and Zichri asked the crowd, "Into these baskets?"

"Yes!" chorused the crowd for the third time.

Having received those affirmations from the witnesses, Zichri and his companions began harvesting the sheaves and placing the grain in the baskets, until the three men had cumulatively harvested about one ephah.[19]

When the three of them were finished, Zichri shouted to the crowd, "The sheaf of first fruits is harvested!"

The crowd cheered, and the rabbis began leading the people in another psalm. Following the psalm, the rabbis led them back down the Mount of Olives, with the Sanhedrists and their harvest bringing up the rear.

As they went, Zichri caught sight of the garden of Gethsemane and remarked to one of his fellow elders, "You should have been here two nights ago when we arrested Jesus in that garden."

"Why?" asked the other Sanhedrist.

"Because, doing the will of God is very satisfying," replied Zichri.

"Amen," was the reply.

Across the Kidron valley, through the Sheep Gate, up the stairway, and into the temple complex went the crowd, singing as they went. When they arrived at the temple, the crowd parted, half to each side, and the elders walked side-by-side through the middle of the crowd to present the sheaves to the priests. The priests said a final prayer, another cheer went up, and the crowd

---

[19] About 5.8 gallons, in US measure

and elders dispersed to their lodgings.

The rabbis carefully stored the sheaves at the temple for the upcoming midday offering.

Jerusalem: Joseph's Tomb, outside the City Walls
The Dark of Night

Twilight had turned to night in the garden, ending the Sabbath and beginning the first day of the week. A gibbous moon, only three days away from being full, would be rising in the east at the third hour of the night,[20] yet even before the moon provided its light, visibility was still good for the soldiers guarding the tomb. The sky was absolutely clear, all the constellations shone brightly, and the band of the Milky Way was easily seen. The combined starlight, augmented by the light-colored limestone all around, provided sufficient illumination for the soldiers to perceive any figures who might approach in the darkness.

The soldiers took their duty seriously, but the job was a thankless one, and when there were no visitors to the tomb—which there wouldn't be until tomorrow morning sometime—the job was profoundly boring. Mostly, the conversations revolved around food and getting back to their comrades-in-arms stationed at Fort Antonia, adjacent to the temple mount.

Albinus was on duty, and he turned to his fellow guardian and said, "Looks like another good night for star-watching," when a rumbling sound started. The two soldiers instinctively lifted their spears to a posture of readiness, but no sooner had they done so, that the ground began shaking. Lurio, Scaurus, and the centurion Petronius, previously asleep in the tent, scrambled out while simultaneously grappling for their weapons and struggling to assess the situation.

And they just made it to standing positions when it happened.

There was a flash and a mighty crack, like the sound of a whip. For an instant, Albinus thought lightning had struck in the

---

[20] I.e., 9 p.m.

middle of the four men. But in the next instant, when the temporary blindness from the flash faded, Albinus saw them.

They looked like men, but they were not. One was a head taller than any man he had ever seen; the other, head and shoulders taller. The two figures exuded might and authority, more than any of Rome's mightiest soldiers. From their clothing—as white as the snow—emanated a light all around.

That was enough to petrify any man, but it was the face that Albinus saw that struck deep terror in his heart. It looked like lightning, and it was fearsome. Never had Albinus seen such power and intensity in any man's eyes, and it caused him to shake with great tremors. He tried to hang on to his spear, but his hand went limp, and the spear clattered to the ground. Then his knees buckled, and he collapsed off to the side and away from the tomb. As if on cue, the other three guards and the centurion fell to the ground simultaneously.

Albinus never lost consciousness, though his frame was as immobile as a dead man. He couldn't move any extremity—not even turn his head—but he was able to move his eyes. He watched the two figures step forward between him and the other prostrate guard, to face the golel stone, and one of them made a slight wave of his hand. Amazingly, the stone rolled away under its own power, as if obeying a command. Then one of the figures leapt, with the ease of a deer, landing on the golel in a sitting position. The other figure stepped to the opposite side of the opening; both then faced outward from the tomb.

Immediately, another sound—Albinus would later describe it as a roar—seemed to come from heaven, and a light brighter than the sun began to shine forth from the tomb opening. Albinus was forced to turn his eyes away from the light and to close his eyelids as tightly as possible, but even so, the light came through brightly.

It only lasted a moment, then quickly faded to blackness. Albinus opened his eyes again and turned them back to the tomb opening. Light was coming from the tomb, but not as intensely now. He still couldn't see inside it. The creatures, or beings, whatever they were, had vanished!

Whether they were inside the tomb now, or not, wasn't

foremost on the soldier's mind. He sensed that whatever had been holding him immobile was releasing its grip. He struggled to all fours, grabbed his spear from the ground, staggered upright, and ran as hard as he could down the path to the Gennath Gate. As he started running, he noticed that his fellow four soldiers were running in the same direction, as fast as they could go.

No one stopped at the Gennath Gate. Immediately after passing through the gate, they instinctively made a hard left to avoid passing right in front of Herod's Palace, with other Roman soldiers stationed at all of the entrances.

They ran hard towards Antipas' Palace, then took a sharp right and ran south through a street of the Upper City. After two more blocks, they slowed to a jog and continued at that pace until they arrived at the large outdoor Theater.

The five men slipped into the Theater and stopped in the orchestra section, below the seating area. They were sweating and panting, and burst into rapid talking over each other, in loud whispers.

"Did you ever..."

"No. What was..."

"Gods? I don't know..."

"Like lightning! Did you see the tomb open?"

"Should we go back?"

"Are you crazy?"

"What happened to..."

"Stop it, stop it!" hissed Petronius. "Just shut up!"

Everyone stopped and looked at Petronius, hoping he would provide direction and courage. Petronius was older than the rest and respected for his experience, but at the moment, his face showed his fear.

"Just shut up and give me a chance to think," he said and began pacing back and forth.

He paced back and forth only a short distance, then turned and addressed his charges.

"Look, centurion Sosia told me about some of the things that happened three days ago at Golgotha and how he thought this man, the guy in the tomb, was a son of God. When he said that, I thought he'd been out in the sun too long. Maybe he was right. But we can't go back there and think we can fight those two—whatever—creatures or gods. They could have slain us all when we were on the ground. We stand no chance against them.

"Also, whether or not we find them still there, it doesn't matter. They opened the tomb. They probably took the body. But even if they didn't, the seal is broken. We've abandoned our posts. We are likely to be executed for it. Or made to wish we had been executed.

"We can't desert and run for another province; they would track us down very quickly, and we might well be crucified, or at least you four; I might be given an easier death because of rank," said Petronius.

The panic of only minutes earlier was now replaced with a different panic in the four listening soldiers, as they saw the dire predicament they were in.

"We only have one chance of surviving this," advised Petronius. "That is, we need to get to the chief priests early this morning to tell them what happened. They were the ones who asked Pilate for the guard to be set; they're the ones worried about the body being stolen. Maybe they can act as a buffer. Damn, I never thought I might die a dishonorable death in such a godless place as this."

"A godless place like this"—it was just an expression—but the five soldiers spent a few hours of the night in the empty theater, worried and praying to every god they knew, including the god of the Jews, to deliver them from their perilous plight.

Nagging at Petronius was the thought that they had left the tent and some equipment and arms in the garden. It would not help their case before Pilate to be missing their gear. He gathered the soldiers, and they returned to the garden, which was quiet. The tomb was open but dark inside and devoid of any corpse. They collected the tent and other gear, and withdrew to another secluded place outside the city wall to wait for daylight and an opportunity to approach the chief priests.

First Light

From Bethany to Jerusalem
Nisan 18, In the Darkness, Just before Dawn

Mary Magdalene was able to sleep better this night after the weekly Sabbath, but her gnawing sorrow still caused her to awake repeatedly throughout the night.

She was in her own room and long ago had learned to judge the time of the night from the phase of the moon and its position in her window, high on the wall, which faced west to Jerusalem. When she first saw the waning moon appear, at the window's lintel, she knew it was just past the ninth hour of the night,[21] and later when she saw it had dropped below the level of the sill, she knew that sunrise was not far away.

By the light of that moon, Mary arose and prepared herself for the trip to Jerusalem. She quietly crept to Mary Clopas' room, called softly, and was pleased to hear Mary acknowledge that she was already up. Mary Clopas awoke her husband Clopas, and in a few minutes, all three of them were ready to go.

Lazarus was a light sleeper, and he arose to see them off and offer a prayer for protection and the success of their purpose.

The first two-thirds of the walk to Jerusalem was a long incline uphill to the top of the Mount of Olives, but it was easier than usual, as they were the only travelers on the road at this hour, and the night was pleasantly cool. The bright moon was towards the west, in the direction they were headed, and it seemed like a beacon.

After walking silently a short distance, they began sharing among themselves stories of what Jesus had said, what he had done, and how he had blessed each of them.

Clopas and his wife Mary had heard the story of Jesus raising Lazarus from the dead—as had most of Jerusalem—but they

---

[21] I.e., 3 a.m.

wanted to hear it from Mary Magdalene. Mary was happy to share the story for their sakes and to honor Jesus, but she omitted the part where Jesus had said to Martha, "I am the resurrection and the life; he who believes in me shall live even if he dies." With Jesus in a grave, it simply would have been too painful to say that, and even remembering those words of his increased her sorrow.

They crested the Mount and started down the steeper side towards the city. Reversing the route they had used two days ago, they followed the path outside the wall, around the south side of the city, and in through the Essene Gate at the southwest corner. About 200 cubits beyond the gate, they were at Zebedee's home.

Salome was waiting for them, ready with a small woven bag of the perfuming oils and additional spices, and she stepped out the door with the strap of the bag over her shoulder. Clopas said goodbye to the women and entered the house, as the remainder of the journey was women's work. The three women—Mary, Mary, and Salome—started north to Antipas' Palace, as the sky was brightening in the east. The sun was still out of sight below the dark silhouette of the Mount of Olives ridge to their right.

When almost to Antipas' Palace, Mary Clopas suddenly stopped short and exclaimed, "Mary, Salome!"

"What?" they responded in unison with alarm.

"The stone! Who will remove the stone? Who will roll it away from the tomb for us?"

No one had thought of that detail. By going to the tomb so early to avoid curious onlookers, they also had deprived themselves of any men's assistance.

Salome asked, "Should we return to the house and get some of the men to come with us?"

"No," Mary Clopas said, "by the time we would get back to the tomb, there could be a crowd there."

For a moment, the women were stymied. Then Mary Magdalene spoke up.

"Let's continue to the tomb. God will make a way."

The other women looked at Mary, unsure where that had

come from. They certainly didn't share her confidence; nevertheless, as Mary began walking again towards the Palace, they followed suit.

The women banged the knocker on the Palace door, and a moment later Joanna and Susanna joined them, glad to be doing anything to honor the One who meant so much to them; indeed, the One who had healed both of them.

To the Tomb

As they walked to the tomb, Mary Clopas related to Joanna and Susanna the problem of moving the stone from the grave. But there was really no time to think of a solution because of the short distance remaining. They turned right and passed through the Gennath Gate, with Salome carrying the precious anointing oils for the group.

The sun was breaking over the Mount of Olives as they turned the corner at a thicket of short trees by the corner of Joseph's garden. The first beam of orange morning light bypassed the north side of the temple, crested the western wall of the city, and illuminated the garden.

Dawn had arrived; first light had come.

All five women looked up, saw the tomb, and gasped in shock and bewilderment. It was *open*. The large circular golel stone had been removed to one side.

Four of the women were totally perplexed as to what had happened, but not Mary Magdalene. With her hand over her mouth, she anguished, "They have stolen his body!"

"Who, who?" the others begged to know.

"The chief priests!" Mary hissed. She spun around, lifted her mantle enough to enable her to run, and sprinted back the way they had come to find help.

The other women stood motionless and confused. Mary Clopas' first impulse was to follow her friend, but being a generation older, she knew she couldn't keep up with Mary

Magdalene.

"Why would they have stolen his body?" asked Susanna.

"I don't know. I don't understand why anyone would do that, or what anyone would gain from it politically, no matter how much they hated him," said Joanna, thinking aloud.

"Should we just go home?" asked Salome.

Mary Clopas shook her head, "How do we know that his body is not in there?"

Mary's question caused the others to realize they had all jumped to a conclusion—a reasonable possibility, but nevertheless not a certainty.

"We need to go look," proclaimed Susanna.

The four women walked cautiously to the tomb opening, listening carefully. Whoever had rolled the stone might still be in there, and the women had no one to protect them. Susanna, being the youngest and boldest, stooped down and entered first. As it sounded like nothing had happened to Susanna, the other women entered, one by one.

The tomb was more spacious than most, and there was a pit dug into the limestone bedrock deep enough that they all could stand fully upright and move around each other. As their eyes adapted to the reduced light of the cave, they could see a ledge cut into the wall to their right. On the ledge was a linen shroud with linen wrappings and a face cloth separate from the others that had been folded up neatly.

Mary Clopas, pointing to the graveclothes, said, "This is where they laid him, but his body is gone."

She turned towards the others and opened her mouth to speak again.

Suddenly two men appeared out of nowhere, one seated at the head of the ledge, away from the door, the other at the foot, closer to the door. The one at the right looked younger than the other.

"Aaah!" Salome gave a little shriek as all the women startled.

The two men looked strong, but had gentle expressions. Their clothes were extraordinary—dazzling white, almost glowing. They asked simultaneously, "Why do you seek the living One among the dead?"

Amazed and terrified, the women all bowed their faces to the ground.

The angel at the right said, "Don't be amazed, and don't be afraid. I know that you are looking for Jesus the Nazarene who has been crucified. He isn't here; he has risen from the dead, just as he said would happen. Remember what he spoke to you back in Galilee. Remember he said that the Son of Man would be delivered into the hands of sinful men, that he would be crucified, and that he would rise again after three days. All this happened just as he said it would."

As the women were recalling Jesus' words, the angel then said to them, "Come and see the place where he was lying. Look here, this is the exact place where they laid him. Now, go quickly and tell his disciples and Peter that he has risen from the dead. Listen, he is going ahead of you into Galilee. There you will see him, just as he has said before. Know for certain that I have told you."

The women left the tomb anxiously. Once they were all outside, they hiked up their mantles and fled quickly towards Zebedee's home. They were trembling, filled with fear over meeting the angels, and they were astonished, filled with great joy over the breathtaking message that they carried.

Mary Magdalene's First Report

On her way to find help, Mary made good time down the road through the Upper City, encountering very few people. She made the decision in transit to first alert Peter, the most prominent among the Twelve. It would only be another half-block to alert John at Zebedee's. Mary Magdalene came to Mark's house and knocked on the door. A groggy servant answered, and Mary said that she needed to speak to Peter right away. The servant passed the message to Mark, who went upstairs to the upper room and woke Peter up.

Peter was mystified as to the reason for the call, but he threw on his mantle and sandals, and came downstairs, half stumbling in the process. Opening the door to the courtyard, Peter saw that it was indeed Mary, as Mark had said.

"Mary," Peter greeted.

"Peter! They have stolen Jesus' body!" she exclaimed, still panting from the run.

Peter stepped out onto the street, closing the door behind him. He started moving up the street.

"Wait," Mary interposed, "we need to tell John."

"Yes," Peter agreed, and changed direction toward Zebedee's.

Peter and Mary hurried to collect John, and Mary told him, "They have taken the Lord's body out of the tomb, and we do not know where they have put him!"

They were soon on their way to the tomb. The three ran together, with John (being faster) in the lead, followed by Peter, and then Mary.

Despite being terrified of the Roman and Jewish authorities, John and Peter were compelled to check out Mary's report. To minimize the chance of contact with Romans or Sanhedrists, John chose a route that skirted Caiaphas' house and ran about halfway between Herod's Palace, where Pilate was, and Antipas' Palace. The streets were still in shadows, although the tops of the buildings were now illumined by the rising sun. Unbeknownst to them, they had passed the four women running from the tomb in the opposite direction on a parallel street.

John reached the tomb first, stooped down, and looked inside. From what he could see, the linen wrappings were lying there, but that was all—there was no body. While he was pondering this, Peter arrived at the tomb, stooped down, and entered it.

As Peter stood up, he surveyed the scene. It made no sense. Right there on the stone shelf were the linen wrappings. Why on earth would anyone wanting to move his body, have unwrapped it? Peter thought. Even more, if someone had unwrapped the body, why were the graveclothes not scattered or in a pile somewhere, as he would have expected, but in the same position that a body would have been lying? And at the end of the linen wrappings, with the shroud within them, he saw the face-cloth, folded neatly and slightly apart from the other wrappings.

Grave robbers would not have been that fastidious.

John, who had hesitated outside, then entered the tomb and stood beside Peter. He also surveyed the scene and was likewise puzzled by the arrangement of the cloths.

Nevertheless, John believed Mary's report and said, "Mary was right. They stole the body."

"It was a despicable thing to do," said Peter, "to show this last contempt for him."

Neither man had any idea of what had transpired the night before. And neither man recollected Jesus' prior words to them, or the Scriptures, that he must rise again from the dead.

Peter crouched down and exited the tomb, followed by John. Mary Magdalene stood outside waiting for them.

John spoke gently to Mary, "I don't know why anyone would do this. It's so reprehensible, so sad."

Mary inquired, "What are you going to do?"

John answered, "We wouldn't know where to look. We can't go to the priests or Romans and ask them to look; maybe they are the ones who have done this. I think we should all go home."

Mary recognized the hopelessness of the situation but said, "You can go; I'm going to stay here."

John felt compassion for Mary's suffering, so he put his hand on her shoulder, and said a prayer that God would cause the body of the Lord to be found. John's prayer, as with so many faithless prayers, was not directed toward God, but rather to its human audience—Mary, in this case. John had no expectation that the body of Jesus would be recovered or ever returned to his grave.

So, the two disciples returned to their own dwellings, walking together for most of the trip. Both men were depressed—Peter to the point of feeling that he had no reason for living. The thought that even Jesus' deceased body was being desecrated compounded his misery.

As they walked, John asked, "Why do you think they took his body, but left the graveclothes?"

"I don't know," responded Peter.

"Why do you think the graveclothes weren't disheveled, or

strewn about?"

"I don't know," said Peter.

"What *do* you know?" asked John.

"Nothing, except someone stole his body, and that was an evil thing to do," said Peter.

John suggested, "I think I figured out why they removed it. They don't want anyone going there to honor him or to make a monument of the tomb. They fear unrest and the anger of the people."

"Maybe," shrugged Peter, "but it doesn't matter now. Nothing matters now."

The two disciples continued the rest of their walk together in silence. When they arrived at the point where their paths diverged, they each said their *"Shalom."* But John stood watching as Peter walked away, concerned for his dear friend.

After Peter had walked a few paces, John called, "Peter!"

Peter turned. "God be with you, Peter," John said.

Feeling his shame again, Peter dropped his eyes to the ground and responded, "God be with you also, John."

The Women Carry a Message

At first, the women tried to talk. They urgently wanted to talk among themselves, but running made it nigh impossible. In between panted breaths was heard:

"Two angels!"

"Alive!"

"They said he's alive!"

And so they gave up the attempt at discourse, and focused on running—if it could even be called that, limited as it was by their garments and the older women among them. As they passed between Herod's Palace on the right, and the Upper Market on the left, they saw a few merchants coming to open their shops. They all felt an urge to shout the news but refrained and said nothing to anyone on their way to report it to the disciples.

Reaching Zebedee's home, they knocked on the door continuously until he answered, and then burst into such a cacophony of voices that Zebedee could make nothing of it.

"Whaaat?" spoke Zebedee loudly. "Come in, and calm down. And maybe just have one of you speak?"

The women burst energetically into the room. Again, they all spoke at once, and poor Zebedee, trying hard, still couldn't make out what they were saying.

"So, there's something wrong with the tomb?" he asked.

"It's empty!" one shouted.

"Yes, Mary Magdalene told us that earlier," he said.

"There are two angels in it!" said Salome.

"So, then, it's not empty?" Zebedee pondered aloud.

"Jesus isn't there, but neither was he stolen like Mary had thought," explained Mary Clopas. "The angels told us that he has risen from the dead!"

Zebedee stroked his beard, trying to understand. Mother Mary had overheard the news and entered the room, with a perplexed look on her face.

"So, where is Jesus?" asked Zebedee finally.

The women quieted down. "We don't know. The angels didn't say, and we didn't think to ask," answered Joanna.

"And what did these angels look like?" asked Zebedee.

Susanna explained, "They looked like men. One looked younger than the other. And they had brilliant white clothing, like nothing ever seen."

Zebedee wasn't convinced that Jesus had risen from the dead. "How do you know that these 'angels' didn't steal his body?" he asked.

The women were silent for a moment.

"We just know. These weren't ordinary men. They were messengers from God. And they told us to tell his disciples that they would meet Jesus in Galilee," frowned Salome. "You need to stop being so unbelieving. Where's John?"

"He ran together with Mary Magdalene and Peter to the tomb," said Zebedee, "I expect he will be back soon."

Salome strode across the room to Mother Mary, who looked very uncertain.

"Do I dare hope?" Mother Mary asked.

Salome didn't want to raise her sister's hopes, only to have them crushed again. She hugged Mother Mary and thought about what she had just seen.

"I know what we saw. Those were angels, and God doesn't lie. You can believe God will have the last word," Susanna told her. Although she ached to give Mother Mary more hope than this, she could not offer, in good conscience, more than she herself possessed.

It wasn't long before John returned. The women repeated the message of the angels verbatim to everyone in the house with John present.

John said, "Peter and I went to the tomb with Mary Magdalene—we must have arrived there right after you all had left. But we didn't see anything except an empty tomb with some graveclothes."

Having relayed the message from the angels, the women prepared to leave the house and complete the instructions received from the angels to "tell the disciples and Peter." There were still ten more men who needed to be told.

After they had left, Clopas asked John, "What do you think of what they said?"

"It sounds like nonsense to me," John said. "I was just there, and I didn't see any angels. Also it doesn't make sense that some angels would have given that message to the women, to be relayed to Peter and me, rather than just tell us when we were there.

"All I know for certain is that the tomb is empty, and I can think of only one thing to explain it—the priests stole his body out of spite to prevent an honorable burial. After murder, they would see the desecration of a tomb as no sin at all."

As John spoke, engrossed in his conversation with Clopas, he failed to notice Mother Mary standing silently across the room, and listening intently to his words. In Mary's ears, John's conviction overpowered the excitement of the women who had just left, and his words obliterated the nascent bud of hope that had sprouted in her heart a moment before. As quietly as a shadow, she turned and left the room in tears.

The Gardener

While the women had been giving their message at Zebedee's home, and Peter and John had been returning from the empty tomb, Mary Magdalene had remained, standing outside the tomb weeping. For two days now—the day before the Sabbath, and the Sabbath—she had been looking forward to this morning with all her heart. The perfumes she had lovingly prepared, she had been planning to use to anoint his enshrouded body as a final act of devotion. But it was not to be. It seemed the animosity of the priests was so great that they had committed this final crime out of sheer malevolence.

As she wept, she stooped and looked into the tomb to fix in her mind the image of the cloths that had covered his body.

She gasped. There inside the tomb, on the stone ledge, she saw two angels arrayed in brilliant white sitting, one at the head and one at the feet, where the body of Jesus had been lying.

And they spoke to her, "Woman, why are you weeping?"

Mary was startled and frightened, unsure of what to say, or why these men were in the tomb. She nervously blurted, "Because someone has taken away the body of my Lord, and I do not know where they have put him!"

She didn't wait for a response, but started backing away from the tomb opening, and turned quickly to go.

But when she had turned around, she saw a man standing nearby. It was Jesus, but Mary didn't know it was him for the tears in her eyes.

The man spoke gently to her, "Woman, why are you weeping? Who are you looking for?"

Thinking that this was the gardener, she said to him, "Sir, if you have carried him away, tell me where you have put him, and I will take him away."

Jesus said to her, "Mary!" She turned to face him and exclaimed, *"Rabboni!"* (which means "Great Teacher" in Hebrew). Mary ran to Jesus, fell at his feet and wrapped her arms around his ankles.

Jesus then said to her, "Don't try to hold me here, for I am not ascending to the Father right now. Instead, take word to my brothers and say to them, 'I am soon ascending to my Father and your Father, to my God and your God.'"

Mary bounded to her feet and leaped in the air a couple of times, giddy with joy, then lifted her mantle to clear her ankles and ran.

She slowed to a brisk walk as she encountered the shadow cast by the western wall of the city, before passing through the Gennath Gate and into the early morning sun. Mary felt as though she would burst—her mind raced with the most exciting news of *all* time, and she felt its weight. But the joy in her heart was too much to contain. Everything around her seemed smaller, even trivial. She looked heavenward and said aloud, "Even the sky cannot contain this joy!" And neither could she, as the glow of her face and her tears of joy ably testified.

Clopas Leaves for Emmaus

Clopas gathered some items in a bag for an overnight trip to Emmaus, and spoke to Zebedee.

"So, I expect to be gone for only a day. I'm going to meet up with my farm manager—he's a disciple too—in the city before we head out together. I'm very eager to return to you and hear if there is any more news by then. And I plan to stop at the tomb on our way out and see it for myself, since the road leading to Emmaus begins right near the tomb."

"Until tomorrow then," said Zebedee. Clopas said *shalom* to Zebedee and headed to the heart of the city.

The Women's News Reaches Mark's Home

Despite the unexpectedly lukewarm reception of their message at Zebedee's house, Salome, Mary Clopas, Joanna, and Susanna were once again beside themselves with excitement, having regained it during their short walk between residences.

The women arrived at Mark's home and knocked on the gate to the courtyard. Shortly thereafter, a servant-girl answered. The women announced that they were looking for Peter who was lodging there, and the servant-girl took the message to Mark.

Mark instructed the servant to invite the women into the house, while he went upstairs to inform Peter, who then came down with Mark from the upper room. Peter greeted the women, and Mark stood nearby and listened while the women delivered their message.

"Peter!" exclaimed Salome, "we went to the tomb with Mary Magdalene this morning at dawn. After she ran to get you and John, we went into the tomb to see what was there. There was no body. But while we were inside, two angels appeared to us. And they gave us a message."

"Yes!" exclaimed Mary Clopas, interrupting, "And they said, 'Why do you seek the living One among the dead?' When they said that, we all bowed low. Then one of them said, 'I know that you are looking for Jesus the Nazarene who has been crucified. He isn't here. He has risen from the dead, just as he said would happen.'

"The angel told us to remember all the things Jesus had spoken to us back in Galilee, about being crucified and rising again after three days. Then the angel said 'Come, see the place where he was lying. Now, go quickly and tell his disciples and Peter that he has risen from the dead. Listen, he is going ahead of you into Galilee. There you will see him, just as he said.'"

Peter seemed dazed.

"Did you see Jesus?"

"No, just the angels."

"*All* of you saw them?"

"Yes!" the women said in unison.

"And they said he has risen from the dead?"

"Yes!" they chorused again.

"But they didn't say where he is now?"

"No," said the women.

Peter straightened his shoulders. "Are you sure they said 'Tell his disciples *and* Peter'?"

"That's exactly what the angel said," answered Joanna.

"Thank you," said Peter, "Where are you going now?"

"We are on our way to Bethany, to tell the rest of the Twelve," replied Salome.

"May God carry you," said Peter.

Peter and Mark escorted the women to the gate; the women said goodbye and departed. Peter and Mark stood looking at each other.

"That's amazing!" blurted Mark, "They said Jesus is alive!"

Peter corrected, "They said that some angels said Jesus was alive."

"Don't you believe them?" Mark asked.

"I don't know what they saw. Or think they saw. They mean well, but they are grieving, and their emotions are high. Even so, just in case there might be angels there, I'm going to run up to the tomb and check for myself. You should stay here."

The Soldiers Move to Save Themselves

Petronius had been waiting anxiously for the right moment, and it was now at hand. From the angle of the sun, he knew that Caiaphas should be up for the day and probably conducting business in the Royal Stoa, the colonnaded hall along the south end of the temple complex. Although anxious about the meeting, he wanted to get it done.

"Lurio," Petronius summoned, "you're coming with me to call on the chief priests." Petronius also gave instructions to the others to continue waiting outside the city.

As they began walking to the temple complex, Petronius advised, "March smartly, and keep your head up. Don't show any concern. I want to put this problem entirely on their shoulders."

Peter Looks for Angels

Peter had jogged north to the tomb so engrossed in thought about the women's report that he paid virtually no attention to any risk of notice by Roman or Jewish authorities. When he reached the garden, he regained his focus, and continued across to the tomb opening. Catching his breath, he stooped down and looked in.

It looked the same as before when he had arrived with John: no body, and the burial cloths were in the same positions. As for angels, there were none.

Peter dropped to his knees there, and considered praying, perhaps to ask God to send an angel, or even just a sign of some kind. But he couldn't. He couldn't bring himself to believe the women had seen an angel. He couldn't shake the painful thought that even if God *had* sent angels to the women, why would God send *him* a message? He had turned his back on Jesus when it really mattered.

Peter stood up, turned to go, and noticed the pile of memorial stones left by others. He picked up a small stone and added it to the pile, saying softly, "Jesus." And the tears started again.

Mary's Extraordinary News

Zebedee was startled to hear the knock on the door. It was much too soon for the women to have returned, and he wasn't expecting anyone else today.

"Maybe Clopas forgot something," he thought aloud.

Opening the door, he was surprised to see Mary Magdalene. She charged into the house without awaiting an invitation, taking him aback. But he was really stunned by the look on her face. This wasn't the downcast, grieving women who had called at the house for Salome just before dawn. This woman looked taller, stronger, and *glowed.*

"He's alive! He's alive!" she shouted.

"What are you saying?" Zebedee asked, confused. "He...who?"

"Jesus! Of course! Jesus is *alive!"*

Zebedee was still holding the door open, and instinctively thinking Jesus might be right behind her, he leaned towards the doorway and glanced out to the street. "Where?" he asked.

Mary's shouts were drawing the entire household into the room, including John and Mother Mary.

"At the tomb! I *saw* him in the garden there!"

Zebedee closed the door. "Please tell us."

In Zebedee's mind, there was a quick flare of hope that her statement was true, but it was quickly extinguished by the thought that no, things like this don't happen, not even with someone as extraordinary as his nephew.

Mary proceeded to describe her experience of seeing the angels in the tomb; hearing Jesus call her name; not recognizing him at first; and his command to tell his followers that he was soon ascending to the Father.

John was expressionless, and Mother Mary, trying hard to process the message, was visibly shaken. Zebedee looked at Mary Magdalene with sympathy. This tragedy had been severe on everyone there, and Mary Magdalene was obviously an emotionally sensitive individual, lacking the constitution to weather the strain.

Zebedee spoke to her, "Mary, why don't you sit for a while and rest. Can I offer you something to eat?"

"You don't believe me, do you?" Mary Magdalene exclaimed. "I *saw* him, I *touched* him. *It was him!*"

The Magdalene looked at John, who pressed his lips together and looked at the floor to avoid her gaze.

"Oh!" she exclaimed, and stamped her foot in frustration. "Oh, you men of little faith!" She brusquely left them for another room.

John recognized her exclamation as a quotation from Jesus, when Jesus had been frustrated by the disciples' unbelief in trying to heal an epileptic boy. Although John felt the quotation was inappropriate at this time, he didn't respond.

John looked at his father. Zebedee raised an eyebrow with an unspoken question.

"I wish it was so. I really wish it was," John answered.

Mother Mary, shaking physically and emotionally, didn't know what to think of the report.

On the Road to Bethany

Salome, Mary Clopas, Joanna, and Susanna could not stop talking about the marvelous sight of the angels at the tomb, and the even more extraordinary news given them by the angels. They considered it to be the highest privilege and joy to carry this glorious message to the disciples who were mourning in Bethany.

Passing the garden of Gethsemane, Mary Clopas informed the others that the garden was the site of Jesus' arrest. Yet now, the information was only of historical interest, a footnote adding to the glory of their news, and not the dark, sad thought it was when Mary Clopas first heard about it from Mary Magdalene.

They reached the top of the Mount and continued eastward, beginning the descent to Bethany. It was now mid-morning, and a man traveling in the opposite direction approached them. When he was a stone's throw away, he raised his hand as though in greeting.

"Shalom! Rejoice!" the man called out.

The women froze. The man's face was in shadow, but the form, the voice, were too familiar.

There can be situations in life when a person encounters something so extraordinary, so remarkable, that the images received by the eye cannot find a place for processing in the mind, and both body and mind pause. So it was with all four women.

The man continued toward them, and when he had closed half the distance, he called out again, with a discernible smile, "Peace be with you!"

It *was* Jesus! There was no need for him to say anything more, as the four women rushed down the dirt road. They fell at his feet, took hold of him, and worshiped him.

Jesus said with a smile, "Do not be afraid. Go and take word to my brothers to leave for Galilee. There they will see me."

Then he vanished from their sight. The women got up and chattered excitedly, analyzing every detail of their brief encounter. Particularly amazing to them was Jesus' vanishing, something so completely unexpected! After the energized discussion, they remembered their mission and commenced walking again down the road with even greater urgency.

As they approached the town of Bethany, Susanna remarked

provocatively, "You know, I recognized Jesus first."

Mary Clopas responded, "I don't know about that. I recognized him at the first 'Shalom.'"

"Oh, I was pretty sure it was him even before he said 'Shalom,'" countered Susanna.

Joanna, not wanting her best friend to become too proud, said, "Your confidence is quite remarkable, Susanna, knowing your difficulty distinguishing an apple from a pomegranate!"

Jerusalem: The Royal Stoa on the Temple Mount

The walk for Petronius and Lurio was only about three-fourths of a mile. Arriving at the temple complex, they entered through the stairs at Robinson's Arch, which put them right close to the Stoa. Informing a temple guard of their business, they waited briefly before being called in to a meeting of Caiaphas, Annas, and other high priests, just as Petronius had hoped would happen.

Petronius explained in detail what he had seen at the garden tomb, and Lurio confirmed his account when asked a few questions by the priests. Caiaphas wanted additional confirmation on the missing body, so he asked the soldiers to wait outside and dispatched a subordinate to verify that the tomb was empty. Next, he sent another subordinate to call some of the elders to join the priests for an impromptu meeting.

As soon as the elders had joined them, Caiaphas addressed the elders and related the events that Petronius had just described. Some of the elders and priests were quite concerned, and one asked, "What do you suppose really happened?"

Caiaphas answered, "I've been trying to figure that out, myself. First, we can discount the superstitious interpretation that the Roman guards have given to it; they are ignorant people. Even so, I don't think the soldiers are lying because they seemed genuinely spooked from the experience. So, what they reported is undoubtedly what they think they saw. I would rule out mass hysteria since it's unlikely an entire squad would be moonstruck at the same time. And Pilate certainly couldn't be responsible as there is no possible benefit for him.

"That leaves Jesus' disciples. Maybe they are more clever than I had estimated. Maybe they used some poison to inflict the soldiers with insanity so they ran off. I don't know how they did it, but it looks like they were successful."

Caiaphas' scout who had gone to examine the tomb arrived then, and reported that the body was in fact missing.

"So there you have it," Caiaphas asserted to the group, "the body *is* gone, and the only persons who would have taken it would be his followers."

"This is a real problem," said Annas sternly, as though Caiaphas didn't know it already. "You know this worthless fellow predicted that he would die and rise from the dead. Now his followers can say that he did. Just what are you going to do about it?"

Caiaphas bristled at his father-in-law's impertinence, but stifled his irritation and offered a plan, "We need to buy off the soldiers and have them say that his disciples stole the body while they were asleep. If we get this story out quickly it will circumvent any rumors his followers might try to spread."

With further elaboration and great drama, Caiaphas described to the men the potential repercussions to all of them of *not* bribing the Romans. Having thus raised their fear level sufficiently, Caiaphas then took an offering for the bribe. (Of course, Annas and his son-in-law had all necessary means to cover the bribe easily, but those who worship money are always the most frugal with their own and spendthrift with that of others.)

With the bribe money in a small leather pouch in his hand, Caiaphas called for the soldiers. He handed the pouch to Petronius and gave a firm command to them both, "When you return to your barracks, you are to say, 'His disciples came during the night and stole his body away while we were sleeping.' And if this should come to the governor's attention, we will win him over and keep you out of trouble." Petronius and Lurio bowed slightly, pivoted, and walked out.

When the soldiers and the elders had left the building, Annas took Caiaphas aside and addressed him with disdain.

"That Galilean said he would destroy the temple and rebuild it in three days. Nobody is going to destroy this temple, or remove the house of Annas from controlling it, on my watch. You were as stupid as a Roman pig for not posting a temple guard by that tomb."

Caiaphas spat at Annas' feet, turned on his heel and left the Stoa in a fury.

Bethany: Lazarus' Home

Salome, Mary Clopas, Joanna, and Susanna arrived at Lazarus' home, and were warmly greeted. Just as they had done at Zebedee's place, the women talked over themselves excitedly as they tried to relate, in one single instant, all that they had seen and heard that morning.

"Please!" shouted Martha in amazement, "Can we have the story in order?"

And so, as they settled down, the women explained how they had gone to the tomb with Mary Magdalene and had seen that the stone had been rolled away; how Mary Magdalene had run off to summon the disciples, thinking Jesus' body had been stolen; how they had entered and seen angels in the tomb, and what the angels had said; how they had informed the disciples in Jerusalem about the angels; and how, on the way to Bethany, they had encountered the risen Jesus himself.

Lazarus reacted immediately with praise and thanksgiving, lifting face and hands heavenward, grateful to God for the best news he had ever heard. Martha reacted with praise bubbling through tears of joy. The nine disciples, however, stood stoically with little expression.

Salome saw the countenances of the disciples and addressed her son, "James Zebedee, where is your joy?"

Speaking the mind of the nine men, he replied, "Uh, mother, I haven't seen Jesus or the angels."

Philip added quietly, "You said he vanished. Where is he now?"

Nathanael questioned, "Why didn't he come with you, if he's alive?"

And Thaddeus questioned, "Why would he reveal himself to you four, and not to us? We were with him day and night for almost three years."

Lazarus spoke to the nine, "Now, listen. The women went looking for Jesus' dead body to anoint, and they found him alive. They went *looking*. Maybe it's time for you all to go looking for him; you are more likely to find him that way than by sitting around here feeling sorry for yourselves."

"Amen!" underscored two of the women.

Considering Lazarus' prescription, the disciples determined to stifle their fears and accompany the women back to Zebedee's home in Jerusalem, to investigate the matter further. They gathered together the few things they had for possessions and made ready to leave.

All except Thomas. He stood apart, along with Lazarus and Martha.

"What's wrong, Thomas?" asked Andrew, "Aren't you coming?"

"No!" He was emphatic.

"Why not?" asked James the Younger.

"I don't mean to discourage you all, but think about this. In the Scriptures, only three people were raised from the dead. Elijah raised one, and Elisha raised two. That's all. Abraham didn't raise anyone, nor did Joseph, or Moses, or Daniel. We've seen Jesus raise three people: Jairus' daughter, the widow of Nain's son, and Lazarus here. So Jesus raised as many as in all Scriptures before him. But hear me now: No one has ever raised himself from the dead. No one. Not ever. It's never been heard of, from the beginning of time. At first, I had difficulty accepting Jesus as the Son of God—the Messiah. But he was, and I came to see it. But now, if he were to rise from the dead, *himself*, then he's not just the Son of God—he *is* God."

After taking a deep breath, Thomas concluded, "I'm sorry. I just can't accept that."

His words had a sobering effect on the group, and all were

silent for a moment.

Joanna spoke to Thomas, "Say what you will, Thomas, but I *saw* him, and I *touched* him, and I *know*." Then the four women left with eight of the disciples.

When the group had left, Thomas looked at Lazarus and asked, "So tell me, Lazarus, how can you believe that he is alive?"

"I think," said Lazarus, "it helps if you've been dead once yourself."

Jerusalem: the Praetorium
Midmorning

The five Roman guards returned to their barracks in Jerusalem with extra wealth on their persons. Petronius had divided the bribe between them, keeping the greater part for himself, for two reasons. First, he was the officer of command among the group, and second, he wanted to have something in hand to assuage Pilate's wrath, should it be needed. He assumed that it would.

The soldiers dutifully did as instructed by Caiaphas and spread the word that Jesus' body had been stolen by his disciples. The story spread quickly among both the soldiers and the Jews, and it was none too soon, as the news about the open, empty tomb was just beginning to circulate along the city's grapevines. Even to this very day, the story fabricated by the chief priests continues to be spread among the Jews.

But it reached Pilate within an hour, and he called for Petronius to explain himself.

The centurion Sylvius was on duty outside Pilate's office; inside were Pilate, his counselor Gallus, and the two soldiers on bodyguard duty.

Pilate studied Petronius for a few seconds before speaking.

"So, what's this story I'm hearing about the tomb?"

"Sir, I apologize, but the man's followers stole his body while we were all sleeping."

Pilate waited, expecting more, but Petronius added nothing.

"That's it? That's all?" Pilate asked, astonished.

"Yes, sir. That's what happened."

Pilate stood up, flabbergasted. Petronius was a good soldier and this was completely out of character.

Throwing one hand up in frustration, Pilate vented, "I don't know what you're thinking. I can't accept your apology; you know this is a tremendous breach of duty. Completely unacceptable!"

"Sylvius!" Pilate shouted, and Sylvius entered the room.

"Sir, there is something more you need to know," interjected Petronius.

"Oh, what's that?" asked Pilate, now irritated.

"Can we speak in private?" asked Petronius.

Pilate looked quizzically at the centurion. Ordinarily, the answer would have been no, but the whole situation seemed so strange, Pilate was curious enough to dig deeper. He nodded at Petronius and waved the other men out of the room.

When the door had closed, Petronius stepped forward, and pulled from his belt a pouch that he set on the table. Pilate reached forward slowly, lifted and hefted the weight.

"And if you have any more questions, the chief priests can answer them," Petronius added.

Pilate sat down, nodding slowly, trying to make sense of this. Obviously, the priests had paid for this story to be spread. That is, the same men who were afraid that his disciples would steal the body were now *paying* to say that his disciples had stolen the body. Yet, the disciples couldn't have stolen the body with the guards there, Pilate was sure of that. How odd. And then, what happened to the body? Not that he cared too much, but could the priests have taken it? Doubtful—but nothing about this whole business made *any* sense at all.

Pilate picked up the pouch again, stashed it, and said to Petronius, "You can go now. But, let's not broadcast that you all were sleeping. That's never acceptable."

"Yes, sir!" Petronius said, relieved. He left the room, leaving the door open, and the bodyguards and Gallus reentered.

"What was that about?" asked Gallus.

"You heard it. The body was stolen while they were sleeping,"

Pilate replied.

"How could they all have been asleep?" asked Gallus.

"They must have gotten into some wine," replied Pilate.

"And the noise of moving the stone didn't wake anyone?" queried Gallus, incredulously.

"Must have been good wine," smiled Pilate with a shrug. "Anything else?"

"No, we can continue later," said Gallus. "Excuse me for a bit."

Gallus left the room with his eyebrows raised. Under his breath, he said to himself, "I'm not going to ask the obvious— how sleeping men could have known who had stolen the body."

Then another thought struck Gallus; he smiled wryly and said aloud, "I don't know what the payoff was, but I would have liked a piece of it."

Jerusalem: Mark's Home
Late Morning

Peter was alone in the upper room of Mark's home. Over and over in his mind, he rehearsed the messages of Mary Magdalene, that Jesus' body had been stolen, and the testimony of the women, that they had seen angels who said Jesus was risen from the dead. The angels had also told the women to go tell his disciples *and Peter* the news, and that Jesus would precede them to Galilee.

The disciples and Peter. And *Peter.*

"What did those words mean?" Peter asked himself. "Why was my name separated from the 'disciples'? Was that a special consideration, or am I no longer considered a disciple?

"I denied him. How can I be a disciple? I think the women were seeing mirages or something. How can he be alive? If he was alive, why didn't I see him?

"Even if he was alive, how could he possibly welcome me? Oh, I wish I had died with him!"

His anguished thoughts tormented him, and they wouldn't cease.

"Peter!" the voice was Mark's; he had come upstairs to fetch Peter. "Mary Magdalene is downstairs looking for you."

Peter didn't want to see Mark, or Mary, or anyone. Instead, he had a sudden urge to leave Jerusalem, return to the Sea of Galilee, find a boat, and float in the middle of the sea by himself, in the gentle breeze with birds passing by, alone, forever.

"Peter, are you coming?" Mark interrupted his thoughts.

"Uh yeah," grunted Peter, as he started for the doorway and followed Mark downstairs.

Mary, still overjoyed by her encounter at the tomb, was hoping her message would be received with more enthusiasm by Peter than it was at Zebedee's house.

"Peter, I've seen him! I've seen Jesus—at the tomb, after you and John had left. I touched him; he really *is* alive. And he gave me a message to share—he said, 'Go to my brothers and say to them, "I am ascending to my Father and your Father, and my God and your God."' Is that not joyous?"

Expressionless, Peter stared at Mary.

"Did you hear me? Are you as unbelieving as John?" Mary exclaimed.

"Mary, whether I believe you or not, I—that is—all I can say is—everything is different for me now. But thank you for telling me."

Peter turned, to return upstairs. Mary, knowing nothing of Peter's denial of Jesus, looked questioningly at Mark, who shrugged his shoulders. Mark turned to follow Peter.

Once in the upper room again, Mark questioned Peter.

"Peter, why are you not excited about her news? Don't you believe her?"

"I believe Mary saw a vision. Or a spirit. Or an angel. Something like that," Peter replied.

"But she said she touched him. Don't you want to go to the tomb for yourself?"

"Mark, I've been to the tomb twice this morning. I don't think a third time would be any different."

"But how could you speak to Mary Magdalene that way? What did you mean by 'everything is different for me'?" Mark demanded.

"You wouldn't understand, Mark. You just wouldn't

understand."

Mark left the room concerned and perplexed. Peter sat down at the table, at the place he had been sitting before his life came apart, where he had been by the side of Jesus. He parsed Mary's words in his mind.

"... tell my brothers ... my *brothers* ... that would be the disciples ... the women said, tell 'His disciples and Peter' ... 'brothers' therefore does not include me ...'my God and your God' ... does not include me; God is silent, and heaven is bronze,[22]" Peter thought.

Peter put his elbows on the table and his face in his hands. Though he didn't want to relive it, his mind pulled him back into the memory of that fateful evening, when Jesus had said that the disciples would all fall away.

"Even if all fall away, I will not," Peter had boldly proclaimed. The remembrance of his words and the shame of his denial formed a sword that eviscerated his pride. The Peter that had been was no longer.

Peter thought about Jesus' words that had followed his proclamation, "I tell you the truth, this very night, Peter..."

"Huh?" Peter thought, Jesus hadn't said his name.

"Peter." The voice repeated. Peter lifted his face, and jerked with fright. There to his side, where he had been sitting on that night, was Jesus.

His eyes were full of love and tenderness. He reached out and touched Peter.

"I forgive you, Peter. I forgive you, my disciple—my brother," Jesus said.

Peter collapsed against Jesus, who wrapped his arms around him. The balm of complete acceptance burned out the acid of Peter's self-loathing. And he cried convulsively: body, soul, and spirit.

Jesus gave instructions to Peter to rejoin the other disciples, saying, "I have much work for you to do." Then he vanished.

---

[22] The heaven which is over your head shall be bronze, and the earth which is under you, iron. (Deu 28:23)

Downstairs, Mark and his mother could hear Peter's cries. Concerned, they said another prayer asking God to heal his broken heart. They did not know it was happening as they were praying.

Sunday Noon to Night

From Bethany to Jerusalem
Nisan 18, the Sixth Hour (Noon)

Eight disciples (James Zebedee, Andrew, Philip, Nathanael, Matthew, James the Younger, Thaddeus, and Simon the Zealot), together with the four women (Salome, Mary Clopas, Joanna, and Susanna), were on their way to Jerusalem. The women were leading, eager to return to the city, and the men followed reticently.

Joanna began, "I'm so eager to return to Galilee after Passover. When Antipas is in Jerusalem, he wants to impress everyone, and that puts a lot of pressure on Chuza, me, and the rest of the household. But more than that, I can't wait to see Jesus again in Galilee like he said."

"I agree," said Salome, "and after this week, I wouldn't care if I never saw Jerusalem again. I much prefer Capernaum with no Sanhedrin and few Romans. Oh my, I can't believe I said that; the temple has always meant so much to me. Anyway, right now I'm eager to tell Zebedee, John, and Mother Mary that we saw Jesus on the road."

Mary Clopas said, "And I cannot wait to tell Clopas and Mary Magdalene that we've seen Jesus! They will be very disappointed they weren't with us to see him."

Susanna said, "I wonder where Mary Magdalene is now. She could still be at the tomb, or at Zebedee's. Or maybe she has decided to return to Bethany."

"Well if she's returning to Bethany we might meet her on the road," said Salome.

The disciples shared none of the enthusiasm of the women. They feared the chief priests, the Sanhedrin, the Romans, and Herod Antipas. They judged the city to be full of enemies who might come after them with the same animosity they displayed when they had pursued Jesus.

At the back of the group were Nathanael, Thaddeus, and Simon the Zealot.

Simon asked Thaddeus, "What do you suppose the women really saw? Anything?"

Thaddeus answered, "Of course they saw something. Sure, they are emotional, but we all have been too. It can't be just someone's imagination, or a dream, when all four of them saw the same thing."

"So what did they see?"

"I think it was a vision from God. I think they saw Jesus in their spirits, or they saw the spirit of Jesus," replied Thaddeus.

"Why do you think so?"

"Because he vanished from them. If Jesus was brought back to life, with flesh and blood, then I don't think he could do that. Lazarus was previously dead, and he doesn't disappear now," explained Thaddeus.

Nathanael spoke up, "I think they saw something more."

"What do you mean?" asked Thaddeus.

"Well, I don't know. But they said they *touched* him. I didn't know you could touch a vision or a spirit.

"Since I have never seen a vision, I wouldn't know either, but maybe it happens," remarked Thaddeus. "So what do you think we will find?"

"Hopefully we won't find trouble, but other than that possibility, I couldn't tell you. I'm not a prophet, you know," said Nathanael.

"Oh, I can see you're not a prophet," responded Thaddeus.

"Yeah? How so?"

"Because prophets," proclaimed Thaddeus, "have much nicer beards."

"I don't know why I talk to you," complained Nathanael. "It certainly isn't for the wisdom."

Jerusalem: The Temple
The Sixth and One-Half Hour (12:30 p.m.)

In the morning, priests had taken the sheaves of barley that had been stored the previous evening, and beaten out the grains from the seed-heads using canes. The grains were then placed, in a single layer, on bronze pans with holes and parched over a fire. After parching, the grains were ground in a stone mill. The resulting coarse flour was passed through a series of successively finer sieves until only the finest remained. That quantity was an omer,[23] or about one-tenth of what had been harvested.

The omer of fine flour was placed in a gold bowl and carefully mixed with a log[24] of olive oil and a small handful of frankincense. The bowl was covered with a beautiful woven cloth of blue, scarlet, and gold threads, to protect it for the ceremony that followed about an hour later.

When the time arrived, an immense, festive crowd had gathered in the temple court to worship and witness the offering of the omer. Their excitement was both religious—this was an ancient ordinance given by Moses—and practical: The nation was forbidden from eating barley or barley bread in the new year until the offerings had been made.

Hundreds of white-robed priests began the ceremony with pomp, liturgy, prayers, musical instruments, and singing. Eventually, a hush fell on the crowd when two priests appeared with Caiaphas the high priest, at the long ramp leading upward to the altar platform. They walked in unison up the ramp, with Caiaphas in the middle of the other two—one holding the gold bowl containing the omer, and the other holding a gold jug containing red wine.

There was a moment of complete silence, after the trio had reached the front of the altar, facing the crowd. Then, the priest to Caiaphas' right presented his gold bowl to the high priest. Caiaphas picked up the omer of dough and solemnly held it forward with both hands.

Caiaphas proclaimed, "This is the first fruit of the earth, which God has graciously given for the health and blessing of his people."

---

[23] About 4.6 pints, in US measure
[24] About 1.3 cups, in US measure

Then he "waved" the dough, with exaggerated motions: first upward, then downward, then to his left, then to his right. He then placed the omer back into the gold bowl, but extracted a handful with his right hand, and held it aloft as he offered a prayer for a bountiful harvest. He turned, stepped toward the fire burning on the altar, and offered that portion of the omer to God in the fire.

Next, the priest on Caiaphas' left presented his jug to the high priest. Caiaphas took the jug, held it toward the crowd, and prayed, "Lord God, we give you thanks for the wine you have provided, and as it is poured out, we remember all you have provided for your people."

Caiaphas then turned and walked on the pathway around to the southwest corner of the altar. The horn at that corner was capped with two silver funnels. Caiaphas lifted the jug and poured the wine into the funnel designated for drink offerings, and the wine descended through a channel inside the altar, into a subterranean chamber to receive it.

The three priests, having completed the offering of the bread and wine, descended the ramp and moved to the opposite side of the altar—the north side. There they joined a group of priests who were standing ready with a constrained, unblemished male lamb one year old. Caiaphas placed his hands on the lamb and prayed, "We entreat you, O Lord God: We have sinned, we have done perversely, we have rebelled, we have done those things we ought not, and we have failed to do those things we ought. But, we return in repentance, and let this be for our covering."

Caiaphas then took a knife and slit the throat of the lamb, while another priest caught the blood in a silver vessel. Caiaphas took the vessel, and followed by a phalanx of priests, carried it to the northeast corner of the base of the altar. He sprinkled the blood on the two sides there. The priests and Caiaphas next proceeded to the southwest corner and sprinkled the remaining blood on the two sides of the altar there.

While Caiaphas was sprinkling the altar, the priests that had remained with the slain lamb worked quickly. They hung the offering on an iron hook, flayed it, then moved its carcass to one of the eight marble tables north of the altar. On the table, they cut the offering into pieces and washed the legs and entrails. Six priests gathered the pieces and joined Caiaphas at the bottom of the ramp on the south side of the altar.

A chorus of priests to the sides and rear of the altar began singing a worship song, *a cappella*. While they sang, Caiaphas led the other six priests up the ramp and around to the eastern side of the altar. He said another prayer of repentance and dedication, then one-by-one, took the pieces of the lamb from the priests and tossed them onto the fire burning on the altar, as the people worshiped. Additional pomp and fine liturgical music followed, but the important parts of the ceremony had finished, and the people were now free to harvest their barley fields.

From Jerusalem to Emmaus
Midafternoon

Clopas made his way slowly through the packed city streets and arrived at the lodging of his business partner Yosef, only to discover he was out on an errand. When Yosef finally returned from the markets, he grabbed his traveling bag and the two men got underway. They headed northwest through the crowded streets towards the Gennath Gate and the road that leads past the garden tomb and westward to the village of Emmaus, their destination in the country about seven miles from Jerusalem.

On the way through the city, Clopas had explained to Yosef what had transpired in the morning before he had left Zebedee's house. Clopas was careful to relate the report of the women exactly as he had heard it, without adding any interpretation to it. Yosef was also a follower of Jesus and had been deeply distressed by his death. He had already heard about the empty tomb, as the city was abuzz with the report and speculation around it, but the news from Clopas was gripping.

Reaching the garden tomb, they found more people there than they had expected. Some had come simply to pay their respects, particularly those from beyond the city who had been prevented from coming the day before because of Sabbath travel restrictions. But many more of them had come because word was spreading about the empty tomb.

None of the crowd was entering the tomb, in order to avoid ceremonial uncleanness; however, a very long line had formed of people who wanted to see it closely. Clopas and Yosef wanted to look into the cave too, so they queued up to wait in line with the others. While in the line, they overheard a woman ahead of them say to her husband, "Some are saying that his disciples stole the body".

Clopas leaned towards Yosef and whispered, "That's nonsense. Why would anyone spread such a rumor?" Yosef whispered back, "Tongues run farther than minds."

Upon reaching the opening, they each stooped down and looked inside. They could see empty graveclothes on a ledge, but no body. That much they could confirm.

And so the men left the garden and continued on their way westward on the Emmaus Road.

Yosef asked, "So, do you believe the report of the women?"

Clopas replied, "My wife Mary doesn't make up stories and is a woman of good understanding. So I'm sure they saw angels. I do find it harder to believe what the angels supposedly said, that Jesus is alive."

"Did they say what the angels looked like?"

"They said they looked like tall men, even though they were seated, and they had shining white clothes."

"Have you ever seen an angel?" asked Yosef.

"No."

"Neither have I, but I would like to. So, do you think the angels were lying?"

"No, I don't," answered Clopas, frowning as though the question was absurd.

"Well then, why don't you believe the angels' statements that Jesus is alive?"

"I don't disbelieve it. And I don't believe it," said Clopas, "but it's difficult to believe, that's all. Trust me, I would like to believe; you know he is my nephew. I am just withholding believing anything until I know more."

At that moment, the two men heard someone walking behind

them and drawing closer. They turned and saw a hooded figure.

"Shalom! Mind if I join you?" the man asked.

"That would be fine," answered Clopas. "Are you headed home after Passover?"

"Oh, you could say that, yes," the man answered, as they all began walking together.

"So, what were you men discussing so intently as you were walking, before I caught up with you?" he asked. Clopas and Yosef stopped and stood still, looking sad.

Clopas answered, "Are you the only one visiting Jerusalem who is unaware of the things that have happened here in these last few days?"

The man asked, "What things?"

Clopas and Yosef explained, "The things about Jesus the Nazarene, who was a prophet and mighty in deed and word in the sight of God and all the people. Tragically, our chief priests and rulers delivered him up to be sentenced to death, and the Romans crucified him. And we had been fervently hoping that he was the One who was going to redeem Israel.

"Now, besides all this, three days have passed since these things happened, and this morning some women among us brought astonishing news. They had gone to the tomb early in the morning, to anoint his body with perfumes, and did not find his body. Amazingly, they came back saying that they had seen a vision of angels who said that he was alive. Some of those who were with us went to the tomb and found it exactly as the women had said, but they did not see him."

The man replied, "Oh foolish men, you are so slow of heart to believe everything the prophets have spoken! Was it not necessary for the Messiah to suffer these things and to enter into his glory?"

Clopas raised his eyebrows, amazed by the stranger's bold reply and wondering what this man apparently knew that they did not. The three of them began walking again, and the man started explaining himself. He began quoting Moses, elucidating the passages in the Torah concerning the Messiah and explaining why these Scriptures were referring to Jesus the

Nazarene.

The stranger continued his comments beyond the Torah to all of the writings of the prophets, illuminating verse after verse about the Messiah, showing how these Scriptures also applied to Jesus and were fulfilled by his life. Clopas and Yosef hung on every word, astounded.

Clopas thought to himself, "This fellow must be a rabbi. I wonder if he ever had the opportunity to hear Jesus teach?"

As they approached the turnoff for Emmaus, Clopas said, "This is the village we are going to; are you going further?"

"Yes, I have much further to go," the man replied.

"In that case, why don't you stay with us? It's getting toward evening, and the day is almost over. Besides, we have enjoyed listening to you."

Yosef agreed, "It would be our pleasure to have you stay with us; truly it would. You *must* at least join us for a meal."

The man agreed, so he accompanied Clopas and Yosef as they made their way into Emmaus to the lodging that Clopas had procured. The owner of the lodging had previously prepared a meal in expectation of the men, so Clopas, Yosef, and their guest directly sat down to eat.

"Would you honor us by saying a blessing over the bread?" Clopas asked their guest.

"Of course," the man replied, "*Baruch atah Adonai Elohainu melech haolam hamotzi lechem min haaretz.* (Blessed are you, Lord our God, King of the Universe, Who brings forth bread from the earth.)"

Then he picked up a piece of bread, repeating the end of the blessing, "*hamotzi lechem min haaretz* (Who brings forth bread from the earth)," and broke it.

Immediately, both Clopas and Yosef recognized the man; it was Jesus! Then he vanished from their sight.

"Jesus!" Clopas exclaimed.

"It was him! It was him! It WAS Jesus! Did you see that? HE JUST DISAPPEARED!" Yosef was beside himself. He gingerly reached his hand into the space Jesus had just occupied, encountered nothing, and then waved it back and forth to convince himself that he really was gone.

"Gone!" Yosef was thunderstruck. "He's here, and then, gone!"

Clopas said, "Wasn't your heart burning like mine, while he spoke to us on the road, while he was opening all those Scriptures to us?"

Yosef agreed, "Yes, my heart was burning. I've never heard anyone but Jesus open the Scriptures like that."

"We need to return to Jerusalem right away and let everyone know!" said Clopas. Both men arose from the table. Clopas paid the lodging proprietor and apologized for their sudden change of plans, while Yosef, abruptly returning to the moment, grabbed a couple of small round loaves of bread from the table and stuffed them in his bag for the return trip.

That very hour they started back to Jerusalem at a brisk pace.

"One thing I don't understand," remarked Yosef, "is why didn't we recognize him earlier than we did? Why was it only while he was breaking the bread?"

"That is a good question, Yosef. I know I didn't look at him closely until then, but I should have recognized him anyway. I think maybe our eyes were prevented from recognizing him until he wanted to reveal himself to us," replied Clopas.

Yosef walked with great enthusiasm. He said, "I feel so privileged that he appeared to us, that he explained the Scriptures, that he broke bread with us. And I can't wait to tell everyone what I saw. 'There he was, then poof! Gone!'"

They both laughed.

The Eleven Begin to Regroup

Peter came down from the upper room to the lower level of the house, and walked into the room where Mark and his mother were. His expression was distant, as though his mind was in another place.

"Peter, are you doing well?" asked Mariam.

"Yes, I am doing very well," answered Peter, and then, focusing his gaze on her, said, "Very well. I have seen Jesus—in the upper room—and he is alive. I need to tell John, and I expect to return within the hour."

Mark and his mother looked at each other. Peter turned to go. After he had left the house, Mariam said, "I am very concerned about him."

Mark said, "I'm going to go look." He ran upstairs, looked around, and returned. "Jesus isn't up there now, anyway," Mark reported.

"I believe Peter saw Jesus—either that, or a vision of Jesus," Mark suggested.

His mother looked at him and, considering his young age, thought it better to say nothing than to discourage his hope.

Peter left the house of the upper room for the third time since taking refuge there following Jesus' trial. During the previous two visits to the garden tomb that morning, he had deliberately chosen routes that bypassed the house of the high priest, partly from fear, and partly from shame—for it was in Caiaphas' house where he had denied knowing Jesus. This time, however, as he made the half-block trip west to the home of John and Zebedee, he stopped at the corner of the road going north past Caiaphas' house. Seeing the house only two blocks away made Peter feel a twinge of melancholy, but the crushing depression he had been feeling had thoroughly dissipated.

Being reminded of the vile injustice committed by the chief priests, Peter muttered, "You men have no idea what you have done."

John, Zebedee, Mary Magdalene and the others at Zebedee's were glad to see Peter when he arrived. John immediately noticed Peter's change of countenance, and he promptly learned the cause for it as Peter related his experience to them all.

"John, Zebedee. I saw ..." Peter's voice caught with emotion, and he spoke the words with difficulty, "Jesus, He ... Jesus, He was ..." Peter put his hands on John's shoulders and said haltingly, "He's ... a-*live!*" Peter began to weep.

"You've seen him?" John asked. Peter nodded in response.

"Where?"

"Upper room," Peter managed to say.

"Is he still there?"

Peter shook his head no.

John was at a loss. "So what now?"

A natural leader, Peter instinctively responded to the vacuum of direction implied by John's question.

"We need to regroup at the upper room," Peter said. "Do you know if the rest of the eleven are still in Bethany?"

"They were still there early this morning when I left from Bethany," interjected Mary Magdalene.

Zebedee added, "We are expecting Salome and the other women to return from there before long. I wouldn't be surprised if the nine accompany them back because of their report about the angels."

Peter said, "So, if they show up later today, John, bring them over to the upper room. If they don't show up today, then we'll need to reach them tomorrow.

"I feel the need to return to the upper room. But I hope to see you later today," Peter finished. Then he said his goodbyes to everyone else and left.

After Peter was gone, Zebedee asked John, "What do you think?"

"I'm pretty sure all these sightings of Jesus are his spirit communicating with us," speculated John. "Why else does he keep vanishing? Someone in the flesh doesn't disappear."

Mary Magdalene looked dismayed at John and said, "I truly pray your unbelief will vanish."

Mother Mary was standing at the back of the room, having listened closely to every word spoken. With her heart heavy with sorrow and conflicting emotions, she knew she couldn't count on her feelings to guide her thoughts. Once again, she pondered the words about Jesus she had received from the beginning, from the angel Gabriel, from the shepherds and Magi, and from Simeon and Anna in the temple. She recalled Jesus' first miracle in Cana, when he turned the water into wine, and thought that she felt as empty as those water pots had been. But the promises she had received of what Jesus would be—those words were her precious hope; she clung to them tenaciously.

She wished for some sign from God. At that very moment Mary Magdalene came over to Mother Mary and gave her a hug; Mother Mary wondered if that hug was the sign.

Jerusalem: Zebedee's Home

To reduce the possibility of attracting notice, the traveling party from Bethany skirted the city wall around the south and entered by the Essene Gate. From there they reached Zebedee's in short order.

John and the eight disciples were relieved and overjoyed to see one another. John inquired about Thomas and was informed of his choice to remain in Bethany and the reason for it.

The women recounted how they had met Jesus on the road to Bethany, and Mary Magdalene shared her encounter with Jesus at the tomb; thus, the women mutually encouraged themselves and strengthened Mother Mary's hope. Zebedee and the disciples listened closely and said little.

Andrew inquired with concern about his brother Peter, and John related Peter's visit to the house an hour or so prior. He also repeated Peter's desire for them all to regroup at the upper room; however, he left out Peter's testimony of encountering Jesus, thinking it better for Peter to convey that to the group himself. For that reason, and because Zebedee's home would be cramped with all of the extra, unexpected visitors, the disciples made ready to proceed to the upper room.

When John and the other eight disciples had left, Zebedee felt like an outsider in his own home, filled predominantly as it currently was with exuberant, talkative women. The only other subdued adult in the house was his sister-in-law, Mother Mary, and he wanted to give her space to grieve. So Zebedee retreated to the courtyard and sat down, glad for the reprieve. He had not dealt sufficiently with his own thoughts or grief, and with the astonishing reports coming in, he strained to arrive at any firm conclusions.

He raised his eyes and hands heavenward, "God, it's like a great storm on the Sea of Galilee; I can't see anything but the waves. Please still the waters and bring us light."

Clopas and Yosef reached Zebedee's house as the day was declining and found the family and guests sharing an improvised meal together. Everyone was surprised to see them, expecting instead their return on the morrow. After they joined the rest at dinner, Clopas and Yosef explained how a stranger had joined them on their travel to Emmaus and was recognized as Jesus when he broke bread with them at the table. Yosef described the vanishing part with wide eyes, great drama, and extensive hand motions.

In turn, Mary Magdalene and the women retold for the two travelers their respective encounters with Jesus. When Clopas learned that the eleven were gathered at the upper room, he and Yosef cut their meal short and proceeded to Mark's to share their story, accompanied by Zebedee.

Jerusalem: The Upper Room in Mark's Home

Mark and his mother were excited to see John with eight other disciples appear at their door, and gave them a warm greeting. Mark led them all upstairs to Peter, and provided them with a few more lamps, while Mariam graciously began preparing platters of fish and vegetables for her guests.

The disciples were fearful of the Jewish authorities; therefore, they instructed Mark how to knock so they would know when it was him, and then bolted the door after he had left. Peter and the disciples were heartened by each other's presence, and the disciples explained to him Thomas' whereabouts.

When they had all sat down for a longer discussion, John and Peter described for the others their experiences at the tomb in the early morning, and then John asked Peter to relate his experience of seeing Jesus in the afternoon, which Peter felt honored to do. Peter abbreviated the message that Jesus had given him, and instead focused on trying to convince the other disciples that he had indeed seen Jesus in bodily form—especially because he could see from their postures that they were not accepting his testimony.

Before they could ask questions, they were interrupted by Mark knocking at the door. He brought in platters of food for dinner, then returned downstairs again.

"How do you know that you weren't seeing a vision?" asked Nathanael.

"Because I *touched* him," answered Peter.

"But if his physical body was here, how could it disappear?" asked Simon the Zealot.

"I have no answer for that," acknowledged Peter, "but neither can I explain how Jesus commanded the storm to cease, or the lepers to be cleansed, or how he raised Lazarus. Even before he was crucified, he showed many times that he had power over the physical world."

"But power to have a physical body that can just appear and disappear at will?" asked Thaddeus, "Who could do that but God alone?"

"Let me tell you something most of you don't know. Remember the time Jesus healed the epileptic boy? Of course you do. If you also remember, that was immediately after Jesus had taken me, John, and James up on a mountain by ourselves. Let me tell you what happened up on the mountain.

"Jesus started praying. And the three of us, we prayed a little, but we fell asleep. While we were sleeping, Jesus changed, and it woke me up. His appearance was different, and his face was shining, like the sun, it was so bright. And his clothing shone too, whiter than any white I've ever seen. So I woke up James and John.

"Immediately, Moses and Elijah appeared, and they were talking with Jesus. I knew who they were because Jesus called them by name. They were glorified, too—but not as much as Jesus.

"They were talking together about Jesus' coming departure from Jerusalem. At the time, I didn't know what that meant. But on the way down the mountain, Jesus instructed us to tell no one what we had seen until the Son of Man had risen from the dead. The three of us discussed what 'rising from the dead' meant, but again, we didn't know at the time. Now, I believe he was talking about what has just happened.

"And because he has risen from the dead, I can freely share this story with you now. James, John, isn't my testimony true?" asked Peter.

They both confirmed that it was, although neither was convinced of Peter's conclusion.

Peter continued, "Besides, you all remember when he spoke to us in Galilee and predicted that he would be handed over to the Gentiles, and be killed, rising again after three days. It happened just like he said."

They remembered his words but were not convinced.

Thaddeus objected, "Yes, I remember. But again, what does 'rising from the dead' mean? The reports we are hearing sound like people are seeing his spirit."

Philip countered, "Thaddeus, if people are just seeing his spirit, wouldn't you expect to find his body still in the grave?"

"That's a good question, and I don't know," said Thaddeus, "but another problem in my mind is that I don't remember anywhere in the Law or the Prophets where it says the Messiah is going to just walk out of a tomb. Or even die in the first place. I thought the Scriptures say that the Messiah is to remain forever."

"What about where David wrote in one Psalm that 'You will not allow your Holy One to undergo decay'?" asked Nathanael. "That sounds to me more like dying, but not decaying, rather than never dying."

"Okay, Rabbi Nathanael," said Thaddeus, frowning, "but could that not mean that God took the body, like he took Elijah in the whirlwind, and perhaps Moses' body too—remember his body was never found—and that Jesus is appearing now in visions?"

Peter insisted, "I *touched* him. How could that be a vision?"

Matthew said, "You and John said the graveclothes were all in place where he had been lying, except the face cloth. How could Jesus have gotten up, and out of the graveclothes, without them getting scattered all over? Or how could he even get out of them without help, anyway?"

Right then there was a knock at the door, which startled

everyone, but after a few more knocks they knew it was Mark. When they opened the door, Mark showed Clopas, Yosef, and Zebedee into the room and asked if he could stay, to which the disciples cheerfully consented. Mark locked the door, and the newcomers joined the disciples reclining around the table.

James the Younger, who had been quiet up to this point, declared to the newcomers, "Peter has told us the Lord has really risen, and appeared to him!"

Clopas responded to his son, "That is exciting news, James! Yosef and I have seen him, too!"

"Tell us, we are eager to hear," said John.

So for a second time, Clopas and Yosef recounted their experiences on the road and how Jesus was recognized by them while breaking the bread. Yosef again described the vanishing part with great drama and hand motions.

Simon the Zealot spoke, "See, I think Jesus is giving us visions from heaven. That's what I think."

Yosef said, "That was no vision. He was really there, walking and talking and sitting at the table with us. Visions don't pick up a piece of bread that is in a bowl and break it."

"Did you touch him?" inquired Thaddeus.

"No," said Clopas, "but he touched the bread and broke it."

Thaddeus asked, "How can flesh and blood just disappear and reappear different places?"

Suddenly, Jesus came and stood among them, and said, "Peace to you."

They were stunned and terrified. Yosef let out a yelp, Philip dropped the chunk of cucumber he was about to bite into, and Nathanael's bushy eyebrows merged with the curly hair on his forehead. They thought they were seeing a spirit!

"You all need to stop your unbelief and soften your hard hearts. You've heard the reports from the women and Peter. You've heard the testimonies of multiple witnesses. Why have you not believed my witnesses? Why are you troubled and afraid, and why are doubts arising in your hearts?

"Take a look at my hands and my feet; see for yourselves that it is me. Touch me and see, for a spirit does not have flesh and bones as you see that I have." After Jesus had said these things, he showed them his hands, his feet, and his side.

While they still had great trouble believing what their eyes were seeing, their emotions were overwhelmed with joy and astonishment.

Then to prove that they were not seeing a ghost, he said to them, "Do you have anything here to eat?" They gave him a piece of broiled fish, and he took it and ate it in front of them. As he did that, they gathered around him, watching closely in continued astonishment. Nathanael's eyes were still wide.

The disciples rejoiced greatly when they saw the Lord; to have him among them again wiped out all the anguish of recent days and replaced it with indescribable elation.

After consuming the fish, Jesus said to them, "Now, recall those things that I spoke to you while I was with you, that everything which is written about me in the Law of Moses and the Prophets and the Psalms must be fulfilled. Just as I told you, so it has happened, and now you've seen it."

Then he opened their minds to understand the Scriptures, and he said to them, "This was written in the Scriptures, that the Christ would suffer and rise again from the dead on the third day, and that repentance for forgiveness of sins would be proclaimed in his name to all the nations of the world, beginning from Jerusalem. You are witnesses of these things."

Jesus repeated his initial greeting, "Peace be with you," and continued, "As the Father has sent me, I also am sending you."

After he had said this, he breathed on them and said, "Receive the Holy Spirit. If you forgive the sins of anyone, their sins are forgiven them; if you do not forgive them, they are not forgiven."

Then he vanished from their sight.

Despite his reproach for their unbelief, none of them was unbelieving now, and their joy swept away all other emotions. They started to talk excitedly among themselves about what Jesus had just spoken to them and about the Scriptures, how they suddenly could understand the prophecies related to the

Christ, and about the words Jesus had spoken to them back in Galilee about his pending death and resurrection—how those words finally all made sense. The depth of revelation and insight was utterly thrilling! Before they had been blind; now they could see.

Mark was eager to return downstairs to inform his mother of Jesus' visit to the upper room. Zebedee, Clopas, and Yosef returned to Zebedee's house to share this news also. The disciples settled down for the night in the upper room, although they had difficulty sleeping for the joy and excitement.

The women at Zebedee's were jubilant to hear confirmation of their earlier sightings and to know that the disbelief of the disciples had finally been vanquished. Mother Mary wept with joy now, secure in the knowledge that her son had overcome death and the grave, but aching to see him as the others had.

It was night outside, but in the hearts of a growing circle of Jesus' followers, a glorious dawn had risen, and it was an entirely new day.

Between the Resurrection and Galilee

On the Roads Again
Nisan 19

The following morning—that is, Monday—Mary Magdalene and Mary Clopas determined to return to Bethany to inform everyone there of the latest developments.

Clopas and Yosef headed for Emmaus again to complete the purpose of yesterday's interrupted journey. As they passed the garden tomb once more, they saw a small crowd of people there, primarily to gawk at the empty tomb—a subject of increasing conversation in the city.

Yosef said to Clopas, "The tomb doesn't look at all the same to me now."

Clopas answered, "For me also. Yesterday, it seemed ominous and forbidding, a great mystery; today, it is just a cave. And its emptiness fills me with thanksgiving to God."

Within the tomb, unseen to the travelers, Joseph of Arimathea and his servants were collecting the graveclothes, reverently folding them. Upon exiting, they rolled the stone back across the opening, and Joseph picked up the cord from the broken seal. Although he didn't mind the visitors in his garden—too much— Joseph felt that the people peering into the tomb were being ill-mannered.

Very curious as to what had actually transpired, Joseph suspected that the story about the disciples stealing the body had been fabricated by the priests and elders. And then there was the question about the soldiers and what they might have seen. As Joseph started back towards the city, he encountered Nicodemus.

"Nicodemus, shalom," said Joseph. "I've closed the tomb. Here are the graveclothes and the seal."

Nicodemus took the cord in his hand and examined it, looking at the attached wax bullae impressed with the seals of Caiaphas and Petronius.

"I believe something very unusual has happened here, Joseph," remarked Nicodemus.

"And I am of the same opinion," agreed Joseph. "The idea that the soldiers slept while someone stole the body is absurd on its face, and the word in the Council is that the chief priests bribed the soldiers to say that. But, there is more. Look at this!"

Joseph took the folded linen shroud and unfolded it near the middle.

Nicodemus glanced at the shroud and exclaimed, "Joseph, it's an image of Jesus! How could that happen?"

"I have no possible idea. It almost appears like the fabric is faintly scorched. But there is no odor of burnt fabric. And here is another odd thing I noticed: The spices we wrapped in the cloths were nowhere to be found in the tomb," replied Joseph. "And 100 pounds of loose spices cannot disappear so completely."

A look of amazement swept over Nicodemus' face. "It reminds me of the chariot of fire that took Elijah to heaven. Perhaps God took the body to heaven in a blaze of fire."

"Perhaps it was something like that. What concerns me is what might happen next—what God will do. I presume you have heard about the curtain in the temple?"

"I have," answered Nicodemus, "And when I asked one of the chief priests if perhaps God was trying to tell us something, he rebuked me and said it was torn by the earthquake. But that is physically impossible, of course, and the rest of the temple suffered no damage.

"I grieve that the chief priests are ignoring the Scriptures and the faith handed down from the Patriarchs. God is saying something here, and I fear what it may be. Our leaders have committed a great sin."

Joseph nodded agreement, and the two men started back to the city together with great consternation.

On the way, Joseph raised a question, "Why do you think we are the only members of the Sanhedrin who understood that Jesus was the Messiah?"

Nicodemus considered a moment before answering, "Pride and jealousy. They could not accept that the Messiah would appear as a carpenter from Nazareth, rather than from a powerful family. They forget that Jacob and David were poor shepherd boys once."

Joseph said, "With the mighty works that Jesus did, they should have known. Yet I still struggle with his origin being from Nazareth rather than Bethlehem as the prophet Isaiah predicted."

"Oh, you didn't know?" asked Nicodemus. "I inquired about that, and he was indeed born in Bethlehem. Shortly thereafter, his family fled from there to escape the violence of Herod."

"Thank you," said a gratified Joseph. "I didn't know that. Although, it just confirms the seriousness of our situation."

Mary Magdalene and Mary Clopas arrived in Bethany and updated Lazarus, Martha, and Thomas with the very latest news. First, Mary Magdalene reported her own encounter with Jesus at the tomb. Then they related Jesus' appearing to Peter individually, and lastly, they told them about the previous night's meeting in the upper room when Jesus appeared to the group of disciples.

When the women had completed their reporting, Lazarus exclaimed, "Thanks be to God! More confirmation!"

Thomas listened intently but was silent.

Mary Magdalene made the decision to remain at Bethany for the time being, to assist her sister Martha with the household.

Mary Clopas, however, wanted to return to Jerusalem that day in order to be present when Clopas returned from Emmaus on the following day. Lazarus wanted to travel with her so that he could hear firsthand from the disciples who had seen Jesus, and he persuaded Thomas to come along.

Jerusalem: The Upper Room in Mark's Home
Nisan 19 to Nisan 24

Arriving in Jerusalem, the trio first went to Zebedee's home to drop off Mary Clopas. Lazarus and Thomas remained there a short time fellowshipping with the disciples. But Lazarus' main interest, since he had already heard the testimony of all the women who had seen Jesus, was meeting with the "Twelve" (still so-called, even though Judas was gone). So he and Thomas soon excused themselves and walked the short distance to Mark's house.

Arriving at the upper room, Lazarus was warmly received, as he and his sisters had been a blessing to the Twelve for a long time, and his miracle of being raised from the dead held a special place in their hearts and minds.

Despite Thomas' reluctance in coming, he was glad to see his brothers.

"Thomas!" exclaimed Matthew, "So good to see you! You should have been here last night!"

"So I have heard," Thomas answered, "But Lazarus and I would like to hear about it from you all."

"Of course," the other disciples told him. "We have seen the Lord!"

Then they described the entire encounter, including all that Jesus had said and done.

Even so, Thomas was not persuaded. He said to them resolutely, "I'm telling you, unless I see the scars of the nails in his hands, put my finger into the imprint of the nails, and put my hand into his side, I am not going to believe it."

The disciples spent some time that day trying to convince Thomas but made no headway; however, Thomas decided to remain with the disciples awhile in the upper room.

Tuesday came and went without Jesus appearing to any of his followers. Lazarus returned to Bethany to his sisters.

Wednesday morning came, the last day of the Feast of Unleavened Bread—a holy day of rest. Thomas said, "I am going up to see the tomb." Despite everyone's fear of the Jewish leaders, Nathanael and Matthew said they would go also, and the three of them headed north through the city streets. When they arrived, there was not much to be seen, as the stone door of the tomb had been rolled back into place. There were a small number of visitors who had also come to see the tomb, and the pile of memorial stones was now taller than a man.

Thursday came, and most of the Jews visiting Jerusalem for the Passover feast began to leave the city and return home. Joanna, her husband Chuza, and Susanna returned to the Galilean capital city of Tiberias with Herod Antipas' retinue.

In the upper room, the excitement of the disciples diminished by a measure. Those who had seen Jesus were craving to see him again, and they began to wonder why he was not manifesting himself.

On Friday at midmorning, Thomas spoke to Matthew.

"I probably don't need to say anything," Thomas said.

"No, I am pretty certain I can guess what you'd say," Matthew replied.

"Yeah, nothing needs to be said, because nothing is what I see," Thomas said.

"So if nothing needs to be said, why don't you try not saying anything?" retorted Matthew.

"Right, so I'm saying nothing."

"Now I think we may have some agreement. Maybe next time we can have a conversation about something," said Matthew, a bit irritated, as he walked away from Thomas.

Nathanael asked Matthew, "So what were you discussing with Thomas?"

"Nothing!" Matthew grumbled.

Saturday Sabbath passed uneventfully. Some of the disciples began to discuss if they should return to Galilee rather than remain sequestered in the upper room.

Thaddeus said, "Remember, the women said the angels told them that Jesus would go before us to Galilee."

James Zebedee responded, "That's true, but Jesus hasn't given us any instructions about when to leave. I think we should remain in Jerusalem until our direction is more clear." Peter and John agreed.

Jerusalem: The Upper Room
Nisan 25

On Sunday at mid-morning, the disciples ate breakfast at the same table in the locked upper room where they had shared their last supper with Jesus, and the mood was subdued. It was one week after the first appearance of Jesus, but also one week since the last. Following breakfast, Thomas made an announcement.

"It's been a week that I've lived in this room, and I haven't seen Jesus yet. Mark and his mother have been gracious hosts, but I don't want to impose on them any longer. Passover is over, and I need to find some way to make a living again, so I'm going to head for Galilee today. I'd be happy to have any of you accompany me if you would like to. I think the time has come to go."

No one said anything in response as Thomas went to pick up his small travel bag and tossed it over his shoulder. He turned to say his farewell.

As he turned, Jesus suddenly stood in the room, right beside the table, and looked straight at Thomas. The disciples at the table all initially reacted with fright.

"Peace to you," Jesus said to the disciples. Thomas' mouth dropped open, and his bag landed on the floor.

He then said to Thomas, "Put your finger here, and examine my hands; and put your hand here, into my side; and do not be unbelieving, but believe."

Thomas answered him, "My Lord and my God!" Then he dropped to his knees and bowed low.

And Jesus said to him, "Do you believe because you have seen me, Thomas? Blessed are those who have not seen me and yet believe."

Jesus continued, "The message I sent to the women through the angels, I repeat to you all: I am going ahead of you to Galilee. You will see me there. Now leave for Galilee today; do not remain here. Peace to you."

Then Jesus disappeared.

Return to Galilee
Nisan 15 to Nisan 30

James Zebedee and James the Younger went immediately to Zebedee's home and informed those present of Jesus' latest appearance. They also said the Twelve would be leaving for Galilee as soon as everyone was ready. Zebedee, Salome, and the others in the house had been waiting to accompany the disciples on the trip back.

In about an hour's time, the party began the return trip to Galilee. They exited the Ephraim Gate on the west side of the city and turned northward in the direction of the road leading to Samaria before it entered Galilee. Immediately after turning, they passed the hill of Golgotha, with its empty, upright stipes.

John remarked to this brother James, "This place looks so different now—as somber as ever, but not frightening."

"Yes," replied James. "Jesus defeated Rome."

"And death," said John.

The trip took six days by foot.

On the first day of travel, Thomas deliberately chose to walk alongside Matthew.

"I probably don't need to say anything," Thomas said.

Matthew grinned, "No, you probably don't."

"But I'm going to anyway. I'm sorry for my unbelief."

"You don't need to apologize to me," said Matthew. "I didn't believe either until I saw him for myself."

"I was being thick-headed. And, I also want to say that Jesus is more...well, beyond anything I could have imagined," said Thomas.

"Well, those are two truths so indisputable that they don't even need to be said," replied Matthew, giving Thomas a friendly nudge.

Thomas returned the nudge, saying, "That's the truth."

The trip was long, dusty, and warm in the sun-filled days, even though it was springtime. During the cool nights, they lodged in caravansaries (hostelries) along the route. These were mercifully much less crowded than if they had left the city with the multitudes just four days earlier. Although Zebedee and Salome could have afforded to stay in an individual room, they chose to spend the nights in the courtyards of the caravansaries, along with their son James the Younger and the other disciples. Mother Mary was put up in a room with Clopas and Mary Clopas.

When they were within sight of the Sea of Galilee, Philip asked Nathanael, "Do you wonder what Jesus might have in store for us next?"

"Yes, all the time. I have a thousand ideas of what might happen next."

"A thousand. Really?"

"Not really, but accounting isn't my strength."

"Do you care to share any?"

"It would be useless," replied Nathanael, "because whatever Jesus does next, you can be certain it won't be any one of my thousand ideas."

"Then why think about them?"

"How can I not?" asked Nathanael. "Right now it's the only thing I want to know."

On the way, Zebedee offered lodging for the Twelve at his home; the disciples thanked him for the offer but politely declined. They had already decided not to burden him with guests and, instead, to stay at Jesus' former home, the house in Capernaum that had served as his base of ministry for the previous three years.

The traveling party passed along the western shore of the Sea of Galilee, to the north side where Capernaum was located. Mother Mary, who Jesus had placed under John's care, settled into the Zebedee home along with Zebedee, Salome, Clopas, and Mary Clopas. John informed Mother Mary that he would be stopping by regularly to see her, then joined the rest of the Twelve at Jesus' former residence.

The men had reached their destination. But nobody knew why Jesus had instructed them to return, or when or where he would manifest himself in Galilee, or what to do in the meantime except wait.

As they settled down for the night, Andrew lay looking up at the thatched ceiling. His mind returned to the day some people with a paralytic friend had dug a hole through it and let their friend down through the hole on a stretcher, how Jesus had healed the man, and how afterward Andrew and a couple other disciples had repaired the hole in Jesus' roof.

Andrew spoke to Peter, "You know, eleven of us now fill this small house, yet it seems very empty."

Peter replied, "I know what you mean, Andrew. Remember when Jesus healed the paralytic fellow here?"

"I was just thinking about it."

"Well, he said just before healing him that he was doing it so the scribes would know he had authority to forgive sins."

"I remember it like it was yesterday."

"At the time, I had trouble accepting those words myself—that he could forgive sins. How differently I feel now, and how grateful I am," Peter said, sighing.

Galilee

The Twelve and those with them had arrived back in Galilee on Friday, Nisan 30, less than two weeks from the first appearance of Jesus after his suffering and death. The following day, a Sabbath, was a day of rest from the long trip and a time of reacclimating to the more relaxed atmosphere of Capernaum.

On the day after the Sabbath, James the son of Zebedee decided to walk to the water's edge, and he was joined by his brother John, former fishing partner Peter, and his brother Andrew. James had grown up on the water and loved everything connected to it. The feel of the cool breeze, the warmth of the sun, the sight of the acrobatic waterfowl, the high-pitched calls of the birds, and the soft rhythmic sound of small waves lapping against the anchored boats and the shore invigorated his soul. He took a deep breath and savored the tranquility of the moment. A few of his father's boats were tied up along the pier, and others had been taken out by hired hands for a day of fishing.

The four disciples sat wordless on the short stone seawall for a while, soaking in the beauty of the sea, tinted as it was by hues of the early morning sun, and enjoying the sweetness of the air—a welcome change from the odorous, noisy streets of Jerusalem.

John asked, "Have any of you missed the sea?"

Peter said, "While we were with Jesus? Not at all. But I surely prefer the beauty and the sounds here over the streets of Jerusalem. Yet, after being with Jesus, this place looks smaller, and I see everything differently. I see blind people everywhere. Before I met Jesus, all I could see were the difficulties of fishing. I was the blind one."

Andrew asked the others a question that was in everyone's mind. "When do you suppose we will see Jesus again?"

James answered, "I've been thinking of that. Let me ask you a question: What did John the Baptist say about Jesus, when Jesus approached him for baptism at the beginning?"

"Behold the lamb of God, who takes away the sin of the world."

"And when was Jesus crucified?" James asked.

"On the day of preparation for Passover."

"That's right. Now one more question. What did Jesus say to us, the night before he died, when he handed us the cup of wine?"

"This is my blood of the covenant, which is poured out for many for forgiveness of sins," Andrew answered.

"Do you see it?" asked James, pausing.

"I do!" exclaimed Andrew, "Jesus is the fulfillment of our Passover feast tradition. He's the lamb of God, exactly as John the Baptist told us. Passover has been—for all these centuries—symbolically pointing to what Jesus just did. He *is* the Passover lamb! And he died on the same afternoon that the Passover lambs were slaughtered in Jerusalem!"

John whistled and with teary eyes said, "He *was meant* to die."

James continued, "Now, follow me on this—he died on the preparation day of Passover—a feast day. On what day did we learn he was resurrected?"

"Yom HaBikkurim—the day of First Fruits, or "first-born of the earth," Andrew said.

"That's right," said James, "Now look at the pattern. The sheaf, or omer of barley, is harvested just after sundown following the weekly Sabbath. That's when Jesus likely came out of the tomb. And the grains of the sheaf are bruised, as Jesus was, then they are combined with incense and lifted before the Lord. So—another sacred day fulfilled by Jesus. What's the next holy day that's coming?"

"Shavuot, or Pentecost," said Andrew, "But that's over a month away. Are you saying that we won't see Jesus again until Pentecost?" asked Andrew.

"Well, I certainly hope it would be sooner, but from the pattern, I don't know if we will."

By this time the other disciples had walked down to the water and joined the four sitting on the wall.

"I have a question," said James the Younger. "Why haven't we seen very much of Jesus? Why isn't he with us all the time?"

No one responded immediately as they considered the question.

Thomas spoke first, "Think about the past three years. Jesus was constantly training us in the things of the Father. He's been teaching us about things of the Spirit, so that we can stand as his disciples on our own feet. He always spoke as though he would be leaving us sometime in the future, and I think that time is here. Remember what he said at the Passover meal: 'Children, I am with you only a little longer. You will seek me, and as I said to the Jews, I also say now to you, "Where I am going, you cannot come."' At the beginning, we were all like children in our understanding, but we really have grown.

"Remember the first time we were in a violent storm on this very sea? Jesus was asleep in the boat, on the cushion. The next time we were in a severe storm, Jesus wasn't with us at first; then he came to us walking on the water. Now he wants us to be able to handle the storm ourselves.

"We have a message the world needs to hear. They need to hear about Jesus, and no one can speak about him better than we can."

Simon the Zealot objected, "But what do we begin to say? How do we know where to go? Why would people listen to us? We can't heal anybody. We can't teach like he did."

Thomas answered, "Remember when he sent us out to the towns and villages? He didn't even let us take supplies. Yet, we found that our needs were met and people were healed and delivered. When he sends us out again, he will provide everything we need. You can count on it."

Philip looked at Thomas, amazed by the transformation in his fellow disciple, and said, "Thomas, my brother, you really encourage me."

In the afternoon of the next day, four of the disciples went to the market street of Capernaum for supplies. Peter was restless at the house. Waiting was difficult, and he wanted to do something useful as they all tarried for further direction from Jesus. So Peter walked to Zebedee's and asked his permission to take one of his fishing boats out to go fishing. Since Peter had partnered in fishing with Zebedee's sons before becoming a disciple, Zebedee readily obliged him.

Returning to the house, Peter announced to Thomas, Nathanael, James, John, Matthew, and Thaddeus, "I am going fishing." They all said to Peter, "We will go with you." On the way to the pier, Peter and John grabbed a couple of the nets that were hanging over a line, drying in the sun. They clambered into the boat, and Peter stowed the nets in the bow. John and James checked the side rudder and the four mast support ropes: fore, aft, port, and starboard. Thomas and Thaddeus untied the mooring ropes and tossed them into the boat.

To get underway, Peter picked up an oar and pushed against a piling supporting the pier, while James took an oar and pushed off the pier from the stern. They dropped the oars into oarlocks, and with four disciples working the four oars, they soon were in open water. They unfurled the square sail from the single yard to take advantage of a light wind from the southwest.

Peter directed James to steer the boat towards a good fishing spot as he worked the sail's main sheet. He wanted to go eastward towards Bethsaida, near the estuary of the Jordan River.

Matthew was sitting in the stern, and Nathanael joined him.

"I'm surprised you decided to come fishing," Nathanael said.

"Oh, I figured these fellows might need some advice on how to catch fish," Matthew retorted. "You know they haven't thrown a net in years."

Peter, overhearing them, said to Matthew, "Don't worry about that. Fishermen never forget how to throw a net. Besides, we're heading for one of the best fishing spots on the sea. We'll be having fish for breakfast."

They arrived at the location of Peter's choosing and dropped a sea anchor. After about an hour of throwing nets without results, they weighed anchor, moved a short distance, and tried again.

James was throwing from the bow, and John from the stern. Matthew got up and said to John, "Here, let me have a throw. I'll show you how it's done."

Nathanael said, "Better hang on to his tunic, John, so he doesn't go out with the net."

John handed the net to Matthew but hung on to the draw cord to make sure his father's net didn't end up in the deep. Matthew gave an awkward heave, the net sank, and John pulled the cord to collapse the net and retrieve it.

The net was empty, but Matthew chirped, "Just keep doing it like that, John, and I'm sure we'll have plenty of fish by morning."

"Whatever you say, Matthew," John replied with a grin.

As Matthew sat down, Nathanael said, "The artlessness of that toss was only equaled by its fishlessness."

"Ha!" retorted Matthew, "Note that I caught as many fish in that toss as the entire boat has caught thus far."

"So noted," agreed Nathanael.

For the remainder of the night the earnest fishermen and their boatmates caught absolutely nothing. Apart from some small talk, the conversational threads revolved around Jesus. They discussed their memories of events over the past three years and his teachings. They discussed how Jesus fit the prophetic messianic Scriptures in ways that were only now becoming plain to them. And of course they discussed those things about which they had no idea, such as where Jesus was at the moment, or what Jesus had planned next.

Apart from Matthew, the other disciples spelled one another about every half-hour in the arduous task of throwing and pulling the weighted nets. Even the former fishermen among them found it tiring, as they were long out of practice.

Fortunately, the night was cool, but the work thoroughly warmed them so much that they found it necessary to strip to their tunics while working.

At daybreak, a tired but determined Peter was still tossing his net from the bow. The boat was facing east directly into the breaking sun, and he was throwing to the port side of the boat. Peter was about ready to quit and return to Capernaum, when he noticed a figure on the beach, about 200 cubits[25] across the water.

The man called out to the disciples in the boat, "Shalom! You don't have any fish, do you?"

A couple of them yelled back, "No!"

Then the man said, "Cast your net on the right side, and you will find fish."

"That sounds really familiar," Thomas said, remembering the story he had heard from Peter years before.

Peter and the others remembered it too, and they all perked up. Peter didn't hesitate to immediately throw his net to the starboard side. As he pulled, the water roiled, and the net was suddenly, monstrously heavy. As it came to the surface, all the disciples, leaning to starboard and eagerly looking at the spot Peter's rope entered the water, saw the net break the surface, teeming full of fish.

Upon seeing the fish, John immediately confirmed what they all had been hoping, "It is the Lord!"

Peter, hearing John's declaration, promptly tied off the end of the net pull-cord to an anchor point below the gunwale, put on his fisherman's jacket (for he had previously removed it), and threw himself into the sea to strike out for the shore where the man stood.

Meanwhile, the other disciples brought the small boat to shore, as they were not far from it. Rather than hoisting the net into the boat, which might have torn it, they dragged the net with the fish through the water as they rowed.

When the boat ran aground, the disciples hopped out into calf-deep water and slogged to land; John, being the last out of the boat, brought a line to shore and threw it around a sizeable rock to secure the boat. They all recognized Jesus sitting there, next to a soaking-wet Peter. In front of them was a charcoal fire with fish cooking on it, and bread. The disciples were

---

[25] A distance of about 100 yards

overflowing with joy.

Jesus said to them, "Bring some of the fish you have just caught." Peter jumped to his feet and dragged the net ashore, full of large fish, 153 by Matthew's count. Remarkably, although there were so many, the net was not torn.

Jesus then said to them, "Come, have breakfast." None of the disciples had the audacity to ask him, "Who are you?" It was indeed the Lord, and they could see it plainly, although their amazement and the sense of "this is too good to be true" made it almost feel as if a dream.

Jesus took the bread and gave it to them, and likewise the fish. This was now the third time that Jesus had appeared to the disciples after he was raised from the dead, the two previous times being in the upper room in Jerusalem.

All of the disciples were full of questions and yearning to ask him, but they knew from experience to let Jesus speak first. So, they ate their breakfast quickly and in silence, thrilled to be in the presence of the one they had been seeking and eager to hear what he would say.

When they had finished eating, Jesus turned to Peter and said, "Peter, let's go for a walk."

As they began walking along the shore, leaving the other disciples at the fire, Jesus asked, "Peter, son of John, do you love me, sacrificially, more than these other men?"

Painfully aware of the imperfection of his own heart, the best Peter could muster in reply was, "Yes, Lord, you know I love you as a brother."

Jesus then said to him, "Feed my lambs."

He then asked Peter again, "Peter, son of John, do you love me sacrificially?"

"Yes, Lord, you know that I love you like a brother."

Jesus said to him, "Tend my sheep."

He asked Peter a third time, "Peter, son of John, do you love me like a brother?"

Peter was grieved because Jesus said to him the third time, "Do you love me like a brother?" rather than "Do you love me sacrificially?" And Peter said to him, "Lord, you know all things;

you know that I love you like a brother."

Jesus said to him, "Feed my sheep."

Then Jesus said to Peter, "I tell you the truth: When you were younger, you dressed yourself and went wherever you wanted, but when you are old you will stretch out your hands, and someone else will dress you and take you where you do not want to go."

Now he said this to make known by what kind of death—that is, martyrdom—Peter would glorify God. After he had spoken this, he said to Peter, "Follow me!"

Turning around, Peter saw John following them, the one who had leaned back against Jesus at the Passover meal and asked, "Lord, who is the one who betrays you?" So when Peter saw him, he said to Jesus, "Lord, what about this man?" Jesus said to him, "If I want him to remain alive until I return, what concern is that to you? You follow me!"[26]

Upon returning to the other disciples sitting by the fire, Jesus gave them instructions.

"When you return to Capernaum and are together with the rest of the Twelve, go throughout the cities and towns of Galilee where we have traveled before, and tell my followers to gather on the mountain where I first taught the people. I will meet you there. It is time for you to get started."

The disciples walked to the boat, and Jesus accompanied them. The crew loaded the fish into the boat, John tossed the mooring line aboard and nudged the boat loose, and the men climbed in. When they looked back to the beach, Jesus was already gone.

Peter manned the rudder and four other disciples handled the oars until the boat reached sufficient depth of water. They

---

[26] Later, Jesus' words to Peter concerning John were misunderstood by some people, resulting in a rumor among Jesus' followers that John would not die. However, Jesus never said that John would not die, but instead, "If I want him to remain alive until I return, what concern is that to you?" John himself testified to what Jesus said about this and wrote it down, and John's testimony is reliable.

turned westward to the direction of Capernaum, and Peter turned the rudder over to James and set the sail for a port tack back to the dock. Winds were brisk and the water choppy, so the rowers pulled in the oars for the return and relied entirely on the wind.

Zebedee greeted them as they came in to the dock to tie up. He was astonished at the catch of fish that he saw.

"Peter, you've had an amazing night!" he declared.

Peter smiled. "No, Jesus brought in the fish; I just hung onto the net."

"You must tell me all about it," said Zebedee enthusiastically.

Peter sold the catch to Zebedee, who planned to dry and market the fish. Zebedee was thrilled to have such an unexpected harvest, and Peter was glad to have the disciples' finances replenished.

Matthew was glad to be back on land.

The first thing the exhausted crew did was to relate their meeting with Jesus to everyone at Zebedee's house. Then they walked back to their lodging and retold the event to the four disciples who had gone to the market for provisions.

Andrew was discouraged that he had chosen to go to the market and had missed Jesus.

"Don't let it bother you, Andrew," Peter assuaged. "We needed the provisions, and Jesus said we will see him again after we collect his followers to the mountain."

"Just the same, I'd rather have fish with Jesus than buy vegetables with Philip," said Andrew.

"So, what's wrong with buying vegetables?" asked Philip.

Andrew rolled his eyes.

The disciples who had returned from fishing slept for a few hours that morning and, upon waking, put together a plan to spread the word through Galilee. They divided into teams of two, following the pattern Jesus had used before, except that Simon the Zealot joined James the Younger and Thaddeus, because the Twelve were now just eleven.

Peter, James, and John mapped out the cities to which each team would go.

"So," announced Peter, "we will start with the cities that are furthest away, so people there will have more travel time to come. Each team will visit two cities. It should take three days for each team to visit the cities and spread the word. Then we have a Sabbath; after that, it should take no more than two days for all to return. So tell the people that we will all assemble on the mountain on the third day of the week."

Before midday, they started off to bring an unparalleled message to the people of Galilee.

While walking down the road, James the Younger asked Simon the Zealot, "Simon, when Jesus first sent us out two-by-two, you were paired with Judas Iscariot. Did you ever think he would betray Jesus?"

"Well, I always felt there was something not right with Judas," he answered, "but I couldn't say then what it was. Now, I can see that he was selfishly ambitious and constantly thinking about how to turn everything to his own advantage. I think that was it. But when Jesus prophesied at our last meal that one of us would betray him, although Judas had crossed my mind, I was much more concerned that I could be the one."

"You? Why would you think that?"

"With Jesus, I learned that I didn't know and couldn't trust my own heart," stated Simon.

"I know what you mean," Thaddeus said.

"Me too," agreed James the Younger.

So the disciples canvassed Galilee, telling the people that Jesus was risen from the dead, and that he would be appearing to his followers on the mountain one and a half miles northwest of Capernaum, where Jesus gave his first major teaching. When they started out, they expected the people to respond with excitement and eagerness, but instead, they found a very mixed reception.

Some people—especially the Pharisees, scribes, and synagogue leaders—rejected their news completely. Not only was everyone well aware that Jesus had been crucified, but they also had heard the false rumor that his disciples had stolen his body.

Others were skeptical and unwilling to sacrifice a few days of work to make the trip for something they doubted. But there were those whose faces brightened at the news: the ones whose lives had been transformed by Jesus' presence and teaching, others whose bodies had been healed at his touch, those who had come to love him—they were the ones who eagerly welcomed the news and made preparations to go to the mountain.

Galilee: On the Mountain Jesus Had Designated

The eleven men regrouped in Capernaum on the second day of the week, having spent five days traversing the populated centers of Galilee with a Sabbath rest in the middle. Early the following morning, they walked up the mountain that Jesus had specified, about three-quarters of an hour's distance from the house, to find a few hundred people already gathered there. The summit was gently rounded, with no trees but plenty of grass, and many were sitting.

By mid-morning, the crowd had grown to more than 500 men, with even more women and children. Mother Mary was there, along with Zebedee and Salome, Clopas and his wife Mary, Joanna, and Susanna.

James the Younger commented to Simon the Zealot, "When Jesus performed healing in a more remote place, there was a crowd of 5,000; now to see him back from the dead, the greatest miracle of all, there are only 500."

"Yes, but remember, we also found it hard to believe at first," responded Simon, "so let's be thankful that at least this many have come."

About that time, a man was spotted coming up the mountain from the side opposite the sea. The eleven disciples immediately recognized him as Jesus, and the crowd began buzzing with anticipation. Some were doubtful that it was actually Jesus; however, as he drew nearer, people began to drop to their knees, overcome with awe. The disciples also kneeled, filled with joy.

Mother Mary also fell to her knees and worshiped. She was

overwhelmed beyond description; she cried and laughed at the same time. Lifting her eyes to gaze at her son's face, she recalled the words of Simeon, when Jesus was a week old, that Jesus was to become "a light to the Gentiles, and the glory of your people Israel." Before her own eyes—before her very own eyes—these words were now being fulfilled. Her son was back; he had taken on the greatest challenge of all time and was victorious. For Mother Mary, her faith in God was vindicated.

Jesus looked at his mother, smiled, and acknowledged her with a nod in her direction. Mary felt the reproaches of the past—the long-forgotten reproaches of being pregnant before marriage—replaced with a mantle of glory, and her heart overflowed.

Jesus came up to the summit where the disciples were, and addressed the crowd in a commanding voice:

"All authority has been given to me in heaven and on earth by my Father. You are those who have followed me and have now seen that, although I was dead, I am alive forevermore. You are my witnesses.

"Therefore, go and make disciples of all the nations, baptizing them in the name of the Father and the Son and the Holy Spirit. Teach them to observe all I have commanded you. Remember the many parables I have taught you, and my command to love one another. And I assure you, I am with you always, even to the end of the age. Peace to you all."

After Jesus said those words, he disappeared. The crowd gasped and began murmuring with excitement over this extraordinary manifestation they had beheld.

The crowd began asking questions of the disciples, and Peter took the lead in trying to answer them. Some were puzzled about the commission that Jesus had given them. Peter suggested that they begin by telling their families and neighbors what they had seen this morning, and about the things Jesus had taught them over the years.

A few doubters remained in the crowd. One man asked, "How can I be certain that he really is alive and that I didn't have a vision of some kind?"

Thomas responded to the question with a question: "Have you ever had a vision before?"

"No," the man replied.

"Have you ever heard of an entire crowd of people having the same vision at once?" asked Thomas.

"No," the man replied again.

"Then I think you have the answer," finished Thomas. "Believe what you have seen."

After describing to the crowd their own experiences of Jesus after his resurrection, the eleven disciples offered some parting words and returned to Capernaum and the task of waiting for Jesus to provide further direction.

Nazareth of Galilee

Jesus and his half-siblings had been raised as devout Jews by Joseph and Mary. They had been instructed in the Torah and grew up observing all the ordinances and feasts. When Jesus began his ministry, his brothers—James, Joses, Jude, and Simon—at first had viewed him curiously and with a bit of pride, thinking he might have been chosen by God as a prophet— particularly after the miracle of turning water to wine at the wedding in Cana. After that, everyone had been effusively complimentary to them about their brother.

But very quickly, their views had turned more negative. Jesus had come into the synagogue in their hometown of Nazareth and insulted the people by highlighting two instances in the Scriptures in which God had blessed Gentile individuals in need while overlooking Jews in need. That had enraged the entire town.

And it got worse. Jesus had started to make claims about himself that, although somewhat ambiguous, sounded messianic. Further, he periodically insulted the Pharisees, scribes, and priests, greatly embarrassing his brothers.

When his mother and four brothers had come to take custody of Jesus, certain that he had lost his senses, they had been blocked by the crowd and ignored by him.

None of the brothers believed in him as Messiah—after all, they had grown up together—and they resented the dishonor he was bringing to the family. They didn't even see him as a prophet any longer, but rather as a troublemaker. During Passover, when they had heard of his arrest and crucifixion, the brothers had all fled Jerusalem and returned to Nazareth in haste, for fear of the authorities.

Back in Nazareth, James bar Joseph pondered his deceased older sibling. He felt the grief of both losing a brother and seeing a promising life wasted, together with the fear that he now would be regarded as tainted, by association, within the synagogue and town community.

James had been disgusted when, about a week before, two of Jesus' former disciples had come through the town proclaiming that Jesus would be appearing on a mountain outside of Capernaum. It shocked him to think that these people would use his brother's death to create some sort of hoax.

It was late in the day, and most of the shops had closed, but James was finishing one last piece for a customer in his shop, which opened onto the street. He heard his name: "James."

Thinking it was a late customer, he said, without looking up, "I'm sorry but I am closed for the day."

"James," the visitor said again.

James looked up and saw Jesus standing just inside the entranceway. His body flinched in surprise, and he dropped his tool. Staring intently, he slowly rose from his seat while shaking his head.

"It can't be!" he exclaimed.

"Your own brother," said Jesus, "and I was dead, and I am alive, as you now see."

"My Lord, my God!" exclaimed James, dropping to his knees and lowering his head.

"James, I have a task for you. Tell your siblings you have seen me. Leave with them for Capernaum, and tell my disciples to return to the upper room in Jerusalem directly. I will give further instructions there."

When James lifted his head, Jesus was gone.

Before twilight, James bar Joseph had recounted his encounter with Jesus to all his siblings. Though not completely persuaded, they agreed to leave with James the next morning.

On the Road Once More

It was a two-day trip to Capernaum for Jesus' siblings. Upon arrival, James recapitulated his brief meeting with Jesus in his shop for the Twelve and those at Zebedee's. He then related the instruction for everyone to leave for Jerusalem.

On the next day, the caravan—most of them traveling by foot—began its way back to the city. As a result of a Sabbath that fell in the middle of their journey, the trip took a full week.

But at last, although physically and emotionally exhausted, they were in Jerusalem again. The Twelve took lodging at the upper room, and relatives stayed at Zebedee's house in Jerusalem. Other followers that had come with them from Galilee found lodgings nearby. Less than four weeks earlier, they had all been very relieved to depart the city. Now they were back, and none of them knew the reason why.

Farewell outside Jerusalem

From Jerusalem to the Mount of Olives

The date was the 27th of Iyar, AD 30, a Thursday by the Gregorian calendar, and 39 days since Jesus had first revealed himself as alive from the grave. It was a day the disciples and followers of Jesus would never forget.

They had arrived in Jerusalem the previous day in the early afternoon. Clopas and his wife Mary had subsequently gone to Bethany to inform Lazarus and his sisters that everyone was back in Jerusalem, and they returned to Zebedee's by nightfall.

There was an atmosphere of expectation among them all as it seemed that Jesus was guiding them to something, although the particulars were opaque to their understanding. The command Jesus had given them on the mountain in Galilee to "Go and make disciples" was understandable enough; however, they all felt completely inadequate to fulfill the mission and were mystified as to how to begin.

It was mid-morning, and the Twelve were taking breakfast, when Jesus appeared again.

"Peace to you," he said. They startled, but only slightly this time, and felt a rush of joy.

"Go gather the others with you, and lead them up to the Mount of Olives. I will meet you there."

Without delay, the Twelve went to Zebedee's and relayed the message. Lazarus and his sisters were there, having come from Bethany earlier that morning.

And so, the entire group left Jerusalem to walk to the Mount of Olives east of the city, about half an hour away. The group consisted of the Twelve, the Zebedees, Mother Mary, the brothers of Jesus, Clopas and his wife, Lazarus and his sisters, Mark and Mariam (his mother), and others, more than two dozen in all.

They walked past the garden of Gethsemane and reached the

summit. It was a beautiful, cloudless day, and Jesus was there to meet them. He began, "Shalom! Peace to you." He looked down towards the temple for a moment, his face showing a twinge of sadness, and then he looked at them.

"You must not leave Jerusalem but wait a little longer for what the Father has promised. You have already heard about it from me. Recall how John baptized you in water; similarly, you will be baptized in the Holy Spirit, and not many days from now."

Simon the Zealot asked him what many were wondering: "Lord, is it at this time you are restoring the kingdom to Israel?"

But Jesus said to them, "It isn't for you to know times or periods which the Father has established by his own authority. But, you will receive power when the Holy Spirit has come upon you, and you shall be my witnesses in Jerusalem, and in all Judea and Samaria, and even to the remotest part of the earth.

"Now listen carefully, I am sending forth upon you the promise of my Father, but stay in the city until you are clothed with power from on high."

They all looked at the city, wondering just what Jesus was talking about and what it would look like when they were "baptized in the Holy Spirit."

Then Jesus said simply, "Follow me."

He turned around and started towards Bethany, and the group followed. He took the more direct road downhill towards Bethany rather than the less steep but longer route to the south. Leading them just beyond the "Sabbath Day's journey" distance from Jerusalem, to the outskirts of Bethany (but still on the Mount), he reached the place they called Bethphage, where the disciples had brought him the donkey to ride into Jerusalem two months earlier. Then he turned and addressed them.

"Go into all the world and preach the Good News about me to all creation. Whoever believes in me and is baptized will be saved, but whoever does not believe will be condemned.

"These signs will accompany those who have believed: in my name they will cast out demons; they will speak with new tongues; they will pick up serpents with their hands; and if they drink any deadly thing, it will not hurt them. They will lay hands on the sick, and the sick will recover. All these things will happen among you." After he had said these things, he lifted up his hands and blessed them.

While Jesus was blessing them, he was separated from them and was raised up from the ground while they were looking on. As he was rising into the sky, a cloud formed; it expanded and surrounded him so that he slowly vanished from their sight.

All of his followers stood in great awe, gazing upward into the sky, watching the solitary cloud continue to enlarge and ascend further into the blue.

James said, "He told us that he would go to the Father, but also that he will return again."

"I hope it isn't long," John said.

As they were looking intently upward at this diminishing marvel, suddenly two men in white clothing stood beside them.

Mary Clopas grasped Salome's arm and whispered, "Those are the same two angels we saw at the tomb!"

The angels said, "Men and women of Galilee, why do you stand here staring into the sky? Just as Jesus has now been taken up from you into heaven, so he will come back in the very same way as you have watched him go." Then the angels vanished.

At the temple mount, back in the city of Jerusalem, Caiaphas and another chief priest were observing the evening sacrificial offering being performed. It was about the ninth hour (3 p.m.). The two of them were standing between the altar and the temple, facing eastward towards the Mount of Olives.

Caiaphas said to his fellow priest, "You know, it's been six weeks since Passover, and I haven't heard even a single word about that Nazarene. I'm so glad we got rid of the problem early and I'll never have to deal with him or his cult followers again."

At that moment, his companion caught sight of something, and said to Caiaphas, "Look at that!"

Beyond the Mount of Olives, they could see a small cloud rising, growing larger, and seeming to accelerate upward.

"Have you ever seen anything like that?"

"No, I haven't," replied Caiaphas.

"It seems to be glowing in the middle," the priest said.

"Maybe it's some odd reflection of the sun," mused Caiaphas. "I can't say I comprehend it."

Return to Jerusalem

On the Mount of Olives, back towards Bethphage and Bethany, the happy band of followers had broken into spontaneous worship of Jesus and the Father. After worshiping for a while, they returned to Jerusalem with overflowing joy and abundant anticipation for the "Holy Spirit coming upon them." They knew from the manner in which Jesus had spoken about it that, whatever it was, it had to be *very good*.

Thus they returned from the mount, also called Olivet, which is within a Sabbath day's journey away from the city of Jerusalem.

As soon as they had entered the city, the eleven remaining members of the Twelve went directly to the upper room where they were staying: that is, Peter and John, James (John's brother) and Andrew (Peter's brother), Philip and Thomas, Nathanael and Matthew, James the Younger, Simon the Zealot, and Thaddeus, the son of James. The others lodged nearby at Zebedee's.

These disciples of Jesus continued meeting together with complete unity of purpose. They devoted themselves to prayer in the upper room, together with the women, Mary the mother of Jesus, his brothers, and a growing number of others. They were also continually making trips to the temple, blessing and worshiping God there, although the Twelve continued exercising caution to avoid being noticed by the chief priests and elders.

Philip asked Nathanael, "Do you wonder what's going to happen when Jesus sends the Holy Spirit?"

"Yes, I have plenty of thoughts of what might happen then."

"Do you care to share any?"

"No," replied Nathanael, "because whatever happens, you can be sure it won't be any one of my ideas."

"Well," said Philip cheerfully, "It's the only thing I want to know right now."

"Me too," said Nathanael.

Exactly ten days later, on the day of Pentecost, 120 of Jesus' followers would find out. But that's another story.

As John wrote years later, "There are many other things which Jesus did which, if each one was written, I suppose that the world itself could not contain the books that would be written."[27]

---

[27] Jn 21:25

PART TWO

THE UNIFIED ACCOUNT OF THE RESURRECTION OF JESUS CHRIST

Introduction to Part Two

The story that follows is a compiled, unified account of events in Jerusalem and Galilee from Jesus' last words on the cross to his ascension, a period of exactly forty-four days.[28] This account is a compilation from the primary records found in the first four books of the New Testament, together with a small assortment of verses from the books of Acts and 1st Corinthians.

This account has been arranged as a single historian-on-the-scene might have written it. The wording has been kept as close to the original sources as possible, with only minor adjustments for flow and clarity. All verses in the New Testament that directly relate to these events have been included.

The story of the resurrection is fascinating, dramatic, and inspiring—exactly as written, even without further elaboration. The original material is quite condensed, as you will appreciate by comparing the Unified Account that follows with Part One. Nevertheless, while reading the Unified Account, I hope you will come to appreciate the highly dynamic and emotional anguish of these days to all those who experienced and testified of them.

Notes to Part Two:

1. In this Part of the book, words in *italics* are additions to the original text to add clarity or to smooth transitions. These additional words have been kept to a minimum.

2. Dates in the headings are based on the Jewish religious calendar. The first three months of that calendar are named Nisan, Iyar, and Sivan. Nisan has thirty days, corresponding to a period between March and April of our present calendar, and is why Easter is celebrated at

---

[28] Forty-four days: the day of crucifixion, three days in the tomb, and appearances to His followers for the next forty days (Acts 1:3)

that time of the year.[29] It is useful to remember that Jewish calendar days begin and end at sundown, not midnight as in the modern Western world and ancient Rome.

A few of the dates have been estimated based on expected travel times, but most of the dates are known or calculated based upon information in the texts.

3. The primary location where the story takes place is Jerusalem, the leading city of Judea, in which Jesus was put on trial (multiple times), condemned, and tortured. He died by crucifixion and was interred in a stone tomb just outside the walls of the city. Other locations in the story include Bethany, a small town less than two miles east of Jerusalem; Emmaus, a town about seven miles west of Jerusalem; and Galilee, a region about eighty-five miles north of Jerusalem. Galilee was the home territory of Jesus and his disciples, and where most of his two to three years of ministry took place. For geographical orientation, see the Maps section in the front of the book and the Important Locations chapter in Part Three.

This part of the book is footnoted with many comments (using numerals), and contains endnotes with references to the original passages (using letters). While this is useful for readers who wish to dig deeper, it can be rather distracting. Therefore, you may wish to first read through Part Two while ignoring all the superscripted characters, to appreciate the flow of the story. You can return for a second pass to glean the extra information in the footnotes or to check the verse references in the endnotes if so inclined. The abbreviation "lit." in the footnotes means "literally."

Please appreciate that all of the original biblical material in the Unified Account was written either by eyewitnesses or by those that recorded the testimony of eyewitnesses. This is what they heard and saw.

---

[29] The occurrence of the first day of Nisan can vary quite a bit on our calendar year-to-year, in similar fashion to the occurrence of Easter.

Long-standing traditions tell us that of the five authors of the material used in this Unified Account, four of them were martyred. The one exception, John, suffered exile to a small rocky island in the Mediterranean. That's the price they paid for bringing this news to the world.

Wednesday Midafternoon, Nisan 14

Golgotha, the Roman Crucifixion Site outside the City Walls of Jerusalem. About 3:00 p.m.

Jesus said, "It is finished!"[30] Again he cried with a loud voice, "Father, I entrust my spirit into your hands."[31] Then he gave up his spirit, and breathed his last.[A]

The centurion who was keeping guard over Jesus, and standing right in front of him, saw how he breathed his last, and praised God saying, "Surely this man was innocent!" Then the earth shook, and the rocks were split, and the centurion and his fellow soldiers became very frightened and said, "Truly this was the Son of God!"[32] [B]

Back in Jerusalem, the veil of the temple was ripped in two, from top to bottom.[33] [C]

---

[30] The Greek word, *teléō*, could also be translated "completed" as in the New English Translation, or "paid" (as the same word is used to discharge a debt).

[31] Jesus' last two statements were in this order. The first statement was probably said softly (as it was heard by John, who being family, was close to the cross), perhaps as a remark Jesus made to himself. The latter statement was made forcefully and apparently heard by the entire crowd.

[32] The sky had been ominously dark for the last three hours before Jesus expired. The timing of his death with the earthquake and the end of darkness, together with the strength of Jesus' final cry, gave testimony to his uniqueness. The conjunction of these things was not lost on the centurion.

[33] At that instant, no priests would have been in the temple; rather, they would have been at the front of the temple, attending to the Passover rituals. The veil was about four inches thick and sixty feet in height, so this rending must have generated a substantial sound.

When all the crowds who had gathered for this spectacle *of a crucifixion* saw what had happened, they began to leave, beating their chests.34 But all his acquaintances including many women were there, looking on from a distance. These had followed and ministered to Jesus when he was in Galilee, and while they came up with him to Jerusalem from Galilee. Among them was Mary Magdalene, and Mary *Clopas* the mother of James *the Younger* and Joseph, and Salome the mother of *James and John*—the sons of Zebedee.35 D

In Jerusalem, because it was the *Passover* day of preparation, the Jewish *leaders* did not want the bodies to remain on the crosses into the *Passover* Sabbath (especially since that Sabbath was a high *holy* day).36 They asked Pilate that their legs might be broken, and that they might be taken away.37

So the soldiers came *from Pilate*, and broke the legs first of one man and then of the other who was crucified with him. But when they came to Jesus and saw that he was already dead, they

---

34 All priests would have left the crowd a few hours earlier to prepare for Passover duties in the temple. Those remaining at Golgotha would have included admirers of Jesus, the curious, and the rabble who had earlier shouted, "Crucify him!" After what they saw, they all had motivation to beat their chests out of distress, but for different reasons.

35 Mary Magdalene was close to these two women, as well as Joanna and Susanna (Lk 8:3). Joanna was at the tomb later, and Susanna probably was as well.

36 This note from John identifies the next day as Nisan 15, the Sabbath of Passover, rather than the weekly Sabbath. The concern of the leaders was that unburied dead bodies would violate the law (Dt 21:22-23).

37 The Jewish leaders were not concerned about murdering an innocent man, but they were concerned about religious uncleanness. Breaking the legs would hasten the death of the crucified.

did not break his legs.[38] But one of the soldiers pierced his side with a spear, and immediately blood and water came out. (*I, John*,[39] saw *firsthand* and testify to this, and my testimony is true. I know that I am telling the truth, so that you also may believe.) These things came to pass to fulfill the *prophecy in* Scripture, "Not one of his bones will be broken," and again another Scripture which says, "They will look on him whom they pierced."[E]

---

[38] Jesus died before the others, perhaps because of the exceptional brutality of his scourging. The Roman soldiers seemed to take particular delight in abusing "The *king* of the Jews," a title that enabled them to focus their general hostility toward the Jews onto a single individual. Furthermore, the influence of the demonic realm on the soldiers should not be discounted.

[39] Lit., *he who has seen*

Wednesday Late Afternoon, Nisan 14

The Praetorium in Jerusalem

After these things, when it was evening on this preparation day (that is, the day before the *Passover High* Sabbath), a rich man named Joseph from Arimathea (a city of the Jews), gathered up courage and went in before Pilate and asked for the body of Jesus. Now Joseph was a prominent member of the Council, a good and righteous man who had not consented to their plan and action, and *one* who was waiting for the kingdom of God. Joseph *had become* a disciple of Jesus, but was a secret one, for fear of the Jews.[40]

Pilate wondered if Jesus was already dead, and summoning the centurion, he asked him whether he had already died. *After* learning this from the centurion, he granted the body to Joseph, ordering it to be given to him.[41] F

A Tomb near the Cross, outside the Walls of Jerusalem

Joseph bought a fine, clean linen shroud, took Jesus down *from the cross,* and carried him away.[42] Nicodemus, *another*

---

[40] Given that Jesus was so vilified by the chief priests and much of the Sanhedrin, Joseph's fear was warranted; it was no small act of courage on Joseph's part to make his feelings towards Jesus known. Joseph must have been experiencing the most profound grief, as he understood that Jesus was the Messiah.

[41] It was Roman policy to release bodies of the executed to family or friends. Such was the case with Jehohanan, a first century crucified Jew who was properly buried in an ossuary. The executed who lacked someone to provide them with a traditional burial were disposed of by the Romans in shallow graves.

[42] Taking a body down from a cross wasn't easy, and Joseph was likely older. He surely had help from assistants or servants. The fact that Joseph was able to purchase a fine burial shroud, after all the shops

member of the Council, who had first come to him by night, also came *and joined Joseph,* bringing about a hundred pounds of a mixture of myrrh and aloes.43 They took the body of Jesus and wrapped it in the linen with the spices, as is the burial custom of the Jews.44 G

Now in the vicinity where Jesus was crucified there was a garden, and in the garden was Joseph's own new tomb, which he had cut out of the rock, and where no body had ever lain. So because it was the Jewish day of preparation, and since Joseph's tomb was nearby, they laid Jesus there. Joseph rolled a large stone against the entrance to the tomb, and *they* went away.45 H

Now it was *the end of* the preparation day and the Sabbath was about to begin.46 The women Mary Magdalene and Mary *Clopas* the *mother* of Joses, who had come with him out of Galilee, *had* followed *Joseph and Nicodemus,* and were sitting opposite the grave.47 They saw the tomb and where his body was laid.48 I

---

were legally closed (at noon), indicates that Joseph had connections, and perhaps called in a favor.

43 The text does not say that Nicodemus *bought* the spices; they may have been from his personal stores. The quantity (one hundred Roman pounds, or seventy-five English pounds equivalent) shows that Nicodemus, like Joseph, was wealthy.

44 Coins were typically used to cover the eyes of the deceased. They may have been coins stamped with Pilate's inscription.

45 Joseph would have needed assistance to move a large golel stone.

46 In other words, twilight was commencing and the two men were under time pressure to complete their burial tasks.

47 The women observed the burial process and saw that anointing oils had been omitted.

48 Within the tomb, Jesus' body was laid on a carved shelf to the right side of the entrance (Mk 16:5-6), rather than placed in a loculus, which, if it had been the case, would have made it harder for the women to later apply oils.

Thursday (High Sabbath Day), Nisan 15

The Praetorium in Jerusalem

Now on the next day, the day after the *Passover* preparation *(that is, on the High Holy Sabbath),*[49] the chief priests and the Pharisees went to Pilate, and said, "Sir, we remember that when he was still alive,[50] that deceiver said, 'After three days I will rise again.'[51] Therefore, give orders for the grave to be secured until the third day, otherwise his disciples may come and steal his *body* away and say to the people, 'He has risen from the dead!' and the final deception will be worse than the first."[52]

Pilate said to them, "Take a guard of soldiers and go; make it *as* secure as you know how."[53] So they went and made the grave

---

[49] This was not the weekly Sabbath but rather the Passover day of rest. The chief priests violated the Sabbath restrictions by visiting Pilate in the Praetorium and by sealing the tomb. These were the same people who criticized Jesus for healing on Sabbaths.

[50] Here, the enemies of Jesus admit that he is dead.

[51] The Jewish leaders fully understood Jesus' claims that he would rise from the dead, although the disciples in their grief seem to have forgotten it.

[52] The "first deception" they considered to be his allusions to being the Messiah. The Jews were being disingenuous here; they couldn't have feared his disciples making such a claim, because it could easily be countered by demanding that they produce a living Jesus. Nor did they fear Jesus' power—they must have believed he was simply a deceiver, or they wouldn't have agitated for his death. It seems the best explanation is that they feared the multitudes who revered Jesus, and the tactic of keeping a Roman guard at the tomb was a clever act of blame-shifting.

[53] The Greek word for "guard" signifies Roman soldiers, not the Jewish temple guard. The literal translation is: "You have a guard," which

secure by setting a seal on the stone and posting the guard.54 J

---

could mean a guard already assigned to keep tabs on the Sanhedrin, but more than likely means that Pilate is simply authorizing the use of Roman soldiers to guard the tomb.

54 Pilate did not share the (expressed) concern of the Jews, or any concern that Jesus might rise from death. Previously, he had ignored his wife's request (based on a dream of hers) to have nothing to do with Jesus (Mt 27:19)—revealing a disinterest in any spiritual or supernatural considerations. Rather, his acquiescence to the request was a zero-cost political favor. Note that he takes no effort to ensure that the grave is secure and leaves the implementation of it up to a gaggle of priests rather than anyone with security experience.

Friday (between Sabbaths), Nisan 16

The Market in Jerusalem

After the *High* Sabbath was over, Mary Magdalene, and Mary *Clopas* the mother of James *the Younger*, and Salome, bought spices, so that they might go and anoint Jesus' body.[55] Then they returned *from the market*[56] and prepared the aromatic spices and fragrant perfumes.[57] K

---

[55] The sequence for the women was: (1) Sabbath rest, (2) purchase of spices, (3) preparation of spices, (4) Sabbath rest, and (5) taking the spice preparations (i.e., anointing oils) to the tomb Sunday morning. This sequence pinpoints the crucifixion of Jesus to a Wednesday, as explained further in Part Three.

[56] Probably the Agora market, a world-class group of shops just east of Herod's Palace and the Praetorium.

[57] The application of fragrant oils to the deceased was the last step in the embalming process. The women, familiar with the sequence, recognized that it had been omitted by Joseph and Nicodemus by necessity. They were trying to ensure a completely proper burial.

Saturday (Weekly Sabbath), Nisan 17

In the City of Jerusalem

On the *weekly* Sabbath the women rested according to the commandment.[58] L

---

[58] Having prepared the oils the day before, why didn't the women anoint his body then? Probably because there would have been a crowd of people visiting Jesus' tomb. His death would have made ripples in the city, and people would have come to pay their respects. The women wanted to do this privately, and the first opportunity they would have had to accomplish the task would have been very early Sunday morning, when most of the crowded city would just be waking up.

Saturday Night, Nisan 18

At the Tomb of Jesus, outside the City Wall

In the evening of that day[59] *after the sun had set,*[60] a great earthquake occurred, for an angel of the Lord came down from heaven, approached the stone, rolled it away, and then sat on it. His face was like lightning, and his clothing was as white as snow.[61] The guards trembled from fear of him and became *prostrated* like dead men.[62] M

And Jesus rose from the dead.[63]

---

[59] For the Jews, the "first day of the week" began Saturday at sundown and continued through the daytime portion of Sunday. Thus, Saturday (daytime) is Nisan 17, but Saturday (evening, after dark) is Nisan 18.

[60] For reasons given in Part Three, the resurrection did not occur at dawn Sunday, but between sunset Saturday and sometime before dawn Sunday. This does not diminish the importance of Easter dawn, for that was when the resurrection first became known to the world.

[61] This scene was witnessed only by the soldiers on guard duty. Therefore, despite being later bribed by the priests to say that Jesus' disciples had stolen the body, the real story was leaked by one or more of them. That such a leak would occur is not surprising.

[62] Other examples of people falling to the ground involuntarily by the action of God are when Jesus was arrested (Jn 18:6) and when Solomon dedicated the first temple (1Ki 8:11 and 2Ch 5:14).

[63] This simple statement does not occur in the New Testament, which might be puzzling to some. However, it is good to recognize that the accounts by the four gospel authors are the testimony of *witnesses*. No one saw the instant of the resurrection, and it may be just as well, as they might have been blinded by it.

We have the testimony of multiple witnesses that saw Jesus' dead body and multiple witnesses who afterwards saw and touched the living Jesus. Logically, there was a resurrection between those events!

Furthermore, when the earthquake occurred, some tombs in the vicinity were opened, and the bodies of many godly persons who had died were raised from the dead. They came out of the tombs after his resurrection, entered the holy city *of Jerusalem*, and appeared to many *people*.[64] N

---

[64] For a discussion of these multiple resurrections, see Appendix H.

Resurrection Morning, Nisan 18

Jerusalem and Its Vicinity

Now after the Sabbath, on the first day of the week, Mary Magdalene and the other Mary *(Clopas) started off* early to the tomb, while it was still dark, to look at the grave. *On the way they met Salome, Joanna, and Susanna.*[65] At early dawn, they arrived at the tomb bringing the spices which they had prepared. They were saying to one another, "Who will roll away the stone for us from the entrance of the tomb?"[66]

Looking up, they saw that the stone had been rolled away from the tomb, even though it was very large.[67] O

Immediately, Mary Magdalene ran *off* to Peter[68] and to John,[69] the other disciple whom Jesus loved, *leaving the rest of the women at the tomb.*[70] When the women entered, they did

---

[65] These women were among the closest followers of Jesus, with deep bonds between themselves. They previously had arranged to meet together in the city before walking to the tomb together. They would never have done this separately, for reasons of safety and support, just as the purchase and preparation of the perfumes had also been a group project.

[66] Clearly this was not something that had occurred to them until they were on the way. The women were also unaware that a guard had been posted.

[67] Note that the women saw neither the angel who had rolled the stone away nor the soldiers. The amount of time that had elapsed since the stone was rolled back is explored in the chapter, "When Was Jesus Crucified?"

[68] Lit., *Simon Peter*

[69] The wording suggests first to Peter and then to John, revealing that they were staying in different quarters.

[70] Mary Magdalene drew an instant conclusion that the body had been stolen. She ran off without entering the tomb or waiting for the other

not find the body of the Lord Jesus. While they were puzzled about this, behold, two *angels—in the form of* men—suddenly appeared[71] near them in dazzling clothing. *The angels* said to them, "Why do you seek the living One among the dead?" They saw *one of them,* a young man sitting at the right, wearing a white robe; and they were amazed and terrified and bowed their faces to the ground. The angel said to the women, "Do not be amazed. Do not be afraid. For I know that you are looking for Jesus the Nazarene who has been crucified. He is not here; he has risen—just as he said. Remember what he spoke to you when he was in Galilee, saying that the Son of Man must be delivered into the hands of sinful men, and be crucified, and the third day rise again." And they remembered his words.[72] P

The angel *then* said, "Come, see the place where he was lying, behold, *this is* the place where they laid him. *Now,* go quickly and tell his disciples and Peter[73] that he has risen from the dead; and behold, he is going ahead of you into Galilee. There you will see him, just as he said; behold, I have told you."Q

The women left the tomb and fled quickly with fear and great joy,[74] for trembling and astonishment had gripped them, and they said nothing to anyone *on the way,* and ran to report it to his disciples.[75] *While they were going,* Mary Magdalene came *to

---

women.

[71] The Greek word here, *ephistēsan,* is often translated "stood," but really connotes "to come suddenly upon." It is better translated "appeared" as per the New Living Translation.

[72] Faith comes from hearing, and hearing by the word of Christ (Ro 10:17). As they recalled his words, faith came alive.

[73] This naming of Peter is very poignant. Peter needed special encouragement and may not have even considered himself a disciple after denying Jesus.

[74] Although Mary Magdalene was the first to *see* the risen Savior, these women were the first to *believe* in the resurrection. The "great joy" they must have felt can hardly be imagined.

[75] The women would have run first to Peter and John—as Mary had—since they were in Jerusalem. As John, Peter, and Mary returned to the

Peter's lodging place and said to him,[76] "They have taken away the Lord's *body* out of the tomb, and we do not know where they have put him!"[R]

So Peter *went to John*,[77] and they went forth, and were going to the tomb, *followed by Mary Magdalene.*

The two ran together; and John[78] ran ahead faster than Peter and came to the tomb first; and stooping and looking in, he saw the linen wrappings lying *by themselves*, but he did not go in.

And so Peter[79] also came after him, and entered the tomb; and he saw the linen wrappings lying *by themselves*, and the face-cloth which had been on his head, lying folded and apart from the linen wrappings.[80]

Then John,[81] who had arrived at the tomb first, also entered the tomb, and he saw and believed *Mary's report that the body had been removed*,[82] for as yet they did not understand the Scripture, that he must rise again from the dead. So, the *two*

---

tomb, the four women must have passed them by on a parallel street, something that could easily happen on the many narrow streets in the city. Furthermore, since John led the way back to the tomb, I expect he would have taken a more circuitous route to avoid authorities, whereas the women, having no reason to fear persecution, probably took the shortest route.

[76] Lit., *them*, but Mary must have spoken to Peter first and repeated the message to John

[77] Lit., *the other disciple*

[78] Lit., *the other disciple*

[79] Lit., *Simon Peter*

[80] The presence of the graveclothes *in place* and the neatly folded facecloth must have been a great mystery to both men. It would not be expected that someone stealing a body would remove the cloths or fold anything.

[81] Lit., *the other disciple*

[82] John overlooked the question of why the graveclothes were there, but the possibility of a resurrection was far removed from his thinking at the time.

disciples went away again to their own dwellings.[83]

But Mary remained, standing outside the tomb weeping;[84] and as she wept, she stooped and looked into the tomb; and she saw two angels *dressed* in white sitting, one at the head and one at the feet, where the body of Jesus had been lying.[85]

And they said to her, "Woman, why are you weeping?"

Mary said to them, "Because they have taken away my Lord, and I do not know where they have put him."

After she had said this, she turned around and saw Jesus standing *nearby* but did not know that it was him. Jesus said to her, "Woman, why are you weeping? Who are you looking for?" Supposing him to be the gardener, she said to him, "Sir, if you have carried him away, tell me where you have put him, and I will take him away."[86]

Jesus said to her, "Mary!" She turned and exclaimed in Hebrew, "Rabboni!" (which means, Teacher).[87]

Jesus then said to her, "Don't hold on to me,[88] for I have not yet returned[89] to the Father; but go to my brothers and say to them, 'I am ascending to my Father and your Father, and my

---

[83] The Greek is plural.

[84] The Greek means deep sobbing, not soft crying.

[85] She must have startled: She had just watched Peter and John enter and leave the tomb, and (no doubt) inform her that nothing was there except the graveclothes.

[86] Mary's devotion to Jesus in life and death is beautiful.

[87] It means more than just a teacher. Perhaps "exalted teacher" or "highest teacher" would better capture the sense.

[88] She may have been holding his feet—reminiscent of her earlier anointing of them. Different opinions have been given for why Jesus said these words. But, taking his entire statement to Mary into account, I think it could be paraphrased as, "Don't try to hold me here; just take word for everyone to head for Galilee, and I'll see you all there."

Jesus was not being dismissive, however—Mary had just received an honor no one before or after her would ever receive.

[89] Lit., *ascended* (or, *gone up*)

God and your God.'"[90] [S]

While Mary was at the tomb, the other women—that is, Joanna, Mary Clopas (mother of James *the Younger),* and the other women with them—returned from the tomb and reported all these things *about the angels to Peter and John, and then left them to give this news* to the rest of the eleven apostles and Jesus' other followers. However, these words appeared to the disciples[91] as nonsense, and they would not believe them.[92] But Peter got up and ran to the tomb *again;*[93] stooping and looking in, he saw the linen wrappings only; and he went away to his lodging, marveling at what had happened.[94] [T]

Now Clopas, having heard the women's report of the angels, and of Peter and John's visits to the tomb, left Jerusalem with another disciple for the nearby town of Emmaus.

As the women continued on to Bethany to deliver the angels'

---

[90] The disciples, despite having deserted Jesus at his arrest, are here called "brothers," a distinct elevation from their former status. This differs in meaning from Jesus' use of "brothers" in Mk 3:35, wherein it means, essentially, "comrade." Yet, Jesus does not say "our Father" or "our God," indicating a difference in nature between his relationship to the Father, and ours.

[91] Lit., *them* (initially, Peter, John, and those with them in Jerusalem)

[92] Perhaps the news was rejected partly because the messengers were women and the testimony of women in Jewish law was not given full weight. However, the disciples knew and respected these women. They may also have concluded that if Jesus was alive, he certainly would have contacted the Twelve first—a simple presumption. But, I think the primary reason for their unbelief was that the news seemed *too* good to be true.

[93] Peter made his first trip to the tomb with John after hearing Mary Magdalene's report of the stolen body. Luke also records that Peter made a second visit to the tomb after hearing the other women's report about seeing angels in the tomb, perhaps to see if the angels were still there. Peter did not enter the tomb again on his second visit.

[94] Although Peter was still unbelieving in the resurrection, the accumulating facts were becoming more baffling.

message, behold, Jesus met them and said, "Rejoice!"[95] And they came up and took hold of his feet and worshiped him. Then Jesus said to them, "Do not be afraid; go tell my brothers[96] to leave for Galilee,[97] and there they will see me."[U]

Now while they[98] continued on their way, some of the guard went into the city and reported to the chief priests all that had happened.[99] And after the chief priests had met with the elders and decided together, they gave a large amount of silver money to the soldiers, and said, "You are to say, 'His disciples came at night and stole his body[100] away while we were sleeping.'[101] And if this should come to the governor's attention,[102] we will win

---

[95] Inexplicably, many English translations deviate from the literal Greek here, which is properly rendered "Rejoice." How appropriate it was!

[96] For a second time since the resurrection, Jesus acknowledges the disciples as his brothers.

[97] Why the emphasis to leave for Galilee? This instruction was given by the angels at the tomb and twice by Jesus. Although the text does not say why, Galilee was his base of ministry, it had the largest concentration of his followers, and it was beyond easy reach of the Jerusalem authorities. In the hills of Galilee, Jesus could openly assemble a large gathering in peace.

[98] I.e, the women

[99] This report was given hours after the events. Obviously the guards had laid low in the interim.

[100] Lit., *him*

[101] Ironically, the priests and elders were asking the soldiers to say that the body had been stolen—which was precisely their supposed concern that justified the posting of the guard! They now formulated a disinformation campaign to circulate a false report to preempt (so they thought) the disciples using the stolen body to claim a resurrection. It also enabled them to shift blame from themselves (for failing to make the tomb secure) to the soldiers for failing their duties. The fabricated report contains a logical inconsistency: If the soldiers were all asleep, how could they have known what transpired?

[102] Lit., *ears*

him over and keep you free from concern."[103] And they took the money and did as they had been instructed; and this story has been widely spread among the Jews to this day.[104] V

Now Jesus' first appearance was to Mary Magdalene, (from whom he had cast out seven demons), and she came, announcing to the disciples *Peter and John, and those with them*,[105] while they were mourning and weeping, "I have seen the Lord!" and reported what things he had said to her. *But when they heard that he was alive and had been seen by her, they did not believe it.* W

The other women who had been at the tomb came to the rest of the eleven at Bethany, and told them of seeing the angels at the tomb, and seeing Jesus on the way, and what they had been told. However, these words appeared to them as nonsense. *Yet all the disciples except Thomas arose and went into Jerusalem to find Peter and John.*[106] X

Meanwhile back in Jerusalem, Jesus appeared to Peter[107] *alone.*[108] Y

---

[103] This is a promise to bribe the governor if necessary.

[104] The Jewish leaders made a concerted effort to spread this false rumor. According to Justin Martyr *Dialog with Trypho the Jew* (Chapter CVII, c. AD 150-160), they "selected and sent out from Jerusalem chosen men through all the land [i.e., nations] to tell that the godless heresy of the Christians had sprung up."

[105] This second trip of Mary to the lodgings of Peter and John probably took place thirty to forty-five minutes after she had previously gone there to report the stolen body.

[106] The text only tells us that Thomas wasn't with the other disciples when Jesus appeared to them later that day. Knowing that he was the last to believe among the Twelve, it is reasonable to presume that he refused to leave their hiding place.

[107] Lit., *Cephas* (alt. name for Peter)

[108] We know about this personal visitation from Paul's list of appearances of Jesus (1Co 15:5). It is also confirmed by Luke 24:34. What Jesus may have said to Peter isn't written, but it must have been comforting and restorative.

Sunday Daytime, Nisan 18

The Road from Jerusalem to Emmaus

Now later that very day, Jesus appeared in a different form[109] to two disciples[110] while they were walking along on their way to the country, to a village named Emmaus, which was about seven miles[111] from Jerusalem. The disciples[112] were discussing with each other about all the things which had taken place. As they were conversing, Jesus himself approached and started traveling with them. However, their eyes were prevented from recognizing him. Jesus[113] said to them, "What are you discussing so intently as you are walking?" They stood still, looking sad.[z]

One named Clopas[114] answered and said to him, "Are you the only one visiting Jerusalem who is unaware of the things which have happened here in these days?"[115]

He said to them, "What things?"[116]

And they said to him, "The things about Jesus the Nazarene, who arose as a prophet, mighty in deed and word before God and all the people. And that our chief priests and rulers

---

[109] The Greek word, *morphe*, means external appearance. However, it seems that Jesus only *appeared* to these men to be in a different form (as opposed to *actually* being in a different form), as the text tells us that "their eyes were prevented from recognizing him," and that their eyes "were opened" when Jesus broke bread (Lk 24:16, 31).

[110] Lit., *of them*

[111] Lit., *sixty stadia*

[112] Lit., *they*

[113] Lit., *he*

[114] Lit., *Cleopas*, an alternative spelling of Clopas

[115] The crucifixion of Jesus was the biggest news in Jerusalem this Passover. Clopas was astounded that Jesus didn't seem to know anything about it.

[116] It must have been a challenge for Jesus to keep a straight face here.

delivered him up to be sentenced to death, and crucified him.[117] We had hoped that he was the one who was going to redeem Israel.[118]

"Now, besides all this, it is the third day since these things happened.[119] And also, some women among us amazed us. They were at the tomb early this morning, and did not find his body. They came back saying that they had seen a vision of angels,[120] who said that he was alive. Some of those who were with us went to the tomb and found it exactly as the women had said, but they did not see him."[121]

Then Jesus[122] said to them, "Oh, foolish[123] men—and slow of heart to believe in all that the prophets have spoken![124] Was it not necessary[125] for the Messiah to suffer these things and to

---

[117] The travelers placed the blame squarely on the chief priests and Sanhedrin, not on the Romans. They recognized that their leaders had coerced Rome into authorizing the execution. This widespread opinion undoubtedly generated animosity toward the leaders, who were aware of it. This explains why the Jewish leaders were keen to have a Roman guard over the tomb, rather than members of the temple guard.

[118] The common people were thinking and hoping that Jesus could be the Messiah. The distinction between the people and their leaders is striking.

[119] See Appendix D for a discussion of this statement about the "third day."

[120] The phrase "vision of angels," rather than simply "angels," displays some doubtful hedging. These two men were hopeful but unconvinced. One of the women who had given this report was Clopas' wife, and he did not fully accept even her testimony.

[121] The "fact-checkers" were unable to corroborate the report.

[122] Lit., *he*

[123] Lit., *without understanding*

[124] Jesus chose not to rebuke these men for failing to believe the women, although it would have been warranted. Instead, he rebuked them for failing to believe the words of the prophets, the very source of their hope of a Messiah.

[125] Necessary, so as to fulfill the prophesies

enter into his glory?"

Then beginning with Moses and all the prophets, he explained to them the things concerning himself in all the Scriptures.[126] As they approached the village where they were going, he indicated that he would go farther.[127]

But they implored[128] him, saying, "Stay with us, for it is getting toward evening, and the day is now almost over." So he went in to stay with them. When he had sat down at the table with them, he took the bread and blessed it, and broke it, and gave it to them.[129] Then their eyes were opened and they recognized him;[130] and then he vanished from their sight.

They said to one another, "Were not our hearts burning within us while he was speaking to us on the road, while he was opening the Scriptures to us?"[131] And they got up that same hour and returned to Jerusalem.[132] AA

---

[126] In an instant, the travelers went from schooling the stranger to being taught by the teacher of teachers.

[127] As he would have, had not Clopas and his friend prevailed upon him to continue with them

[128] This is a strong word in Greek. It is an echo of Jacob, when he wrestled with the angel, saying, "I will not let you go unless you bless me" (Ge 32:36).

[129] This is the first communion service in history, administered by Jesus himself.

[130] God opens eyes (Ps 146:8), and he can close them, too (Ro 11:8).

[131] Ever since, ardent students of Scripture have longed for a transcript of that Bible study.

[132] It was greater than a two-hour hike back to Jerusalem, and the day was declining. They may have been pressed to make it before sundown.

Sunday Evening, Nisan 18

The Upper Room in Southwest Jerusalem

And so, *Clopas and his companion* found the eleven,[133] and those who were with them gathered together,[134] *some of whom*[135] were saying, "The Lord has really risen and has appeared to Peter."[136] On the evening of that day, the first day of the week,[137] and with the doors shut where the disciples were,[138] for fear of the Jews,[139] the two recounted their experiences on

---

[133] Actually, only ten; Thomas was absent. Obviously, during this interim period before Matthias was chosen to replace Judas, the group was sometimes still referred to as "the Twelve" and sometimes as "the eleven."

[134] This may have been an intimate gathering or a sizable crowd. It would be nice to know who were there. Notice that it was not limited to members of the Twelve.

[135] The "whom" doing the speaking here are not Clopas and his companion. Nine members of the Twelve (or a subset) had heard Peter's testimony of an appearance from Jesus. (Peter was also present.)

[136] Lit., *Simon*

[137] It had to be close to sundown by the time the Emmaus travelers joined the group.

[138] This location, although not named, can reasonably be expected to be the "upper room" in which they had eaten the Passover with Jesus. Sometime before Passover, Jesus had arranged for the room for the feast, and it can be assumed that he made the arrangement for the entire week of Unleavened Bread, as was customary. Visitors were freely accommodated within Jerusalem, and in turn, typically would leave to their hosts the skins of the Passover lambs and the vessels they used in their sacred observances. (Edersheim, *The Temple—Its Ministry and Services* (1874), Chapter 11, subchapter "Later Celebrations.")

[139] There are no records of the priests and rulers pursuing the disciples

the road and how Jesus was recognized by them while breaking the bread, but the disciples did not believe them either.[140] And while they were talking about these things, as they were reclining at the table, Jesus himself came and stood in their midst and said to them, "Peace to you *all.*"[141] But they were startled and terrified and thought that they were seeing a spirit.[142]

And he rebuked them for their unbelief and hardness of heart, because they had not believed those who had seen him after he had risen,[143] *and he* said to them, "Why are you troubled, and why do doubts arise in your hearts?"[BB]

"Look at my hands and my feet, that it is truly me. Touch me and see, for a spirit does not have flesh and bones as you see that I have." When he had said this, he showed them his hands, his feet, and his side.[144]

While they still could not believe it because of their joy and astonishment, he said to them, "Do you have anything here to eat?" They gave him a piece of a broiled fish, and he took it and ate it in front of them.[145]

---

immediately after the crucifixion, but it's very possible. Since Jesus was accused of insurrection, his disciples would be considered guilty by association.

[140] This disproves the theory that the disciples failed to believe the women because of misogyny or disrespect of women, as this testimony came from two brethren. The disciples didn't believe because they simply were unable.

[141] The Greek for "you" is pluralized here. Many English versions omit "all," but all is intended.

[142] Here the disciples saw, but their stubborn minds still sought an alternative explanation. Thus, the common skeptic's phrase "I'll believe it if I see it" can be a self-deception.

[143] See the Epilogue for further comments about their unbelief.

[144] Jesus showed them his scars from the nails and the spear. The marks of his ordeal have been turned to his glory.

[145] Jesus knew that some were thinking they were seeing a spirit, and it seems he did this to counter that thought. From this event, it is clear

The disciples rejoiced greatly when they saw the Lord.[146] Then he said to them, "These are my words that I spoke to you while I was with you, that all things which are written about me in the Law of Moses and the Prophets and the Psalms must be fulfilled."[147]

Then he opened their minds to understand the Scriptures, and he said to them, "This has been written, that the Christ would suffer and rise again from the dead *on* the third day, and that repentance for forgiveness of sins would be proclaimed in his name to all the nations, beginning from Jerusalem.[148] You are witnesses of these things."[CC]

And Jesus said to them again, "Peace to you *all*; as the Father has sent me, I also am sending you." After he had said this, he breathed on them and said, "Receive the Holy Spirit.[149] If you forgive the sins of anyone, their sins are forgiven them; if you do not forgive them, they are not forgiven."[150] [DD]

---

that disembodied spirits do not eat food, and further, that God is not vegan.

[146] This is their Damascus road experience; this is when faith came alive.

[147] This fascinating revelation from Jesus tells us that the chief purpose of the Scriptures written before him were to point to him, and that God ordained that every single one of them would be fulfilled.

[148] The gospel was first preached on the day of Pentecost, in Jerusalem, forty-seven days after Jesus spoke these words. (Pentecost, meaning fifty, was counted inclusively from Nisan 15, the first day of Unleavened Bread.)

[149] They received the Holy Spirit on the same (Jewish calendar) day as the resurrection; however, they received a special impartation of power when they were baptized in the Holy Spirit on the day of Pentecost. These were two very different events.

[150] This sentence has prompted various interpretations, a review of which is beyond the scope of this book. My view is that it applies in a ministerial sense, but not with respect to anyone's eternal destiny. Peter seems to have exercised this authority in Acts 5:1-11.

Monday, Nisan 19

The Upper Room in Southwest Jerusalem

Now Thomas, one of the Twelve, called the Twin, was not *there* with them when Jesus came *the prior evening.*[151] So the other disciples told him, "We have seen the Lord!" But he said to them, "Unless I see the scars of the nails in his hands, and put my finger into the imprint of the nails, and put my hand into his side, I will not believe it."[152] EE

---

[151] The news about the five appearances of Jesus on the previous day must have reached Thomas in Bethany, so that he was persuaded, despite his fears and disbelief, to rejoin the disciples in Jerusalem.

[152] Jesus could have appeared immediately to Thomas to settle the doubt in Thomas' mind. Rather, Jesus chose to let Thomas marinate in his unbelief for another week, during which Jesus made no further appearances. Thomas probably felt confirmed in his unbelief over those days.

Sunday, Nisan 25 (One Week after the Resurrection)

The Upper Room in Jerusalem

A week later,[153] the disciples were again inside, and Thomas was with them. The doors were locked,[154] and *yet* Jesus came and stood among them and said, "Peace to you *all*."

Then he said to Thomas, "Put your finger here, and see my hands. Put your hand here into my side, and do not be unbelieving, but believe."[155] Thomas answered him, "My Lord and my God!"[156] And Jesus said to him, "Do you believe because you have seen me? Blessed are those who did not see *me*, and yet believed."[157] FF

---

[153] Lit., *eight days*. Virtually all commentators agree that this expression, "after eight days," simply means a week later—that is, the days are counted inclusively. For further elaboration, see The Order of Appearances in Part Three, under the appearance to Thomas.

[154] Or, *shut*; a locked and barred door was no more obstacle to Jesus than a sealed stone tomb and a squad of Roman soldiers.

[155] Jesus leveled a strong public rebuke to Thomas, using Thomas' very own words.

[156] Thomas is the first one in the Scriptures to express that Jesus is divine and not just someone with an extraordinary relationship to God. This may shed light on Thomas' reluctance to accept the resurrection reports.

[157] Following his reproof of Thomas, Jesus gives special commendation and a blessing to certain people: those who believe without having seen Jesus. And as far as we know, the only people who fit the description at that time were the four devoted women who had journeyed to the tomb and heard the news from two angels. They did see Jesus later, but they believed before seeing him.

A Month Away from Jerusalem,
Nisan 27 - Iyar 26

From Jerusalem to Galilee and Back

And so the eleven disciples traveled to Galilee.[GG]

Afterwards,[158] Jesus revealed himself again to the disciples at the Sea of Galilee,[159] and he did so in this way:

Peter,[160] Thomas called the Twin, Nathanael of Cana in Galilee, the sons of Zebedee,[161] and two others of his disciples were together.

Peter[162] said to them, "I am going fishing."[163] They said to him, "We will go with you." They went out and got into the boat but that night they caught nothing. As day was breaking, Jesus stood on the beach, yet the disciples did not know that it was Jesus.[164] Then Jesus said to them, "Children, you don't have any fish[165] to eat, do you?" They answered him, "No."

And he said to them, "Cast *your net* on the right-hand side of the boat and you will find *fish*." So they cast, and then they were not able to haul it in because of the multitude of fish. Therefore, the disciple whom Jesus loved[166] said to Peter, "It is the Lord!"

---

[158] Lit., *after these things*

[159] Lit., *Tiberias*, another name for the Sea of Galilee

[160] Lit., *Simon Peter*

[161] I.e., James and John

[162] Lit., *Simon Peter*

[163] By this time, Peter and the other fishermen had been two to three years away from fishing and probably needed to borrow a boat and tackle. Zebedee would be the obvious provider.

[164] They may not have recognized Jesus simply because of the distance, about 100 yards, and the dim morning light.

[165] Lit., *something to eat with bread*; in this context, fish

[166] i.e., John

When Peter[167] heard that it was the Lord, he put his fisherman's coat on (for he was unclad for work), and threw himself into the sea. But the other disciples came in the boat—for they were not far from land, about one hundred yards away—dragging the net with the fish. When they got out on land, they saw a charcoal fire there with fish set on it, and bread.

Jesus said to them, "Bring some of the fish that you have just caught." Peter[168] went up and dragged the net ashore, full of large fish—153. But although there were so many, the net was not torn. Jesus said to them, "Come, have breakfast." None of the disciples dared to ask him, "Who are you?" They knew it was the Lord.[169] Jesus came and took the bread and gave it to them, and likewise the fish. This was now the third time that Jesus appeared to the disciples after he was raised from the dead.[170]

When they had finished breakfast, Jesus said to Peter,[171] "Peter[172] son of John, do you love me more than these?"[173] He said to him, "Yes, Lord; you know that I love you." He said to him, "Feed my lambs."

He said to him again a second time, "Peter[174] son of John, do you love me?" He said to him, "Yes, Lord; you know that I love you." He said to him, "Tend my sheep."

He said to him the third time, "Peter[175] son of John, do you

---

[167] Lit., *Simon Peter*

[168] Lit., *Simon Peter*

[169] Although they each *knew* it, they must have felt much greater reverential awe for Jesus and an appreciation for the magnitude of the moment that gave it something of a surreal feeling. Also, Jesus may have looked somewhat changed in his resurrected state (perhaps his hair was white, as John saw him in Rev 1:14).

[170] For the disciples, most of the time between the resurrection and ascension was spent waiting and wondering.

[171] Lit., *Simon Peter*

[172] Lit., *Simon*

[173] I.e., more than these other disciples

[174] Lit., *Simon*

[175] Lit., *Simon*

love me?" Peter was grieved because he said to him the third time, "Do you love me?" And Peter said to him, "Lord, you know all things, you know that I love you." Jesus said to him, "Feed my sheep."[176]

"Very truly I say to you, when you were younger you dressed yourself and went wherever you wanted, but when you are old you will stretch out your hands, and someone else will dress you and take you where you do not want to go."[177] Now he said this to make known by what kind of death Peter would glorify God. And when he had spoken this, he said to him, "Follow me!"

Turning around, Peter saw the disciple[178] Jesus loved following them, the one who had leaned back against him[179] at the supper and asked, "Lord, who is the one who betrays you?" So when Peter saw him, he said to Jesus, "Lord, what about this man?" Jesus said to him, "If I want him to remain *alive* until I return, what is that to you? You follow me!"[180]

Therefore this saying spread among the brethren that this disciple would not die; but Jesus did not say to him that he would not die, but rather, "If I want him to remain until I return, what is that to you?" This is the disciple who is testifying to these things and writing them, and we know that his testimony is true.

---

[176] To understand this exchange, it is important to know that two different Greek words are translated "love" here. Jesus' first and second questions use the word *agapao*, but Jesus' last question, and all of Peter's replies, use the word *phileo*. The former is sacrificial love; the latter is brotherly love.

Jesus is forcing Peter to recognize that he is not the hero he previously had imagined himself to be, while also restoring their relationship.

[177] Tradition says that Peter was crucified in Rome. Jesus is informing him of his future martyrdom.

[178] I.e., John

[179] Lit., *on his breast*

[180] Jesus has been characterized in some churches as one who would never discomfort his followers or speak hard truths to them. It is a false notion, as shown here.

And there are also many other things which Jesus did which, if each one was written, I suppose that the world itself could not contain the books that would be written.[HH]

After this, the eleven disciples went to the mountain to which Jesus had directed them,[181] *and a large number of Galilean disciples joined them.*[182] Jesus *there* appeared to more than five hundred brethren at one time, most of whom remain alive until now, although some have passed away. When they saw him, they worshiped him, but some doubted.[183] [II]

And Jesus came up and spoke to them, saying, "All authority has been given to me in heaven and on earth. Therefore, go and make disciples of all the nations, baptizing them in the name of the Father and the Son and the Holy Spirit, teaching them to observe all I have commanded you; and surely, I am with you always, even to the end of the age."[JJ]

After that, Jesus appeared to James, *his brother.*[184] [KK]

Jesus directed his disciples and close followers to return to

---

[181] It is reasonable to expect that this was the same location where Jesus delivered his famous "sermon on the mount" message (Mt 5:1), as the disciples and many of his followers knew the place.

[182] Obviously, these Galilean disciples had to have received notice of this upcoming appearance. The size of the crowd suggests that they came from multiple cities and towns of the area. The notice of this meeting apparently was announced through the disciples.

[183] This group of more than 500 men (not counting women and children) was the largest assembly to which Jesus appeared. Some of these men doubted the resurrection. That doubt was removed when Jesus came closer and spoke to them.

[184] There is no indication that James believed in Jesus as the Messiah prior to this visitation; in fact, there is evidence to the contrary (Mk 3:21,31; Jn 7:5). James may have fled Jerusalem when Jesus was arrested because it was common then for authorities to retaliate against kin for the offenses of one person. James was from Nazareth in Galilee, and it's quite probable that he had acquired Joseph's carpentry business after Joseph died and Jesus launched his ministry. Therefore, it is likely that this visitation happened in Galilee—even in Nazareth.

Jerusalem.[185] *They proceeded to Jerusalem, and the eleven disciples stayed again in the upper room.*[186]

---

[185] Although this instruction is not recorded, the disciples would have had every reason to have remained in Galilee, unless Jesus had specifically directed them to return to Jerusalem.

The group that returned from Galilee to Jerusalem was of some size, drawn from the 500 brethren who saw Jesus there—they probably comprised most of the 120 in the upper room on the day of Pentecost.

While Luke makes no mention of the Twelve's round-trip to Galilee in either his gospel or Acts (which he wrote), he does make an allusion to it when he recorded that Jesus "gathered them together" in Jerusalem (Acts 1:4), after appearing to his followers over forty days. If the disciples had remained in Jerusalem the whole time, there would have been no need to "gather them." Unfortunately, Luke's omission has resulted in much misinterpretation of his account.

[186] The disciples were staying in an upper room in Jerusalem after their return from Galilee. (Acts 1:13)

Thursday, Iyar 27 - the Ascension

The Mount of Olives, Just East of Jerusalem

Gathering *his disciples*[187] together *on the Mount of Olives,*[188] Jesus commanded them not to leave Jerusalem but to wait for what the Father had promised, "Which you heard of from me; for John baptized you with water, but you will be baptized in the Holy Spirit not many days from now."

So while they were together, they were asking him, "Lord, is it at this time you are restoring the kingdom to Israel?"[189]

He said to them, "It is not for you to know times or periods which the Father has established by his own authority; but you will receive power when the Holy Spirit has come upon you, and you shall be my witnesses in Jerusalem, and in all Judea and Samaria, and even to the remotest part of the earth. Now behold, I am sending forth upon you the promise of my Father,[190] but stay in the city until you are clothed with power from on high."LL

Then he led them out as far as Bethany. And he said to them, "Go into all the world and preach the gospel to all creation.[191]

---

[187] Lit., *them*

[188] The disciples had been waiting in the upper room, so Jesus would not have needed to gather them, had he chosen to appear there. Further, Luke says, "he [Jesus] led them out as far as Bethany," which was on the downhill slope of the eastern side of the Mount of Olives. Therefore, it seems Jesus must have directed his disciples to travel from the upper room to some point on the Mount, whether it was Gethsemane, the top of the ridge, or somewhere else. From there, he led them further east, although perhaps only to the outskirts of Bethany.

[189] Astonishingly, Jesus' closest followers had not realized the global implications of his mission.

[190] The coming of the Holy Spirit involved also Jesus and the Father; it was an event of the entire Trinity.

[191] This statement from Mark appears broader than the command

Whoever believes and is baptized will be saved, but whoever does not believe will be condemned. These signs will accompany those who have believed: in my name they will cast out demons; they will speak with new tongues; they will pick up serpents with their hands, and if they drink any deadly *poison* it will not hurt them; they will lay hands on the sick and they will recover."MM

After he had said these things, he lifted up his hands and blessed them. While he was blessing them, he was separated from them and was lifted up while they were looking on, being carried up into heaven, and a cloud received him out of their sight. *Thus* the Lord Jesus was received up into heaven and sat down at the right hand of God, far above all rule, authority, power and dominion, and every name that is named, not only in this age but also in the one to come.NN

And as they were looking intently into the sky while he was going, suddenly two men in white clothing stood beside them. They also said, "Men192 of Galilee, why do you stand *here* looking into the sky? This Jesus, who has been taken up from you into heaven, will come in just the same way as you have watched him go into heaven."

And after worshiping *Jesus*, they returned to Jerusalem with great joy, from the mount called Olivet, which is near the city, a Sabbath day's journey away.OO

As soon as they had entered *the city*, they went up to the upper room where they were staying; that is, Peter and John and James *Zebedee* and Andrew, Philip and Thomas, Nathanael193 and Matthew, James the Younger,194 and Simon the Zealot, and

---

Jesus gave to the 500 brethren (per Matthew); it seems to allude that the good news is for the benefit of mankind and also for the joy or instruction of angelic beings. (cf. Eph 3:10-11; 1Pe 1:12).

192 The Greek word is best translated as "men," yet it does not mean that no women were present. Throughout Jesus' ministry, women were present (Lk 8:1-3), and we can expect they were present here also.

193 Lit., *Bartholomew*, another name for Nathanael

194 Lit., *of Alphaeus*, meaning the son of Alphaeus, another name for Clopas. This is the son of Clopas and Mary.

Thaddeus.[195] These all with one purpose were continually devoting themselves to prayer, along with the women,[196] and Mother Mary,[197] and his brothers.[198] And they were *also* continually in the temple blessing God.[199] PP

Now Jesus did many other signs[200] in the presence of the disciples, *between his crucifixion and ascension,*[201] which are not written in this book; but these have been written so that you may believe that Jesus is the Christ,[202] the Son of God; and that believing you may have life in his name.QQ

---

[195] Lit., *Judas of James*, another name for Thaddeus

[196] "The women" certainly included those esteemed followers who had taken anointing oils to the tomb.

[197] Lit., *Mary the mother of Jesus*

[198] Jesus' other siblings had become convinced of the truth of his messianic claims during the disciples' time in Galilee. Perhaps the testimony of Mother Mary or their brother James played a role in that.

[199] Several weeks earlier, the disciples had been fearfully hiding behind locked doors. Now they worshiped God openly in the temple with great joy and no concern for the authorities. This transformation testifies to the truth of the resurrection and the power of their experiences with the risen Jesus.

[200] I.e., attesting miracles

[201] This timespan in italics is taken from the context of John's words (Jn 20). It is reasonable to presume that most of these signs occurred during the approximately two-week period while the disciples stayed in Galilee, considering that Galilee was (1) Jesus' base of ministry, (2) Jesus' home region, (3) the place that both the angels and Jesus commanded them to go, and (4) far from the crowd that had violently rejected him. What those signs were and what quantity is meant by "many" are completely unknown today, so it is impossible to speculate about them.

[202] In other words, the testimonies of the four gospel accounts should be sufficient for belief. In Jesus' words, "Blessed are those who have not seen [me] and yet believe." (Jn 20:29 CSB)

Part Three

Explanation of the Unified Account

Introduction to Part Three

Biblical commentators have long recognized the difficulty of reconciling the differences between the resurrection accounts in the four gospels. Perhaps for equally as long, they have explained those differences as being the result of four different persons providing testimony to the event. Now certainly, we should not expect that separate writers recounting an extraordinary, rapidly moving, and emotional event would provide virtually identical descriptions of it. In fact, if that were the case, we would naturally suspect collusion or plagiarism. However, while this observation is useful for explaining why the differences exist, it is not helpful for developing a composite picture of what transpired.

Various writers, both academic and popular, religious and cynical, have concluded that the four accounts simply cannot be harmonized. A good short summary of these opinions (with references) is provided in Wenham's *Easter Enigma*,[203] should you decide to explore these alternative views. However, because the resurrection accounts have been reconciled and integrated herein, I think it is better to consider whether or not the Unified Account of Part Two in this book is cohesive and cogent. This part of the book, Part Three, makes that case by providing background information and describing the thought processes, assumptions, and conclusions that went into putting together the Unified Account in Part Two. (And thus Part One, which is built upon the scaffold of Part Two.)

A secondary purpose of Part Three is to share details and insights I've discovered through research and immersion in the story for many months. To me, these are precious, and I wish to share that value.

---

[203] John Wenham, *Easter Enigma* (Eugene, OR: Wipf & Stock Publishers, 1992), 9-12.

A number of pieces of background information are helpful to better understand the story. For that reason, in the following sections we will examine:

- The writers of the accounts and their intended audiences and purposes for writing

- The characters and their relationships

- The layout of Jerusalem, especially the relative locations of places important to the story and the time it would take to travel from one place to another

We will also make reference to the following historical information:

- The customs, culture, and political situation of the Jews in early first century Palestine

- Roman practices

- Extra-biblical sources, such as early church historians and other first-century and early second-century writings

Ironically, one of the major problems in constructing the Unified Account turned out to be the five women at the tomb. Or was it three of them, or two, or just one? Those are the reported numbers of women involved depending on which gospel account you read. And the number of women at the tomb is only one of several problems regarding the women involved with the resurrection event. Why is that so interesting and ironic?

Because, as you will see, the women hold the principal keys to understanding the entire story.

When Was Jesus Crucified?

When *was* Jesus crucified? It's a question that relates directly to an understanding of the events that followed, including the resurrection. And importantly, why does any of this chronology matter, beyond historical curiosity and fodder for academic papers?

These questions are relevant because the chronology of Jesus' final week impacts the reconstruction of these events in many ways. As one example, knowing Jesus was arrested on the night of Nisan 14 (as explained below) tells us that the moon would have been quite bright—just one day shy of a full moon—thus providing ample light for the disciples as they fled down the road towards Bethany. (Bethany was, from the garden of Gethsemane where Jesus was arrested, their sole line of retreat, and they had friends there.[204])

So then, let's examine in turn what can be determined about the month, day of the month, hour, day of the week, and year of these events. Of these details, the particular year in which these events happened is the least important for the purposes of this book (although we shall examine the question), but they are all pertinent in various ways for assembling the resurrection accounts into a complete picture.

Some Necessary Background on Jewish Timekeeping

A Jewish day in the first century began at sunset and ended at the following sunset so that nighttime preceded daytime. This is still observed today among Jews who reckon the weekly Sabbath day of rest as beginning at sundown Friday and continuing to

---

[204] Now a certain man was sick, Lazarus of Bethany, the village of Mary and her sister Martha. This He said, and after that He said to them... "Our friend Lazarus has fallen asleep; but I go, so that I may awaken him out of sleep." (Jn 11:1, 11)

sundown Saturday. In addition, the term "day" was used in the gospels, as it is today, to mean either a sunset-to-sunset day, or just the daylight portion thereof, depending upon context.

In the first century, Jews subdivided days into two 12-hour periods, one for nighttime and one for daylight. Each of those two periods was divided into twelve equal hours; however, the lengths of the hours varied across the year, as the ratio of daytime to nighttime varied. Thus, summer daylight hours were longer than summer nighttime hours. Jesus was crucified and resurrected close to the vernal equinox, that is, the time of year when daylight and nighttime hours would have been nearly equal in length.

Romans, like the Western world today, counted the hours of a day beginning from midnight (for "civic" days).[205] Jews, however, counted daylight hours from the beginning of daylight, and the New Testament reports time from the Jewish perspective. And so, in converting New Testament time to modern time, it's useful to approximate the "first hour of the day" as corresponding roughly to 7:00 a.m., the "second hour" to 8:00 a.m., and so on. The "first hour of the night" would likewise correspond to 7:00 p.m., etc. These hours should be considered approximate, however, as sunup and sundown vary with the seasons, and any given "hour" means the whole hour, not the instant when the hour changes.[206]

Furthermore, the best timekeeping devices available during this time period were hourglasses and sundials, luxuries beyond the means of the average person. Therefore, while we should presume that most people at the time were adequately capable of approximating the hour by an eyeball estimate of the sun's or moon's position, we also shouldn't regard their estimates to be to-the-minute precision.

Jewish priests in Jerusalem determined the beginning of each

---

[205] The Romans also counted hours for "natural" days just as the Jews did. See Appendix C.

[206] See Appendix C for further explanation on converting Jewish time to modern time.

month through observation of the moon. Since a lunar month averages about 29.5 days, a standard 12-month Jewish year had only 354 days. (Their months alternated between 29 and 30 days.) Without correction, a series of such years would cause the seasons to occur later and later on the calendar, and this would become a problem for the timing of planting, harvesting, and festivals. The Jewish leaders made necessary, occasional corrections (called "intercalations") to the calendar by inserting "leap" days and months.

The intercalations of the Jewish calendar have a potential impact only upon the determination of the year of these events. Appendix A describes the process they used and its impact on the chronology relevant to this book.

The Month

Jesus' death and resurrection occurred during the Jewish religious feast of Passover, that is, the Jewish celebration of the miraculous release of their ancestors from slavery in Egypt. All four gospel accounts mention this chronological association.[207]

The Passover feast, in turn, has always been celebrated annually during the month of Nisan,[208] that is, the first month of the Jewish religious calendar. Nisan begins usually between mid-March and mid-April on the Julian calendar, or in other words, in the spring season. It does not begin on a fixed Julian date because the Jewish calendar is lunar based, not solar. God, through Moses, fixed the timing of Passover on the Jewish calendar, as recorded in Exodus:

> "This month [i.e., Nisan] shall be the *beginning of months* for you; it is to be the first month of the year to you.... Your lamb shall be an unblemished male a year old; you may take it from the sheep or from the goats. You shall keep it until the *fourteenth day* of the same month, then the whole

---

[207] Mt 26:19; Mk 14:16; Lk 22:15; Jn 18:28
[208] Before the Babylonian captivity, this month was called Abib (or Aviv).

assembly of the congregation of Israel is to kill it at twilight."
(Ex 12:2, 5-6; brackets and emphasis added)

In the first century, the Jewish months began by decree when certain observers in Jerusalem spotted a new moon (specifically, the first visible crescent of a waxing moon). Thus, the day of the month was always fixed relative to the phases of the moon: the first of every month was (always) a new moon, the eighth was a waxing quarter-moon,[209] the fifteenth was a full moon, the twenty-second was a waning quarter-moon, and so on.

Jesus was crucified and resurrected during the month of Nisan, the first month of the Jewish calendar, during the Passover feast. The testimony of the gospels further provides us with the day of the month, which relates these events to the phase of the moon.

The Day of the Month

John was very specific about the day of the month on which Jesus was crucified:

> Then the Jews, because it was *the day of preparation*, so that the bodies would not remain on the cross on the Sabbath *(for that Sabbath was a high day)*, asked Pilate that their legs might be broken, and that they might be taken away. (Jn 19:31, emphasis added)

During the first century in Jerusalem, the day of preparation was the day when the Jews prepared for the great feast that began at sundown, at the beginning of Nisan 15.[210] In other

---

[209] A quarter-moon is a moon that is half-illumined but called "quarter" because it occurs when the moon is at a quarter point in its monthly cycle.

[210] Every Friday was also a day of preparation for the weekly Sabbath immediately following, but John makes it clear that this Sabbath was a "high" day—a particularly sacred day—meaning Nisan 15. No other day

words, the preparation day was *Nisan 14*, and this is the day that Jesus was tried, crucified, and died. Mark, Luke, and Matthew confirm this date as well.[211] (If you are wondering how Jesus could have celebrated the Passover meal the night before Passover lambs were sacrificed at the temple, see Appendix B for an explanation.)

So, Nisan 14, the date given through Moses for the sacrifice of the Passover lamb, was also the same calendar date when Jesus died on the cross—a perfect fulfillment of the Passover tradition. It is most sobering to realize that as Jesus was dying on a cross outside the city, priests within the city at the temple—many of whom had clamored for his crucifixion—were commencing the sacrifice of Passover lambs and oblivious to the fulfillment of their cherished tradition happening less than 700 yards away.

The Hour of the Day

Mark tells us plainly that Jesus was nailed to the cross at the third hour, that is, about 9 a.m.:

> It was the *third hour* when they crucified Him. (Mk 15:25, emphasis added)

In other words, this occurred about mid-morning. Mark also records that the sky darkened around noon and remained dark until Jesus expired at approximately 3 p.m.[212]

---

could have been meant.

[211] When evening had already come, because it was the preparation day, that is, the day before the Sabbath (Mk 15:42). It was the preparation day, and the Sabbath was about to begin (Lk 23:54). Now on the next day, the day after the preparation, the chief priests and the Pharisees gathered together with Pilate (Mt 27:62).

Note that the event in Matthew 27:62 happened the day after Jesus died—thus he died on the preparation day.

[212] When the sixth hour came, darkness fell over the whole land until the ninth hour.... And Jesus uttered a loud cry, and breathed His last. (Mk 15:33, 37)

Matthew and Luke both corroborate Mark's account that darkness occurred over the entire land between noon and 3 p.m., and they both indicate that Jesus was on the cross at least by noon, although neither one of them gives the starting time of the crucifixion to compare with Mark's account.

John, in stark contrast, seems to say that Jesus was crucified at noon or shortly afterwards[213]. This apparent conflict has drawn several attempts for an explanation, the simplest and most compelling being that a copyist's error occurred early in church history, and that the genuine reading of John should be "the third hour," or 9 a.m., in agreement with Mark. The evidence for this explanation and descriptions of less compelling explanations are detailed in Appendix C.

The Day of the Week

Church tradition has long held that Jesus was crucified on a Friday and raised from the dead at dawn on a Sunday morning.

Neither is correct.

There are three reasons why a Friday crucifixion can be discounted, and these are presented in increasing order of weight:

First, if Jesus died on a Friday, then on the preceding weekly Sabbath, Jesus and his traveling companions would have been violating Sabbath travel restrictions, which, as observant Jews, they would not have done.

John describes what Jesus was doing six days before the Passover (that is, six days before Jesus' death): "Jesus,

---

[213] Now it was the day of preparation for the Passover; it was *about the sixth hour*. And he said to the Jews, "Behold, your King!" So they cried out, "Away with Him away with Him, crucify Him!" Pilate said to them, "Shall I crucify your King?" The chief priests answered, "We have no king but Caesar." So he then handed Him over to them to be crucified. (Jn 19:14-16, emphasis added)

206

therefore, six days before the Passover, came to Bethany..." (Jn 12:1). For a Friday crucifixion, this trip to Bethany would have occurred on a Sabbath. Jesus' travel to Bethany from Jericho would have thus violated Sabbath travel restrictions.

However, a Wednesday crucifixion would have Jesus arriving in Bethany on the preceding Thursday.

Second, a Friday crucifixion would not fulfill Jesus' own prophecy concerning his death and resurrection, famously quoted in Matthew:

> "...for just as Jonah was three days and three nights in the belly of the sea monster, so will the Son of Man be three days and three nights in the heart of the earth." (Mt 12:40)[214]

In order to properly interpret this verse, we must understand that "a day and a night" is a phrase used to explicitly distinguish an entire 24-hour day from simply the daylight portion of a day. Given the nature of timekeeping in the first century, it would be inappropriate to apply twenty-first century ideas of millisecond precision to this prophecy. Nevertheless, it is entirely reasonable to presume its fulfillment to be fairly close to three full days. Certainly, it is even to be expected, when we recognize that God so coordinated the death of the Lamb of God to fall on the same day of the year, and at the same time, as lambs were being sacrificed in the temple—so that Jesus' death fulfilled the prophetic tradition, *simultaneously*. Should we then suppose that God would be grossly imprecise in his prophecy of the length of time when Jesus would be in the tomb? It would seem unlikely.

A Friday crucifixion flatly contradicts this prophecy. If Jesus died on Friday afternoon, he would have been in the grave for only *one* day and *two* nights, or just *one-half* of what was prophesied.[215] First-century timekeeping was not that imprecise,

---

[214] "In the heart of the earth" is idiomatic for "in the tomb."

[215] Since Jesus died at about 3 p.m., he would have not been buried

and God's Word is not so elastic as to permit alignment between the prophecy and a Friday crucifixion. All the hand-waving and clever explanations used to try to make these align simply serve to undermine the validity of written prophecy in general—and even of the resurrection as an historical fact.

A Thursday crucifixion also fails to fulfill the prophecy of Matthew 12:40. If Jesus had died Thursday afternoon, he would have been in the tomb for *two* days and *three* nights at best. Again, the daytime portions of Thursday and Sunday cannot be included, as the interment took place just before sundown, and the women were at the tomb promptly at sunrise.

A Wednesday crucifixion, at first glance, also may seem to fail to fulfill the prophecy, as Jesus would have been in the tomb for *three* days and *four* nights—one night too many. (Logically, of course, if he was in the tomb four nights, he technically did complete the requirement of being in the tomb three full days, but let's set that aside for now.)[216]

Now, when exactly (during the week) did Jesus *rise* from the dead? Tradition holds that Jesus was resurrected Sunday morning. Why? Because the women discovered his body missing at the crack of dawn on Sunday. Yet this only establishes that Jesus was resurrected *at least* by Sunday morning. He could have been resurrected earlier. How much earlier? As early as the end of the previous day.

Saturday was a Sabbath, and although travel was limited, Jesus' tomb was just beyond Jerusalem's wall and within easy Sabbath-travel distance for anyone in the city. The tomb would

---

until about twilight. Therefore, he was in the grave (at most) Friday (night) and Saturday (day and night). Friday (day) cannot be counted, as the omitted application of spices to the body testifies that Joseph and Nicodemus were pressed for time to inter the body before twilight (when the Sabbath began). Sunday (day) cannot be counted as the women were at the tomb at daybreak. The conclusion is the same whether we use Jewish or Roman views of a "day."

[216] Some readers may wonder of the relevance of Clopas' comment on the Emmaus road to this discussion; this is covered in Appendix D.

have seen heavy foot traffic during that day because of Jesus' notoriety and people paying their respects or visiting out of curiosity. But the flow of visitors would have stopped as dusk approached. If Jesus was resurrected shortly after sundown Saturday, the prophecy would have been perfectly fulfilled, though no one would have known until the women arrived at dawn.

Is there any textual evidence that Jesus left the tomb well before the women arrived? There are hints, and one direct statement of confirmation.

Matthew records:

> And behold, a severe earthquake had occurred, for an angel of the Lord descended from heaven and came and rolled away the stone and sat upon it. And his appearance was like lightning, and his clothing as white as snow. The guards shook for fear of him and became like dead men. (Mt 28:2-4)

Surely, this dramatic appearance of the angels and the opening of the tomb must have corresponded with the moment of the resurrection. Yet the Scriptures tell us that none of the pagan soldiers witnessed the resurrected Christ or heard the angelic announcement delivered to the women.[217]

If Matthew had written this detail with the tools available to the modern English writer, these three verses would have been in brackets or parentheses, or he would have used a verb tense to indicate it happened before the women's visit. As a first-century writer in Greek, he lacked such tools to express what is a parenthetical, explanatory note.

---

[217] Now after He had risen early on the first day of the week, He *first appeared* to Mary Magdalene, from whom He had cast out seven demons (Mk 16:9, emphasis added).

Note that Jesus did not *first* appear to the soldiers. Peter is also recorded as saying that Jesus became visible only to witnesses chosen by God (Acts 10:40-41).

Giving careful consideration to the four gospel accounts, it's evident that this event described by Matthew occurred before the women's arrival—and not just immediately before it—for the following reasons:

1. No angels were sitting on the rock when the women arrived. In truth, there were no angels even present (or discernible to their senses) as the women approached the golel[218] stone; the angels only appeared to the women, and suddenly, after they had entered the tomb.

2. No guard was present at the tomb. The women would have been intimidated by the prostrate guards and wouldn't have stepped over them to enter the tomb. Nor did the women mention the guards' presence—an inexplicable omission unless they were long gone.

3. Similarly, the women apparently didn't encounter the earthquake (described as "severe") on their way to the tomb. Had they done so, they most certainly would have postponed the graveside visit and immediately returned to their residences to check on friends and relatives. This means that the time of the resurrection was certainly a number of hours before the women had even left their residences to travel to the tomb.

4. The lie that was concocted by the Jewish elders and spread by the guard was that the disciples had come *by night* and stolen his body while they were sleeping (Mt 28:13). This chronicles a nighttime resurrection.

In other words, it was somewhere between twilight and the middle of night when the angel descended, which would have made his lightning-like appearance even more fearful.

In addition to these hints provided by Matthew, Mark provides a direct statement that Jesus rose well before dawn:

Now *after* He had risen *early on the first day of the week*, He first appeared to Mary Magdalene, from whom He had cast out seven demons. (Mk 16:9, emphasis added)

---

[218] The large round stone used to seal the tomb

It's a mistake to view this verse solely from the Western notion of when a day begins and ends. The first day of the week is what we now call Sunday, of course. But, to a Jewish writer, the day formally began the previous dusk, and "early on the first day of the week" could mean a number of things. The Greek word used, *prōi*, could simply mean "shortly after sunrise." However, it could also mean the fourth watch of the night—that is, from 3 a.m. to 6 a.m.[219] And, *prōi* was used elsewhere in the New Testament to specifically mean "before daylight," or "during the nighttime."[220] Seven verses earlier (Mk 16:2), we are told that at least three women came to the tomb "very early." This verse expresses that Jesus had risen "earlier than *very* early."

Thus, Jesus rose from the grave well before dawn Sunday morning, much before the women's arrival, and so fulfilled his own prophetic words.

One question that might trouble a reader when considering a resurrection as early as Saturday at twilight, or at midnight, or even a few hours before the women arrived, is the question of what Jesus was doing during the interval between his resurrection and his first appearance to Mary Magdalene. The answer is that the texts are silent on that point. However, this should not concern us; we are likewise not informed of what Jesus was doing in the intervals between his various appearances on Sunday, or between Sunday and his appearance to Thomas (a gap of eight days), or between any of the subsequent appearances before his ascension. All of the gospel accounts of the resurrection contain purely eyewitness testimony; they are devoid of any speculations concerning what was happening behind the scenes.

---

[219] *Thayer's Greek Lexicon*, (Biblesoft, Inc.: 2011), Strong's G4404.

[220] In the early morning, while it was still dark, Jesus got up, left the house, and went away to a secluded place, and was praying there. (Mk 1:35)

Now on the first day of the week Mary Magdalene came early to the tomb, while it was still dark, and saw the stone already taken away from the tomb. (Jn 20:1)

The *third* and most compelling reason why Jesus could not have been crucified on a Friday is provided by the activities of women who followed him, as they attempted to honor Jesus by completing what had been omitted in his burial preparations.

It was a Jewish cultural and religious duty for the family and friends of Jesus to provide a proper and adequate burial for him. Fortunately, Pilate had granted Jesus' body to Joseph of Arimathea (thus allowing for a proper Jewish burial), but Joseph—and Nicodemus, who helped him—had very little time between when they took custody of the body and sundown.

Jesus died around 3:00 p.m., and sundown was around 6:00 p.m. Between those hours Joseph had to travel to the Praetorium; obtain an audience with the governor; request the body; wait for Pilate to confirm Jesus's death; travel back to the crucifixion site; remove the body carefully to minimize further damage to it; obtain burial cloths; transport the body to the grave site (fortunately, close by); wash, anoint with spices, and wrap the body; tie the cloths; anoint the body with oils; move the body into the tomb and position it; seal the tomb with a large stone; and say prayers—all by 6:00 p.m. or so.

As it turns out, in the rush to complete these tasks by sundown, Joseph and Nicodemus omitted the final anointing oils. Without a doubt, this happened knowingly because of the unavailability thereof and as a concession to the time limitation. Mary Magdalene and Mary Clopas were present as Joseph and Nicodemus worked, and they saw the omission. For them, it was imperative that their Lord receive the honor of a complete consecration.

How the Actions of the Women Pinpoint the Day Jesus Was Crucified

The Scriptures tell us what the two Marys did to remedy this oversight:

> Mary Magdalene and Mary the mother of Joses were looking on to see where He was laid. When the [High Holy] Sabbath

was over, Mary Magdalene, and Mary the mother of James [the Younger], and Salome, bought spices, so that they might come and anoint Him. (Mk 15:47, 16:1, brackets added)

Now the women who had come with Him out of Galilee followed, and saw the tomb and how His body was laid. Then they returned and prepared spices and perfumes. And on the [weekly] Sabbath they rested according to the commandment. (Lk 23:55–56, brackets added)

The first "Sabbath" above is from Mark; the second one is from Luke. These two references to a Sabbath have caused much confusion. The confounding assumption is that these two Sabbaths are the same day. They cannot possibly be, which is why the bracketed modifiers have been added to the above verses.

If they were the same day, Mark and Luke could not be reconciled—period. Mark says the women bought spices *after* the Sabbath was over. Luke says they took the spices and prepared the oils (from the spices) *before* the Sabbath, and rested on the Sabbath following their preparations. So, if these two writers were speaking of the same Sabbath, then the women prepared the spices before they had purchased them! A single Sabbath makes these two verses flatly irreconcilable.

(Moreover, neither verse is possible individually for a Friday or Thursday crucifixion, as will be shown.)

The problem resolves when it is understood that during Passover week there are two Sabbaths, not one! Mark and Luke are referring to different Sabbaths. First, there is the usual weekly Sabbath—what we would call Saturday—in which observant Jews rest from work and attend synagogue. But on the Jewish calendar there are seven floating Sabbaths, and one of these—Nisan 15, the Sabbath of Passover—can occur any day of the week, just as January 1st on the Gregorian calendar occurs on different days depending on the year. [221]

---

[221] Note that "Sabbath" means "rest," not "Saturday." Any obligatory

A single Sabbath creates an impossible situation for a Friday crucifixion. If we assume only one Sabbath, and Jesus died on a Friday, then as soon as the Sabbath began—at sundown on that Friday, just as the stone door was being rolled over the tomb opening—the women had to rest. (The shops would have been closed from noontime anyway, as they always were on Nisan 14.) They had to rest until Saturday at sundown, twenty-four hours later. However, the shops did not open until Sunday morning because of nightfall. They could not possibly have bought spices until Sunday morning and certainly could not have prepared them. Neither Mark's nor Luke's statements would be possible. A Friday crucifixion simply could not have happened.

Now, recognizing that there are two Sabbaths in the Passover week and that the high holy Sabbath of Passover can occur any day of the week, we can see the solution. Jesus died on the day of preparation for the Passover[222] (which is always Nisan 14), followed by the Sabbath of Nisan 15 (on which the women rested, per Mark), followed by a day on which they bought and prepared spices (Nisan 16), then by the weekly Sabbath (Nisan 17) on which they rested (per Luke). Backing up from Saturday, Jesus was crucified on a Wednesday, Nisan 14. The women performed their work on Friday, Nisan 16, and came to the tomb on Sunday, Nisan 18. There had to be a working day between the two Sabbaths.

A Thursday crucifixion is also impossible for the same reason—it doesn't provide any time for the women to have performed their tasks. With a Thursday crucifixion, both Friday (now the Passover Sabbath and the first day of Unleavened

day of rest is a Sabbath. The Scriptures are clear that any feast's day-of-rest is called a Sabbath. This is shown in God's instructions concerning the Feast of Tabernacles in Ex 23:33-44, and would likewise apply to any other mandated day of rest.

222 And Mary Magdalene was there, and the other Mary, sitting opposite the grave. Now on the *next* day, the day *after* the preparation, the chief priests and the Pharisees gathered together with Pilate (Mt 27:61-62, emphasis added)

Bread) and Saturday would be back-to-back Sabbaths. In this scenario, the women could not have purchased the spices or prepared the anointing oils before Sunday morning, when they visited the tomb.

The details of the women's actions in Mark and Luke are sufficient and conclusive for accepting Wednesday as the day of Jesus' crucifixion. Their actions serve as the primary key that leads to a coherent understanding of the entire narrative.

Women, thank you!

How Did the Idea of a Friday Crucifixion Arise?

The tradition of a Friday crucifixion is very deeply entrenched in the liturgical calendar and mind of the Christian church. Even though the textual evidence warrants a revision, it's doubtful that Good Friday will ever become Good Wednesday. We might inquire how this mistake originated.

Historically, the liturgical calendar did not spring into existence upon the creation of the early church, nor even in the first hundred years of its existence. Rather, it evolved over time. By the second half of the second century, Judaism and Christianity had parted company in most places. The observance of Easter (i.e., annual celebration of the resurrection) is not mentioned at all in the New Testament nor in early Christian sources related to church practice, such as Paul's epistles.

In Jerusalem between AD 325 and 386, bishops Macarius, Maximus, and Cyril established days on the calendar for celebrating particular events in the life of Jesus, including a celebration of "Good Friday" at Golgotha (that is, the location of the crucifixion).[223] The practices thus established in Jerusalem soon spread elsewhere. This may have been the origin of the incorrect identification of Friday as the day of the crucifixion.

For context, the emperor Constantine had outlawed the persecution of Christians in the Roman Empire in AD 312, and AD 325 was the year of The First Council of Nicaea. The church

---

[223] Anders Ekenberg, "The Early History of the Liturgical Year," (Lecture at the University of John Paul II, Cracow, 15 April 2015).

by this time was completely divorced from Judaism and guided by the church at Rome.

Bishops Macarius, Maximus, and Cyril were establishing liturgical calendar celebrations more than three centuries after the actual events. From their names, they were Roman rather than Jewish men,[224] and from their positions, they were culturally Roman. My supposition is that they misread several verses such as Luke 23:54—"It was the preparation day, and the Sabbath was about to begin."

The simple, presumptive interpretation is that this "Sabbath" was a Saturday, and so Jesus must have been crucified on a Friday. Had these men been of Jewish origin and thus more familiar with the floating Sabbaths of the Feasts, they might not have leaped to such a conclusion.

The Year of the Crucifixion and Resurrection

From the Scriptures, and some extra-biblical sources, we can bracket the possible years in which these events occurred, and even arrive at a specific year. There are several different approaches we can take.

The gospel writer Luke provides chronological markers to the start of Jesus' ministry:

> Now in the fifteenth year of the reign of Tiberius Caesar, when Pontius Pilate was governor of Judea, and Herod was tetrarch[225] of Galilee, and his brother Philip was tetrarch of the region of Ituraea and Trachonitis, and Lysanias was tetrarch of Abilene, in the high priesthood of Annas and Caiaphas, the word of God came to John, the son of Zacharias, in the wilderness. And he came into all the district around the Jordan, preaching a baptism of repentance for the forgiveness of sins ... Now when all the people were baptized, Jesus was also baptized, and while He was praying,

---

[224] All three are Latin names. Macarius and Cyril are latinized versions of Greek names.

[225] Tetrarch: the ruler of the fourth part of a country or province

heaven was opened. (Lk 3:1-3, 21)

In this passage, Luke has named seven officials: Tiberius, Pilate, Herod (Antipas), Philip, Lysanias, Annas, and Caiaphas, and tied them all to the baptism of Jesus—which was the inaugural event commencing his ministry.[226] Pontius Pilate governed the province of Judea (southern Palestine) during the years AD 26 to 36; Herod Antipas governed Galilee from 4 BC to AD 39; Philip governed Ituraea from 4 BC until AD 34; and the years of Lysanias' tetrarchy are not known.

Annas was the high priest from AD 6 to 15, when he was deposed by the Roman procurator. Between AD 15 and 18, three different high priests were installed and removed by the Romans. Then, in AD 18, Caiaphas (who was also Annas' son-in-law) was appointed chief priest. Caiaphas apparently had the political adroitness to keep a working relationship with the Romans while not unduly aggravating the Jews, as he kept his office from AD 18 until AD 36, longer than any other high priest of the period. Luke's expression "the high priesthood of Annas *and* Caiaphas" reveals that Annas exerted considerable influence behind the scenes and may have been the real power behind Caiaphas.[227]

---

[226] Precisely speaking, Luke 3:1-3 dates the beginning of John the Baptist's ministry. However, it's most credible to accept that the ministry of Jesus began nearly concurrently with the Baptist's, because John's entire purpose was to herald the coming of Jesus (Lk 3:4-6) through baptism (Lk 3:21). Unlike most public figures, John had no intention of creating a personal following; rather, his singular goal was to introduce Jesus to the world. Furthermore, Luke's extreme precision in these verses only makes sense if Luke's purpose was to document the beginning of Jesus' ministry here—the Baptist was an important but very minor personage in comparison. Even so, John was quite successful in his purpose—everyone knew that John had identified Jesus as the Messiah (Lk 20:4,5).

[227] This is implied when Jesus was put on trial by Annas before he was tried by Caiaphas. "So Annas sent Him bound to Caiaphas the high

Taking all of these dates together, we have a bracket for the start of Jesus' ministry between AD 26 and AD 34.

John's gospel mentions three Passovers,[228] and from this information, the length of Jesus' ministry was more than two years to less than three years.[229] Adjusting our bracket accordingly,[230] that would give us a range of AD 28 to 37 for his crucifixion; however, Pilate presided over Jesus' final trial, so the possible years for Jesus' crucifixion reduce to a range of AD 28 to 36.

Luke's record of the "fifteenth year of the reign of Tiberius Caesar" would seem to identify the exact year when John began his ministry, but there is controversy surrounding this identification—it all depends on the assumption of the start of Tiberius' reign. For now, assuming the widest possible range of dates for the start of Tiberius' reign (covered in more detail in Appendix E), we can calculate his fifteenth year to be somewhere within AD 27 to 30. This would reduce both limits of our range for the crucifixion to AD 29 to 33.

Fortunately, greater precision is possible. John writes of an exchange between Jesus and the Jews in Jerusalem at Jesus' first of three Passover visits during his ministry. This occurred near the beginning of his ministry years:

> The Jews then said, "It took *forty-six years* to build this temple, and will you raise it up in three days?" (Jn 2:20,

---

priest." (Jn 18:24)

[228] A few commentators believe that John 4:35 indicates a fourth Passover (*Benson's Commentary of the Old and New Testaments, Clarke's Commentary, and others*). My reasons for believing otherwise are given in Appendix E.

[229] Jesus died on the third Passover. From the first to third Passovers is two years. The only question is how long before the first Passover Jesus' ministry began (I'm presuming John did not omit any Passovers).

[230] To keep the bracket as wide as possible, we would add two years to the beginning and three years to the end of it.

emphasis added)

At the time of this statement, the second temple complex—begun by Herod I in 20/19 BC—was still under construction.[231] This verse fixes the start of Jesus' ministry to AD 27/28,[232] and therefore, his third Passover and crucifixion to AD 30.

There are other corroborations for the year AD 30 as the year of Jesus' resurrection, and they, along with possible objections to this date, are covered in Appendix E for the interested reader.

In conclusion, Jesus died about 3:00 p.m. on Wednesday, Nisan 14, AD 30.

He rose from the dead during the night, Saturday-to-Sunday, in the first half of Nisan 18, AD 30.

The women arrived at the tomb as dawn broke on the morning of Nisan 18, and first learned of the news that would shake the world.

---

[231] Jack Finegan, *Handbook of Biblical Chronology* (Peabody: Hendricksen Publishers, 1998), 347, §592.

[232] The math is (-20)+46+1=27. The increment by one is necessary because there is no "zero" year; that is, 1 BC is followed by AD 1.

Writers

There are two schools of thought in the field of biblical studies in higher education. The first school of thought views the Scriptures as inspired by God. The second, and larger "higher criticism"[233] school, is comprised of professors who generally conduct their work from three foundational beliefs: 1) God and the supernatural do not exist, 2) the texts were not written by the traditionally ascribed authors or in the traditionally presumed time periods, and 3) the intentions of the original authors, whoever they were, were consistently to promote some political/theological/sexist/misogynistic/racist/oppressive agenda—take your pick.

This author rejects the entire set of foundational beliefs of so-called "modern scholarship" of higher criticism. There are plenty of reasons for doing so; however, that discussion is outside the purpose of this book.

Even so, it is relevant concerning the authorship of the four gospels and the book of 1st Corinthians. The reader should know that there was unanimity among early Christian writers that the gospels were written by their eponymous authors and that the letters to the Corinthians were written by Paul.

Matthew

Matthew, author of the first gospel, was one of the twelve disciples and also known by the name of Levi. He was a tax collector before being called to follow Jesus. As would be

---

[233] Dictionary definition of higher criticism: the study of biblical writings to determine their literary history and the purpose and meaning of the authors. In practice and truth, "higher criticism" amounts to unalloyed hypercriticism in the robe of scholarship. It is similar to deconstructionism applied to other literary texts. There is nothing "higher" about it.

expected from someone of that background, he was precise in his narrative and often recorded numerous details that others omitted.

On the night Jesus was arrested just outside the wall of Jerusalem, all the disciples fled towards Bethany (except Judas, of course, who was among the arresting party that returned to the city). Peter and John subsequently had a change of mind, reversed course, and followed, at a distance, the arresting party back to the city. The rest of them undoubtedly continued on to Lazarus' home in Bethany, where they had been staying for several nights during the previous week. It was their only option. Matthew was with this group of nine disciples.

All the disciples were deeply afraid of the Jewish authorities and their Roman allies. They knew it was the intent of the arresting party (a large group)[234] to arrest them too, a terrifying prospect. Jesus ran interference by supernaturally dropping them where they stood, then informing the prostrate mob that they could arrest him, but not his followers.[235]

Given their understandably fearful state of mind, the nine disciples in Bethany likely remained there, as news of Jesus, Peter, and John slowly trickled out of Jerusalem. Although important news traveled on well-oiled grapevines, it went by foot. And on Sabbaths, travelers and news could not even reach Bethany, as Bethany was beyond the "Sabbath day's journey" travel restriction of 2,000 cubits (or 1,000 yards) proscribed by Jewish law. Since there were two Sabbaths between Jesus' death and resurrection, much of that period was a news blackout to the

---

[234] The Greek word indicates a Roman *cohort*. The size of a cohort was variable, but could have been as large as 600 or more in this case. Many commentaries opine that it was smaller. In any event, the cohort was very large relative to the number of disciples. These soldiers likely came from the Antonia Fortress adjacent to the temple.

[235] So when He said to them, "I am He," they drew back and fell to the ground. Therefore He again asked them, "Whom do you seek?" And they said, "Jesus the Nazarene." Jesus answered, "I told you that I am He; so if you seek Me, let these go their way." (Jn 18:6-8)

Bethany group. The lack of information would have magnified their fears.

Sometime during Sunday, after reports of Jesus' resurrection reached the nine disciples—and despite their disbelief in what they heard—with great trepidation, eight of the disciples, including Matthew, made their way to the upper room to meet with Peter and John. This was where Matthew first encountered the resurrected Christ, and from this time until the ascension, Matthew was an eyewitness to all that he wrote. But where did Matthew obtain his knowledge of events in Jerusalem during the time he was cloistered in Bethany?

Naturally, Matthew would have been a sponge for information from all the other disciples and followers, and especially the women, who were proclaiming the most extraordinary news. Mary Magdalene and Mary Clopas (the "other Mary") were eyewitnesses together to the crucifixion, the burial, and the empty tomb; they separately encountered angels that were inside the tomb.[236] Matthew features both of these women prominently in his account, so one or both were undoubtedly his source(s) for the events of Sunday morning.

Noticeably, Matthew contains several related details that are exclusive to his account. The first is the visit of the chief priests and Pharisees to Pilate on the Passover Sabbath (a violation of their own religious laws), to petition the governor for a guard to be stationed at the tomb. The second is the moment of the resurrection, when the earthquake occurred, the angel rolled the stone away, and the soldiers "became like dead men." The third is the meeting of the soldiers Sunday morning with the chief priests and elders, where the soldiers reported what they had seen, and the Jewish leaders offered a bribe to spread a false report that "His disciples came by night and stole Him away." Matthew appears to be addressing and contravening this rumor, which was being spread "to this day," the day of his writing.

Matthew's knowledge about the soldiers' experiences could

---

[236] This latter fact is not obvious from Matthew's account alone but becomes apparent when the four accounts are compared closely.

not have come from his Galilean compatriots. It must have come from either one of the soldiers in the guard detail, or a chief priest, or a Sanhedrin member (either Pharisee or Sadducee).

It appears more likely to have come from a soldier who was either sympathetic to Jesus or who became a follower in the early days of the Jerusalem church. Why?

Caiaphas, the official high priest, was the primary antagonist to Jesus and very politically astute. In connection with the soldiers, he would have only enlisted the assistance of a handful of Sanhedrin members who were closely allied with him in outlook and sentiment. Thus, it's unlikely the leaked information concerning the bribe and false rumor would have originated from the priests; indeed, they had much to lose were it to become public knowledge.

Also, Matthew reports that the stone was sealed by the priests and the Roman guard. The testimony of a priest likely would have omitted mention of the (detested) Roman soldiers' seal and only recognized the application of their authority (their seal) to the tomb. Lastly, when the guard recounted the graveside happenings to the priests, they would have omitted the information that "they shook for fear of him [that is, the angel]," as this would have reflected on them poorly, and the priests would therefore have never known that detail. What the soldiers experienced, as written in Matthew 28:2-3, sounds like the firsthand testimony of an eyewitness, not something secondhand from the recollection of a Jewish leader who wasn't there.

The Roman soldiers knew what they had seen, and it surely was the most extraordinary and memorable event of their entire lives. Even so, the significance of that moment must have remained an unanswered, burning question in their minds. For that reason, it's not hard to imagine that sometime afterwards, upon hearing of the resurrection of the man whose tomb they'd been guarding, one or more of the soldiers at the tomb would have understood the existential magnitude of the connection and joined the ranks of the believers. This may have been the source through which the testimony of the resurrection moment became known to Matthew. And, as a former tax collector, Matthew may have retained some connections among the Romans.

Mark

Mark, also known as John Mark, was the writer of the shortest gospel account of the life of Jesus. He was not one of the twelve apostles but was an early follower of Jesus. Mark may have been a teenager at the time of these events, living at his parents' home.

Mark was from Levitical lineage, and his family had some means. His uncle (or perhaps, cousin)[237] was Barnabas, a Levite who was a notable leader in the early church and who later took Mark under his tutelage for missionary work.

Mark's family owned a house in Jerusalem, which provided a meeting place for Jesus' disciples.[238] By longstanding tradition, this house was in the Essene Quarter, in the southwest part of the city, an area of relative wealth—but not the extreme wealth of the Upper City. Still, the household had the means to employ a servant girl named Rhoda and the size to host a prayer vigil when Peter was incarcerated some years later.[239]

So where did Mark obtain his knowledge to write his gospel? Certainly, he might have been able to provide his own testimony to a few small details. But he would have had little possible first-hand knowledge of anything prior to the Last Supper or insight

---

[237] In Colossians, (4:10, NASB), Paul relays the greetings of "Barnabas's cousin (Greek: *anepsios*) Mark." Older English translations render this Greek word as "sister's son," making Mark the nephew; newer translations render it "cousin." It may be that *anepsios* could mean either, just as the Dutch word *neef* does today.

[238] Its identification as the location of the upper room is made in the section "Important Locations."

[239] And when he realized this, he went to the house of Mary, the mother of John who was also called Mark, where many were gathered together and were praying. When he knocked at the door of the gate, a servant-girl named Rhoda came to answer. (Acts 12:12-13)

into what happened during Jesus' final week in Jerusalem.[240]

Fortunately, the early church historian Eusebius tells us that Mark served as the voice for Peter's memoir.[241] The gospel of Mark might thus be regarded as the gospel according to Peter. One internal indication that Peter was the principal source is Mark's record of a detail in the angel's instructions to the women that is recorded nowhere else: "Tell the disciples *and Peter.*" It is a poignant detail that carried tremendous importance for Peter. Furthermore, there are other scenes in Mark's gospel that omit a few of the more embarrassing moments for Peter, while others highlight his leadership, when compared to other gospel accounts.[242] All of these testify to Peter's input.

In preparation for the Last Supper, Jesus had directed Peter and John to enter Jerusalem, where they would meet a man carrying a pitcher of water. They were to follow him to a house

---

[240] It's possible, too, that Barnabas, if he became a follower during Jesus' time of ministry, could have provided some information. But that is speculative, and in any case the information would have been limited.

[241] From The Church History of Eusebius, III:39 (quoting Papias): This also the presbyter said: "Mark, having become the interpreter of Peter, wrote down accurately, though not in order, whatsoever he remembered of the things said or done by Christ. For he neither heard the Lord nor followed him, but afterward, as I said, he followed Peter, who adapted his teaching to the needs of his hearers, but with no intention of giving a connected account of the Lord's discourses, so that Mark committed no error while he thus wrote some things as he remembered them. For he was careful of one thing, not to omit any of the things which he had heard, and not to state any of them falsely." These things are related by Papias concerning Mark.

[242] An example of the former: Peter, after saying they had left everything to follow Jesus, added "What then will there be in it for us?" as reported in Mt 19:27 but not Mk 10:28. An example of the latter: Peter said to Jesus, "Rabbi, look, the fig tree which You cursed has withered," in Mark 11:21, the only record.

where a "large upper room" was ready (Lk 22:7-13). From these instructions, it's apparent that Peter and John did not know the place or the people there. Therefore, this was conceivably the first time that Peter met Mark.

In the aftermath of Peter's denial, Peter left the home of the high priest and sought solitude in the upper room (as described in Peter's entry in the section "A Closer Look at the Characters," in Part Three of this book). In the ensuing days, Mark may have served as the courier for information between Peter's and John's locations. This stressful period must have forged a deep bond between Mark and Peter.

This helps explain why, fourteen years later, Peter initially fled to Mark's house upon release from prison; Peter knew it as a sanctuary. And although Mark began his involvement in the fledgling church under the wing of his relative Barnabas and ministered with Paul, it was Peter who served as Mark's primary mentor. Not only was Mark entrusted with writing Peter's memoir—the gospel of Mark—but Peter even referred to Mark as "my son" in one of his letters.[243]

Luke

Luke is an early Christian of the first century who wrote the gospel with his name and the book of Acts—comprising together more than a quarter of the entire New Testament text—yet little is known about his personal life. He is generally thought to have been a Greek who wrote his gospel with a Gentile audience in mind. He had a medical background (Paul referred to him as the "beloved physician"[244]) and he traveled with Paul in his missionary journeys: Three sections of Acts are written in the first person plural. His proficiency of Koine Greek in his writings reveals that he was a well-educated man.

But most relevant to this book is that Luke, although involved

---

[243] She who is in Babylon, chosen together with you, sends you greetings, and so does my son, Mark. (1 Pe 5:13)

[244] Luke, the beloved physician, sends you his greetings, and also Demas. (Col 4:14)

closely with Paul and the early church, was not an eyewitness to the life and resurrection of Jesus, which he expresses in the opening lines to his gospel. So where did Luke obtain his information? Who were his sources?

Luke was a historian of the first order, and his gospel shows careful attention to historical accuracy. As Luke put it:

> Inasmuch as many have undertaken to compile an account of the things accomplished among us, just as they were handed down to us by those who from the beginning were eyewitnesses and servants of the word, it seemed fitting for me as well, having investigated everything carefully from the beginning, to write it out for you in consecutive order, most excellent Theophilus; so that you may know the exact truth about the things you have been taught. (Lk 1:1-4)

So Luke interviewed eyewitnesses to the events he described and compiled a careful chronological account. Luke's account of the events surrounding Jesus' resurrection has certain details and incidences that are unique among the four gospels, and these unique items suggest at least two of his sources.

The first source is Joanna, a woman mentioned only by Luke and in only two verses. She was the wife of Chuza, the steward of Herod Antipas, ruler of Galilee.[245] Joanna is the likely source for Luke's exclusive report of Jesus' interrogation before Herod, as she was uniquely positioned to possess that knowledge: she was probably an eyewitness.[246] Luke also records that Joanna was

---

[245] ...and Joanna the wife of Chuza, Herod's steward, and Susanna, and many others who were contributing to their support out of their private means. (Lk 8:3)

[246] During Herod's time in Jerusalem for Passover, a week-long celebration of Jews from all over the empire, and the major social and political event of the year, steward Chuza's services would have been in particular demand by the tetrarch, and it can be presumed that Joanna would have had complementary responsibilities as well.

one of the women at the tomb Sunday morning.[247] The context of the latter mention suggests that she may possibly have been at the cross, at the tomb when Jesus was interred, and among the women who prepared the spices; at the very least, she was in close communication with the women who were.

The second source is Clopas (or Cleopas), Luke's obvious connection to the conversation Jesus had with the two men traveling to Emmaus on Sunday (Lk 24:13-33) and Jesus' Sunday evening appearance. Some scholars have conjectured that Luke was Clopas' traveling companion, but Luke's opening in his first chapter seems to preclude that possibility.

John

John, author of the fourth gospel, was one of the closest of Jesus' disciples; he sometimes refers to himself in the third person as the "beloved disciple."[248] His gospel stands out among the four in several respects. First, the majority of his gospel concerns itself with events of Jesus' final week and Jesus' appearance in Galilee after his resurrection. Secondly, John describes in unmatched detail the intimacy of Jesus' actions and words to his disciples during the Last Supper, thus providing his readers with a window into the heart and purposes of Jesus as no other account does.

John's record of the resurrection is narrowly his own experience, with a focus on his interaction with Mary Magdalene and his run to the tomb with Peter. He omits the experiences of the other women who had been with Mary as well as the appearance of Jesus on Sunday to Peter (individually) and to the two men traveling to Emmaus.

John was the only one of the Twelve at the cross; the only one to witness and report Jesus' side being pierced; the one who took Mary the mother of Jesus into his care and lodging in

---

[247] Now they were Mary Magdalene and Joanna and Mary the mother of James; also the other women with them were telling these things to the apostles. (Lk 24:10)

[248] Jn 21:20

Jerusalem; and the one who overheard and reported on Jesus' repeated injunctions to Peter to "tend my sheep."

Paul

Paul, the former Pharisee and persecutor of the church, who was converted to a Jesus follower after his famous Damascus Road experience, wrote only six verses that are germane to our study of the resurrection, in 1st Corinthians 15:3-8. These verses provide us with a chronological listing of six post-resurrection appearances of Jesus. In this listing, Paul confirms the private appearance to Peter mentioned in Luke 24:34. He also gives us the only mention of Jesus' appearance to his brother James bar Joseph.

Additionally, Paul provides the only mention of Jesus' appearance in Galilee to a group of "more than 500 brothers"—a group far larger than that of the other recorded appearances. Paul's record of this event explains why the disciples were commanded by the angels and Jesus to travel from Jerusalem back to Galilee. Jesus was strengthening the faith of those he had ministered among for three years. This would have supercharged the nascent church in the region of his greatest support.

A Closer Look at the Characters

Let's take a more comprehensive look at some of the people surrounding the resurrection and the details we know about them.

1. Jesus was the son of Mary and (ostensibly) Joseph, and was raised in Nazareth of Galilee. His father Joseph was deceased by the time of Jesus' death.[249] Jesus had several sisters and brothers,[250] one of whom was named James bar Joseph—not to be confused with disciples James Zebedee (brother of John) or James the Younger.

Jesus' siblings did not believe in him (insofar as his Messianic claims) during his time of ministry,[251] but they did become followers after the resurrection;[252] this change among his siblings is itself a testimony to the historicity of the resurrection.

2. Mother Mary was the mother of Jesus. As stated before, she is identified herein as "Mother Mary" simply to avoid using the longer phrase "Mary, the mother of Jesus." Since there are two other Marys connected with accounts of the resurrection, we need to differentiate among them.[253] At the time of the

---

[249] While on the cross, Jesus said to his disciple John (concerning his mother Mary, who was also present), "Behold your Mother"—thus committing Mary into John's care for protection and support. He would not have said this had Joseph still been alive.

[250] James, Joseph, Judas, and Simon were Jesus' half-brothers, and he also had (unnamed) half-sisters (Mt 13:55-56).

[251] For not even His brothers were believing in Him. (Jn 7:5)

[252] These all with one mind were continually devoting themselves to prayer, along with the women, and Mary the mother of Jesus, and with His brothers. (Acts 1:14)

[253] It is interesting that about 29% of women in first century Palestine were named Mary or Salome. Mary was the most common. This comes from Tal Ilan's *Lexicon of Jewish Names in Late Antiquity: Part I:*

crucifixion and resurrection, she was a widow, around 50 years of age. Jesus was not only her firstborn but also her caretaker. While Jesus was on the cross, he entrusted that responsibility to his cousin and disciple John.

In the gospel accounts, Mother Mary appears near the cross during Jesus' crucifixion and again, fifty-three days later, on the day of Pentecost in the upper room.[254] Despite not being otherwise mentioned in connection with the resurrection, she must have been completely aware of the swirling reports (and rumors), since she was staying with her nephew (disciple John) and his family after Jesus' death.

Given her state of mourning, she must have remained sequestered at the Zebedee home; there is no indication that she joined any of the other women during their movements around the city.

Nevertheless, she undoubtedly saw Jesus when he appeared to groups larger than the eleven disciples. Later, after Jesus' ascension, she was present in the upper room on the day of Pentecost. The extremities of emotions she had to feel during these events cannot be overstated.

3. Clopas was a close relative and follower of Jesus. He was an uncle to Jesus, since he was the brother of Jesus' father Joseph.[255] He is noteworthy in the resurrection accounts

---

Palestine 330 BCE-200 CE. The data comes from multiple sources, but the majority is from ossuary inscriptions.

[254] The Jewish feast of Shavuot (Pentecost) took place on Sivan 6, fifty days after Nisan 15 (counted inclusively). If counted non-inclusively, as we do today, it would also be fifty days from Nisan 14, the day of the crucifixion. Most churches celebrate Pentecost on the seventh Sunday after Easter Sunday, which differs from the Jewish reckoning.

[255] From The Church History of Eusebius, Book III Chapter XI:
After the martyrdom of James [the brother of Jesus] and the conquest of Jerusalem which immediately followed, it is said that those of the apostles and disciples of the Lord that were still living came together from all directions with those that were related to the Lord according to the flesh (for the majority of them also were still alive) to take

because he and an unnamed fellow traveler met the risen Jesus on their way to Emmaus, a village 7 miles to the west of Jerusalem.[256] Before these two travelers, only the women at the tomb and Peter had seen the risen Jesus.

The name Clopas is the same as Cleopas in the New Testament, as these are simply transliteration variants, the former being an Aramaic name and the latter being the closest Greek equivalent to it.[257]

Clopas was married to Mary (of) Clopas, one of the women who journeyed to Jesus' tomb on Sunday morning after the resurrection. In addition to being related to Jesus, this couple must have been intimate followers of his mission, since they were among a very small number of people outside of "the Twelve" (only ten, actually) who were especially honored to see Jesus on that first day of his resurrection appearances.

Clopas and his wife Mary had children: James the Younger, Joses, and Salome (Mk 15:40). James the Younger can be reasonably identified as the same person as "James of Alphaeus," the disciple listed ninth in all four listings of the Twelve. This identification is controversial and will be examined more closely in the section on Relationships; even so, if this identification was not presumed, it would have no effect on Part Two and little effect on Part One of this book.

4. *Mary Clopas* was a relative and follower of Jesus. She was

---

counsel as to who was worthy to succeed James.

They all with one consent pronounced Symeon, the son of Clopas, of whom the gospel also makes mention; to be worthy of the episcopal throne of that parish. He was a cousin, as they say, of the Saviour. For Hegesippus records that *Clopas was a brother of Joseph.* (Hegesippus, here quoted, was a second century historian.)

[256] And behold, two of them were going that very day to a village named Emmaus, which was about seven miles from Jerusalem.

One of them, named Cleopas, answered and said to Him, "Are You the only one visiting Jerusalem and unaware of the things which have happened here in these days?" (Lk 24:13,18)

[257] Wenham, *Easter Enigma*, 144, Note 11.

wife to Clopas,[258] and thus an aunt (by marriage) to Jesus. She was also the mother of the disciple James the Younger.[259] She met the risen Jesus separately from (and earlier than) her husband that first resurrection Sunday. In Matthew's gospel, she is twice referred to as "the other Mary,"[260] and she was present at the cross, the burial, and the resurrection of Jesus.

Mary Clopas, despite being a generation older, obviously had a very close friendship with Mary Magdalene.[261] All four gospels mention the two women together[262] during the period between the crucifixion and resurrection. We can therefore presume they were inseparable during this time, only separating when Mary Magdalene first ran alone to report that the body of Jesus had been stolen (as John's gospel informs us), leaving Mary Clopas and the other women to first encounter the angelic messengers.

5. *Salome* was the wife of Zebedee and mother to disciples James and John. She was also sister to Mother Mary, and thus an aunt to Jesus. She was at the cross when Jesus died and at the tomb on the morning of the resurrection. Because she was

---

[258] But standing by the cross of Jesus were His mother, and His mother's sister, Mary the wife of Clopas, and Mary Magdalene. (Jn 19:25)

[259] There were also women looking on from a distance, among whom were Mary Magdalene, and Mary the mother of James the younger and of Joses, and Salome. (Mk 15:40 ESV)

[260] And Mary Magdalene was there, and the other Mary, sitting opposite the grave. (Mt 27:61)

Now after the Sabbath, as it began to dawn toward the first day of the week, Mary Magdalene and the other Mary came to look at the grave. (Mt 28:1)

[261] There are several clues to the generational difference. Mary Clopas was married and had adult children; Mary Magdalene was single, as were her siblings. Mary Magdalene "ran quickly" to report to the disciples, and Mary Clopas, her constant companion, did not follow— probably because she was at an age and stage of life where "running quickly" wasn't an option.

[262] Mt 27:56, 61; Mt 28:1; Mk 15:40, 47; 16:1; Lk 24:10; Jn 19:25

Mother Mary's sister and because her son John had been entrusted with Mother Mary's care, Salome would have accompanied Mary and John from the crucifixion site to her own home in Jerusalem after Jesus' death rather than joining Mary Clopas and Mary Magdalene in following the burial party to the tomb.

In the days immediately following the crucifixion, Salome was surely Mother Mary's primary comforter, as she was the closest family member of similar age. Salome also participated with the other women in buying and preparing spices, and joined them in their Sunday morning mission to anoint Jesus' body. It must have been difficult for her to leave Mother Mary's side to attend to these tasks, but it speaks to her love for her sister and crucified nephew, as well as to her own courage.

6. *Zebedee,* the husband of Salome and father of disciples James and John, owned a profitable fishing business in Capernaum on the northern edge of the Sea of Galilee.[263] He is not mentioned after the calling of his sons to follow Jesus, but he was probably still in the fishing business at the time of the resurrection, considering that he was the most likely source of the boat and fishing tackle utilized by seven disciples to go fishing not long afterwards.[264] By that time, the four disciples who previously had been together in the fishing business (James, John, Peter, and Andrew) were three years out of that line of work and without boats or nets.

This night-long fishing excursion took place sometime during the approximately month-long period in Galilee, in-between the resurrection and ascension events in Judea.

---

[263] Immediately He [Jesus] called them [James and John]; and they left their father Zebedee in the boat with the hired servants, and went away to follow Him. (Mk 1:20, brackets added)

[264] Simon Peter, and Thomas called Didymus, and Nathanael of Cana in Galilee, and the sons of Zebedee, and two others of His disciples were together. Simon Peter said to them, "I am going fishing." They said to him, "We will also come with you." They went out and got into the boat; and that night they caught nothing. (Jn 21:2-3)

The end product of Zebedee's business—dry, salted fish—was in high demand in Jerusalem, especially during the annual feast days. For business purposes and because they could afford it, the Zebedees likely owned a second home in Jerusalem. This house must have been of some size to have accommodated the Zebedees and assorted relatives at the annual feasts; it was probably the lodging place for Jesus and his disciples when they had visited Jerusalem in previous years—particularly because Jesus and the Zebedee family were closely related.

7. *James bar Joseph* was Jesus' brother, and probably the oldest of his younger brothers, as he is listed first among them in Matthew 13:55 and Mark 6:3. James quickly became a prominent leader in the early church in Jerusalem, where he was recognized as an apostle[265] and known as "James the Just." Jesus made a special post-resurrection appearance to him alone, after the appearance to "more than 500" disciples in Galilee.[266] Surely, this meeting was sufficiently stunning to transform James' assessment of his brother from itinerant preacher to the very Son of God!

Years after these events, James composed the New Testament's book of James. He was martyred in Jerusalem, as described by the historian Eusebius. The Jewish historian Josephus confirmed James' martyrdom and noted that the person responsible for his death was the high priest Hanan ben Hanan (otherwise known as Annas ben Annas), that is, the son of the infamous Annas who first interrogated Jesus after his arrest (Jn 18:13ff). Thus, the perpetrator for James' death was brother-in-law to the infamous Caiaphas, the leading conspirator of Jesus' death.

---

[265] [Paul's account of his first exposure to church leaders] Then three years later I went up to Jerusalem to become acquainted with Cephas, and stayed with him fifteen days. But I did not see any other of the apostles except James, the Lord's brother. (Gal 1:18-19, brackets added)

[266] then He appeared to James [the brother of Jesus], then to all the apostles. (1 Cor 15:7, brackets added)

8. *John* was the only one of the twelve disciples present at Jesus' death. Although he and Peter had followed Jesus back into Jerusalem subsequent to his arrest, only John continued to the cross and witnessed the crucifixion. Following Jesus' death, John took Mother Mary into his household (initially, his father's house) in Jerusalem.[267] Historians assume that this house, the house of Zebedee, was located at the present-day site of the Church of the Dormitian in Jerusalem.

Previously, John had been traveling with Jesus for about 3 years and was consequently a man "without fixed address." His natural inclination after the crucifixion would have been to seek family in Jerusalem for his (and Mother Mary's) lodging. Another reason for this is that John's mother Salome was Mary's sister.

Not far (about a 2 minute walk) from Zebedee's Jerusalem house is located the traditional site of Caiaphas's house. This relative proximity provides a ready explanation for how John could have been known to the high priest[268]—that is, Caiaphas lived in the same neighborhood as John's parents. Other explanations for this connection are: a possible familial connection to the priesthood or a business connection (such as supplying fish to the priests). Or, all three reasons could be true.

A connection between John and the priesthood was a real possibility. John's mother Salome and Jesus' mother Mary were sisters, and Mary's relative Elizabeth (mother of John the Baptist) was married to Zacharias, a priest. Thus, they all could

---

[267] Then He said to the disciple, "Behold, your mother!" From that hour the disciple took her into his own household. (Jn 19:27)

[268] Simon Peter was following Jesus, and so was another disciple. Now that disciple was known to the high priest, and entered with Jesus into the court of the high priest, but Peter was standing at the door outside. So the other disciple, *who was known to the high priest*, went out and spoke to the doorkeeper, and brought Peter in. (Jn 18:15-16, emphasis added)

There is a very long and solid tradition of identifying "the other disciple" as John.

have been of priestly station.

Among the disciples, John seemed to have had a bit more spiritual insight than the others. Not only did he stay with Jesus through the crucifixion, but he was the first one to recognize the resurrected Jesus on the beach in Galilee.[269] Nevertheless, John, along with his fellow ten disciples, was very slow to believe Jesus had indeed risen from the dead.[270]

9. *Peter* was the most prominent of the twelve disciples who, with John, witnessed the trial and condemnation of Jesus. Simon was his original name; "Peter" is the Aramaic name given to him by Jesus; "Cephas" is the Hebrew equivalent; and "a Rock" is the English equivalent. In the Scriptures he is referred to by all these names, plus the combined name "Simon Peter."

During Jesus' trial, Peter adamantly denied knowing him three times, a denial which left Peter emotionally devastated and broken.[271] At this point, a deeply depressed Peter must have left for quiet refuge somewhere other than the crowded Zebedee home in Jerusalem. The next we hear about Peter is on Sunday morning when he received the report from Mary Magdalene that (as she thought) the body of Jesus had been stolen.

Where was Peter in the interim? Given Peter's extreme depression and personal sense of failure, he wouldn't have joined the relatives of Jesus (that is, John, Zebedee, Salome, and Mary) at Zebedee's house. He had no money (Judas having been the group's treasurer—and a thief), and therefore he couldn't

---

[269] Therefore that disciple whom Jesus loved said to Peter, "It is the Lord." (Jn 21:7a)

[270] I have heard John 20:8 interpreted as stating that John was the first to believe in the resurrection: "So the other disciple [namely, John] who had first come to the tomb then also entered, and he saw and believed" (Jn 20:8), but this ignores the next verse: "For as yet they did not understand the Scripture, that He must rise again from the dead" (Jn 20:9).

So then, what did John believe? From the context, he believed Mary's report that the body had been stolen.

[271] And he went out and wept bitterly. (Lk 22:62)

have easily wandered back to Galilee, a five to six day tiring journey. Because of his shame, he wouldn't have joined the other disciples in Bethany, and he had limited connection to Jerusalem, except for Zebedee's home and the "large upper room" of Mark's house, where Jesus and his disciples had recently received hospitality.

I believe he returned to the upper room to seek sanctuary in an uncrowded space, to grieve in solitude, and to languish in depression. The traditional locations of the upper room and Zebedee's home are only about 100+ yards apart, and it's possible that Mark could have served as a go-between for messages between the locations.

The gospel of John provides support for the idea that Peter was lodging separately from John. After Peter and John received Mary Magdalene's first report and ran to the tomb to investigate, they "...went away again to their own homes" (Jn 20:10). Or so reads the NASB translation; about half of English translations render it as "home." The literal Greek is "to their own [i.e., places]." It is plural, and furthermore, the phrase does not distinguish between a permanent home and temporary lodging. Paul also provides support for separate lodgings, when he noted that Jesus appeared to Peter, but not to both of them (1 Co 15:5).

John and Peter were itinerant for the previous three years, and their lodgings in the city were temporary for the occasion of the feast. The Greek text would better be translated "to their own places" (or "residences" or "lodgings"). The most important point is that they were not staying at the same location, and a secondary point is that neither of them would have felt "at home," as they depended on the hospitality of others.

Also, because Mary Magdalene was able to locate Peter and John so quickly,[272] those lodgings must have been in close

---

[272] So she ran and came to Simon Peter and to the other disciple whom Jesus loved, and said to them, "They have taken away the Lord out of the tomb." (Jn 20:2a). Note that the phrasing implies that they were in different locations: "came to... and to..." rather than the simpler and

proximity. The leading candidate for Peter's lodging would be the large home of Mark's family, which was also the location of the upper room for the Last Supper and only a couple minutes' walk from the home of Zebedee. It was thus probably in the upper room, where Peter had denied Jesus, that the resurrected Jesus met Peter sometime after appearing to the women.

10. Thomas was one of the nine disciples who fled to Bethany when Jesus was arrested. He was also the last of the eleven disciples (Judas having defected) to believe that Jesus had risen from the dead. On resurrection Sunday, he apparently did not return with the other eight disciples from Bethany to Jerusalem, as he missed the first meeting of the eleven with the risen Jesus.[273]

Where Thomas resided over the next several days is unknown, but one week after the resurrection, Thomas was present with the disciples when Jesus appeared again to the group. Perhaps Thomas remained in Bethany over that week, but I rather think he would have returned to join the disciples in Jerusalem upon hearing the reports of Jesus' resurrection coming from his fellow disciples.

His refusal to believe may have been strengthened over the course of the week, simply because Jesus was not seen again over those intervening days.

However, I think there was an additional factor in his reluctance to believe the reports. Thomas appears to have considered more deeply than his companions the meaning of Jesus defeating death; he realized that for a man to possess power over death *in himself* meant more than messiahship; it meant divinity—that Jesus was truly God in the flesh.

That was a conclusion Thomas couldn't accept until he saw Jesus with his own eyes.[274] Thomas' declaration upon meeting

---

more natural construction: "came to Peter and John."

[273] But Thomas, one of the Twelve, called Didymus, was not with them when Jesus came. (Jn 20:24)

[274] So the other disciples were saying to him, "We have seen the Lord!" But he said to them, "Unless I see in His hands the imprint of the nails,

the risen Jesus ("my Lord and my God") attests to his understanding of the full weight of this event. He was the first recorded person to make such a declaration.

11. *Eight disciples (The Twelve without Judas, Peter, John, and Thomas):* These eight disciples, namely, Andrew, James bar Zebedee, Philip, Nathanael, Matthew, James the Younger, Thaddaeus, and Simon the Zealot, having fled to Bethany from the arresting party, remained there four days, until later in the day of the resurrection, when they returned to the upper room upon hearing reports from the women.

James bar Zebedee (the brother of John) and James the Younger had parents in the Zebedee's house during this period. Their mothers, Salome and Mary Clopas, respectively, are plausible candidates to have brought news reports to Bethany.

12. *Lazarus* lived in Bethany with his two sisters, Mary (Magdalene) and Martha. They were close to Jesus and his disciples, and had hosted them the week before the crucifixion. Although Lazarus is not mentioned in connection with the resurrection, his home would have been the natural place for the disciples to have fled for refuge from the Jewish authorities upon Jesus' arrest.

Lazarus himself was a recent target of the ruling Jews because people were believing in Jesus as a result of Lazarus having been raised from the dead.[275] And so, through the confusion and sparsity of news during the aftermath of Jesus' arrest, Lazarus must have felt a mixture of emotions: concern, grief, and fear, in conflict with a faith in God resulting from his own extraordinary miracle.

13. *Martha,* the sister of Lazarus, would have had the primary responsibility for hosting the disciples when in Bethany, as she was the owner of the home in which she and her sister Mary

---

and put my finger into the place of the nails, and put my hand into His side, I will not believe." (Jn 20:25)

[275] But the chief priests planned to put Lazarus to death also. (Jn 12:10)

lived.[276] (Lazarus is assumed to have lived there as well, although we only know that he also lived in Bethany.)[277] She is recognized as the more practical of the two sisters, and for that reason, is sometimes regarded as less spiritually attuned, but to her credit, she showed greater faith in Jesus after her brother Lazarus died than anyone else (Jn 11:20-27). Martha and her two siblings loved Jesus, and he loved them.[278]

14. Mary Magdalene was the first person to meet the risen Jesus and the first to carry that news to the disciples. As stated in Part One, she is the same person as Mary of Bethany, the sister to Martha and Lazarus. The three siblings lived in Bethany, about two miles east of Jerusalem, but Mary, by virtue of her surname, must have lived for a period in Magdala on the western coast of the Sea of Galilee.

The siblings had hosted Jesus and his party of disciples on more than one of his visits to Judea. During the week leading up to his death, they hosted Jesus and the disciples again for several nights, and Mary (for the second time) anointed Jesus with expensive perfume. Much more can be said about her, and will be, in the subsequent section.

15. Joanna was a woman of wealth and position, connected to the household of Herod Antipas, tetrarch of Galilee and Perea, by virtue of being married to Chuza, Herod's steward. (The office of steward involved live-in employment for managing domestic concerns, such as the supervision of servants, managing of finances, purchases of supplies, and keeping of accounts.) For most of the year, she lived in Galilee attached to Antipas' household, and in Galilee she was healed (either physically, or from evil spirits, or both) by Jesus and became a follower and supporter.[279]

---

[276] Now as they were traveling along, He entered a village; and a woman named Martha welcomed Him into her home. (Lk 10:38)

[277] Now a certain man was sick, Lazarus of Bethany, the village of Mary and her sister Martha. (Jn 11:1)

[278] Now Jesus loved Martha and her sister and Lazarus. (Jn 11:5)

[279] Soon afterwards, He [Jesus] began going around from one city and

During the major Jewish feasts, Herod's entire household, including Chuza and Joanna, relocated temporarily to the third largest building in Jerusalem (only overshadowed by the temple itself and Herod's palace, the latter used by Pontius Pilate during the feasts).

16. Susanna is a woman of means who followed Jesus in Galilee and supported him and his disciples out of her private resources. Like Joanna and Mary Magdalene, she had also been physically healed and/or delivered of demons by Jesus, and from Luke 8:1-3 we can conclude that these three shared a close relationship.

Susanna is not directly mentioned in relation to the events of the resurrection; however, Luke informs us that at least five women were present at the tomb that momentous Sunday morning (Mary Magdalene, Mary Clopas, Joanna, and "the other women [plural] with them"). Of course, there may have been more than five women, but there were at least five. From Mark, we know that one of the "other women" was Salome. It is fair to assume that Susanna was present because of the close connection she shared with Joanna. Luke's highlighting of these women by name indicates that they were among a small cadre of supporters who followed Jesus all the way from Galilee to the resurrection, and into the early church.

17. Joseph of Arimathea was the man who buried Jesus. Arimathea was a "city" (per Luke; today we would call it a town) in Judea a short distance north of Jerusalem.[280] Joseph was a wealthy man and a prominent member among the seventy-one

---

village to another, proclaiming and preaching the kingdom of God. The Twelve were with Him, and also some women who had been healed of evil spirits and sicknesses: Mary who was called Magdalene, from whom seven demons had gone out, and *Joanna the wife of Chuza*, Herod's steward, and Susanna, and many others who were contributing to their support out of their private means. (Lk 8:1-3, emphasis added)

[280] Arimathea has not been positively identified, but two locations that have been proposed are five or six miles north of Jerusalem.

ruling men of the High Sanhedrin—effectively the Supreme Court of the Jews. Matthew and John tell us that Joseph had become a disciple of Jesus, but John also notes that Joseph kept hidden his attachment to Jesus out of fear of the other Jewish leaders. Nevertheless, leading up to the crucifixion, Joseph had displayed at least passive support for Jesus because "he had not consented to their plan and action [against Jesus]."[281]

Joseph must have been a Pharisee, as he was "waiting for the kingdom of God," which means that he was hoping to see the Messiah redeem Israel. (Sadducees, in contrast, were the agnostics of their day, despite wearing the facade of religion.) Since Joseph followed Jesus, he must have considered Jesus to have been the Messiah; thus, Jesus' death brought him severe disappointment and grief. At risk to himself by exposing his loyalty to Jesus, Joseph "gathered up courage" and requested Jesus' body from Pilate, burying it in his own costly tomb cut into the bedrock just outside the walls of Jerusalem. Tombs of that time were usually sealed by stones cut square at one end and inserted into the tomb openings like a plug; the "very large," round golel stone of Joseph's tomb—rare but not unknown—speaks of his elite position in the city.

18. Nicodemus was another member of the High Sanhedrin. During Jesus' ministry, Nicodemus had arranged a meeting with Jesus at night to learn more about him. Although that meeting, as reported by John (Jn 3:1-21), appears to have left Nicodemus greatly perplexed, he obviously was impressed enough to stand up for Jesus on one occasion in the Sanhedrin.[282]

Nicodemus assisted Joseph of Arimathea in the interment of Jesus' body, providing about 100 Roman pounds (75 English pounds) of spices for that task, a testimony to Nicodemus' reverential regard of Jesus. The two men had to hurriedly

---

[281] (he [Joseph] had not consented to their plan and action) (Lk 23:51, brackets added)

[282] Nicodemus (he who came to Him before, being one of them) said to them, "Our Law does not judge a man unless it first hears from him and knows what he is doing, does it?" (Jn 7:50-51)

prepare the body for burial, a task made difficult by approaching nightfall when the Sabbath began and the heart-wrenching labor of working with a badly mutilated body.

19. *Mark,* also known as John Mark and the author of the gospel by his name, lived at the large house of the upper room with his mother, Mariam.[283] Mark has long been thought of as the "young man" who fled from the garden of Gethsemane as Jesus was being arrested, leaving his nightshirt behind.[284]

Although identifying Mark as the young man has been disputed, it is not unreasonable. First, we have other examples of New Testament authors downplaying themselves, for example: John refers to himself indirectly,[285] as does Paul,[286] and Luke may (although I think it unlikely) have been the "traveling companion" of Clopas in Luke 24:13ff. So, the fact that this young man is not named does not mean that he isn't the author.

However, a stronger substantiation is that the peculiar detail about the young man in the garden makes no sense at all unless it was written by the author Mark about himself. (No other writer mentions it.) Mark's gospel is otherwise very concise, yet this detail is completely superfluous, even discontinuous, to the story of Jesus' arrest. Why would Mark include it unless it was Mark noting his cameo part in the event? Mark would be

---

[283] And when he [Peter] realized this, he went to the house of Mary, the mother of John who was also called Mark, where many were gathered together and were praying. (Acts 12:12, brackets added)

Note that Mary is the anglicized version of the Greek *Mariam.*

[284] A young man was following Him, wearing nothing but a linen sheet over his naked body; and they seized him. But he pulled free of the linen sheet and escaped naked. (Mk 14:51-52)

[285] Peter, turning around, saw the disciple whom Jesus loved following them; the one who also had leaned back on His bosom at the supper and said, "Lord, who is the one who betrays You?" (Jn 21:20)

[286] I know a man in Christ who fourteen years ago--whether in the body I do not know, or out of the body I do not know, God knows--such a man was caught up to the third heaven. (2 Co 12:2)

strongly motivated for making this insertion into the material dictated to him by Peter, as this episode probably represents Mark's closest experience with the pre-resurrected Jesus. It would have meant tremendous credibility for Mark in the early church, even despite its limited gravity. Mark could forever after say, "I was there."

So, if Mark was indeed the "young man" mentioned in Mark 14:51, he probably was in his teens at the time and living with his parents. He would have been aware of, or even have witnessed, the Last Supper.

He may even have been the "man carrying a pitcher of water" who led Peter and John to the house to prepare the Passover. His presence in the garden can now be explained: He either followed Jesus and his disciples out to the garden of Gethsemane, or he ran to the garden with a warning if the arresting party had arrived at the upper room seeking Jesus before pursuing him across the Kidron valley to the garden.

In the years following, we know that Mark was close to Peter and has long been thought to have written his gospel from Peter's dictation while he was with Peter in Rome, as was explained in Mark's entry in the Writers section.

20. *Mariam* was the mother of Mark and matriarch of the house of the upper room. Her name in Hebrew, Mariam, would normally be anglicized to Mary, but with so many other Marys in the story (Mother Mary, Mary Clopas, Mary Magdalene) and because her role in the story is both minor and presumed, her name has been left closer to the Greek form to avoid additional confusion.

This Mariam appears in the New Testament in a single verse.[287] Her home was the place where Peter fled to, years later, when he was released from prison. Despite only one mention of her name, her hospitality and support for the disciples and early church in the face of persecution are noteworthy and laudable.

---

[287] Acts 12:12

Who Was Mary Magdalene?

Outside of Jesus, Mary Magdalene is the most prominent figure in the resurrection account. That makes her a very interesting individual, yet she is something of a mystery. She is interesting, first and foremost, because she was given the extreme honor of being the first human being to have seen the risen Jesus and to announce the jubilant news to the world. But she is also puzzling, because at first glance, the New Testament writers do not seem to say much about her.

She is barely mentioned prior to the crucifixion. Then she appears, and three of the four gospel writers state that she was at the cross when Jesus died. The fourth—Luke—strongly implies it as well. All four gospel accounts say that she was at the tomb at dawn on Sunday. Yet after giving her report to the disciples of having seen Jesus alive, we hear nothing more about her. Yet, to the early church, her name would have been as recognizable as that of Peter, James, and John because of her connection with the resurrection. Surely there must be more to her story.

Indeed, there is.

Luke provides us with the singular mention of Mary Magdalene prior to the cross, in the same passage where we first learn of Joanna and Susanna:

> Soon afterwards, He [Jesus] began going around from one city and village [within Galilee, from the context] to another, proclaiming and preaching the kingdom of God. The Twelve were with Him, and also some women who had been healed of evil spirits and sicknesses: Mary who was called Magdalene, from whom seven demons had gone out, and Joanna the wife of Chuza, Herod's steward, and Susanna, and many others who were contributing to their support out of their private means. (Lk 8:1-3, brackets added)

So, we learn from this passage that in Galilee Mary Magdalene encountered Jesus, who delivered her from seven demons (and perhaps sickness also), and that she began following Jesus and supporting his ministry and disciples. The phrase indicates that this "following" involved physically traveling with the band of disciples—"the Twelve were *with* Him, and *also* some women..."—surely providing some of the logistical support associated with such travels (such as arranging for meals and lodging) in addition to the financial support.

As previously mentioned, Mary (Greek: *Mariam*) was the most common name for a woman in first century Palestine, so it's no surprise that there are three different "Marys" clearly associated with the resurrection. Besides Mary Magdalene, there are five "Marys" mentioned in the New Testament. Is it possible to identify any of them with Mary Magdalene? Arguably so— "arguably" because the identifications I am about to make have been debated for some time. But I believe a strong case can be made for identifying Mary Magdalene as the same person as the "sinner woman" who anointed Jesus in Luke's account (Lk 7:36-50) as well as Mary of Bethany. Let's take a look at the arguments in favor of these two connections. First, we will examine whether Mary Magdalene could be the same person as the woman in Luke 7.

> Now one of the Pharisees was requesting Him to dine with him, and He entered the Pharisee's house and reclined at the table. And there was a woman in the city who was a sinner; and when she learned that He was reclining at the table in the Pharisee's house, she brought an alabaster vial of perfume, and standing behind Him at His feet, weeping, she began to wet His feet with her tears, and kept wiping them with the hair of her head, and kissing His feet and anointing them with the perfume. (Lk 7:36-38)

In that culture, hosting guests for a meal was a form of public entertainment for the neighbors, in which they would come into the house and sit or stand along the walls to listen and watch, but generally not to comment or participate.[288] Meals were taken at a low table, and diners would eat in a semi-reclined position while leaning on cushions, with legs and feet angled away from the table.[289] In the account above, Luke apprises us that the woman was a "sinner," and the Greek word denotes one who is conspicuously sinful—in this context, sexually promiscuous. Most likely, the woman was a prostitute, but her possession of an expensive alabaster vial of perfume could indicate that she was an escort for the upper class or from a family of some means, rather than a common prostitute.

One thing is certain about the woman. Not long before this episode, she had already been transformed by encountering Jesus. That much is apparent from the extraordinary and emotional response she gives to his simple presence there, as she:

a. wept loudly and profusely (the Greek word, *klaíō*, means wail or sob; in contrast with *dakrýō* for silent weeping)

b. stood as close behind him as she could get, such that her tears fell on his feet

c. having inadvertently wet his feet, attempted to dry them by letting down her hair—in the presence of men—a scandalous act in that culture.

On top of that, she then proceeded to anoint his feet from her vial of oil and repeatedly kissed them. This interaction with

---

[288] J. Vernon McGee, *Through the Bible* (Nashville, TN: Thomas Nelson, Inc., 1983), Vol. 4, 279.

Also, "Many came in and took their places on the side seats, uninvited and yet unchallenged. They spoke to those at table on business or the news of the day, and our host spoke freely to them" (Trench, describing a dinner at a Consul's house at Damietta, as cited in *Vincent's Word Studies*). See Marvin Vincent, *Word Studies in the New Testament* (1887), on Luke 7:37.

[289] Kaari Ward, ed., *Jesus and His Times* (Pleasantville, NY: Reader's Digest Association, Inc, 1988), p. 98.

someone else's guest was entirely inappropriate for anyone at that time. No doubt that everyone, except Jesus, was completely shocked by this spectacle. To the woman's credit, the outrageousness of her actions offers a resounding testimony of the work Jesus had already done in her heart.

In the remainder of the account (Lk 7:39-50), Jesus rebukes his host Simon, pointing out Simon's neglectful hosting of his guests, Simon's critical judgment of the woman's heart, and the greater love shown by this woman compared to Simon:

> Now when the Pharisee who had invited Him saw this, he said to himself, "If this man were a prophet He would know who and what sort of person this woman is who is touching Him, that she is a sinner." And Jesus answered him, "Simon, I have something to say to you." And he replied, "Say it, Teacher." ...Turning toward the woman, He said to Simon, "Do you see this woman? I entered your house; you gave Me no water for My feet, but she has wet My feet with her tears and wiped them with her hair. You gave Me no kiss; but she, since the time I came in, has not ceased to kiss My feet. You did not anoint My head with oil, but she anointed My feet with perfume. *Therefore, I tell you, her many sins have been forgiven—as her great love has shown. But whoever has been forgiven little loves little.*" Then He said to her, "Your sins have been forgiven." Those who were reclining at the table with Him began to say to themselves, "Who is this man who even forgives sins?" And He said to the woman, "Your faith has saved you; go in peace." (Lk 7:39-40, 44-50 NASB, *except NIV for verse 47, in italics*)

It's important to grasp the dynamics of these interactions. In that culture, it was customary hospitality for a host to provide three marks of respect for arriving guests: a kiss of greeting, oil for anointing one's head, and water for washing one's feet. Simon the Pharisee provided none of these for Jesus. So, it appears that Simon invited Jesus—the new celebrity in the region—for the purpose of gaining the "inside scoop" to later entertain his peers. Simon's neglect of ordinary hospitality towards Jesus was intentional—he surely would have shown greater deference if the guest was the Chief Priest! It seems that Simon was being disrespectful to make a statement that he considered himself superior to Jesus.

Now, the woman standing behind Jesus probably recognized these omissions and understood the insult. Overwhelmed with emotion, her intention was probably to counter Simon's disparagement and at least anoint Jesus on his head. As she stood there intending to do this and removing the alabastron from around her neck, her tears fell on his feet and started to create tracks in the fine road dust coating them. Impulsively, she kneeled and started to wipe them with her hair. Needing additional moisture, she used the anointing oil for the task. While kneeling, she kissed his feet. It was spontaneous and scandalous, but she didn't care.

Immediately following this text are the aforementioned verses of Luke 8:1-3, introducing us to Mary Magdalene, Joanna, and Susanna. In the original manuscript, there was no chapter break between the story of the unnamed woman who was anointing and wiping Jesus' feet and the introduction of Mary Magdalene. Therefore, there is no discontinuity necessarily implied between these passages, and a legitimate reading is to view chapter 7 as describing the transformation of Mary Magdalene as a follower of Jesus, who then joined his entourage in chapter 8. The position of her name as first in the list of the three women would also be expected if this were the case.

If Mary Magdalene was the "sinner" woman of Luke chapter 7, her name—"Magdalene", which means "from Magdala"—would certainly be fitting, as Magdala, a resort town on the west shore of the Sea of Galilee, was noted for wealth and corruption.[290]

---

[290] Alfred Edersheim, *The Life and Times of Jesus the Messiah* (Peabody, MA: Hendrickson Publ., 1993), 394.
Also, Gustaf Dalman, *Sacred Sites and Ways*, trans. Paul Levertoff (New York: Macmillan, 1935), 127.

For a prostitute, Magdala would have been a preferred location for such work. Other locations suggested for this event (Nain, Capernaum, Jerusalem) are less likely—the first two because of the small size and milieu of those towns, and the third because Galilee is the context for the story, and Jerusalem is not in Galilee.

Aside from these considerations, we can observe a similar personality in the woman of Luke 7 and Mary Magdalene in John 20. Consider the parallel reactions expressed in these two passages [my comments in brackets]:

Luke: ...when she learned [she went immediately] that He was reclining at the table in the Pharisee's house, she brought an alabaster vial of perfume, and standing behind Him at His feet, weeping [literally, sobbing, Gr. *klaíō*], she began to wet His feet with her tears, and kept wiping them with the hair of her head [an impetuous act], and kissing His feet and anointing them with the perfume...

John: ... Mary Magdalene came early to the tomb, while it was still dark [she went to the tomb at the very first opportunity, before the sun had even risen], and saw the stone already taken away from the tomb. So she ran [Gr. implies, ran as in a race; impetuously leaving the women she was with] and came to Simon Peter and to the other disciple ... [then ran back with the two disciples] ... Mary was standing outside the tomb weeping [literally, sobbing, Gr. *klaíō*]; and so, as she wept [Gr. *klaíō*], she ... saw two angels in white sitting, ... And they said to her, "Woman, why are you weeping [Gr. *klaíō*]?" She said to them, "Because they have taken away my Lord, and I do not know where they have laid Him." When she had said this, she turned around and saw Jesus standing... Jesus said to her, "Woman, why are you weeping? [Gr. *klaíō*; she is still sobbing.] Whom are you seeking?" Supposing Him to be the gardener, she said to Him, "Sir, if you have carried Him away, tell me where you have laid Him, and I will take Him away." [impetuous, and presumptuous for a non-family member] Jesus said to her, "Mary!" She turned and said to Him in Hebrew, "Rabboni!" [Aramaic, a term usually reserved for the president of the Sanhedrin, and meaning "My great master"][291] ... Jesus said to her, "Stop clinging to Me [she was, undoubtedly, grasping His feet], for I have not yet ascended to the Father..."

This reaction is not exhibited by the other women who met the risen Jesus; although they took hold of his feet, they worshipped[292] rather than sobbed. The two passages above are both describing a woman to whom Jesus meant everything and the opinions of others meant nothing—a woman of intense feeling who threw convention aside to be as close to him as possible, and who wept copiously at his feet in each case. It is easy to appreciate that these two descriptions *could* be of the same person, and we shall see shortly that we can also relate the story of Luke 7 to Mary of Bethany. She is the only other person in the Scriptures who comes close to displaying this devotion to Jesus.

Some biblical commentators object to the identification of the "sinner woman" with Mary Magdalene, pointing out that the condition of being a "sinner" is not synonymous with the condition of being oppressed by demons, as Mary Magdalene was before meeting Jesus (Lk 8:2). True, but both conditions can coexist for a single individual, and apparently this was the case for Mary Magdalene. We should not presume zero correlation between the two conditions as demons are

---

[291] Per *Vine's Expository Dictionary of New Testament Words*. John also adds an explanation not shown here—translating *Rabboni* into the Greek—"which means *didáskalos*," a reasonable but not wholly equivalent translation on John's part, rendered "Master" in some English translations, and with the even less equivalent "Teacher" in others. "Rabboni" is a term of extreme deference, for which neither the Greek nor the English have a truly equivalent word.

[292] And behold, Jesus met them and greeted them. And they came up and took hold of His feet and worshiped Him. (Mt 28:9)

promoters of sin and degradation, just like Satan himself.[293]

This does not imply that very sinful people are always demonized, nor the reverse; however, we should expect some correlation between demonization and sinful decline,[294] and there is no reason to believe that the two descriptions cannot be simultaneously true of a single individual. Also, demonic activity is not always accompanied by external bizarre behavior, as in the raving Gerasene demoniac.[295] It is noteworthy, even perhaps shocking, that Jesus cast demons out of religiously observant people in synagogues[296]—people who undoubtedly were no more conspicuous (as either sinners or demonized) than the general mass of humanity.

Another objection is that Luke's account does not directly identify the sinful woman. This should not be surprising. In numerous instances, the New Testament writers omitted the names of individuals where their identification could cause harm or shame. An example is John's account of the unidentified adulterous woman about to be stoned to death in John 8:3-11. Another example is that we learn Matthew was a tax collector (an occupation despised in that culture) only because Matthew tells us himself.[297] Mark, Luke, and John omit that information.

Furthermore, naming the woman would not have contributed to Luke's principal aim to the story, which was to describe the

---

[293] The thief comes only to steal and kill and destroy; I came that they may have life, and have it abundantly. (Jn 10:10)

[294] In fact, those who work in deliverance ministries report that this is common.

[295] When He got out of the boat, immediately a man from the tombs with an unclean spirit met Him ... Constantly, night and day, he was screaming among the tombs and in the mountains, and gashing himself with stones. (Mk 5:2, 5)

[296] And He went into their synagogues throughout all Galilee, preaching and casting out the demons. (Mk 1:39)

[297] Philip and Bartholomew; Thomas and Matthew the tax collector (Mt 10:3a)

interaction between Jesus and Simon the Pharisee, in which Jesus exposed the difference between superficial appearances and vital issues of the heart. Identifying the woman by name would not have added any relevant information for this purpose. Her specific actions, though, were highly noteworthy because they were so ill-mannered according to the etiquette of the time. And fortunately for the modern reader's benefit, it is precisely this extraordinary violation of decorum that provides us a connection to another story—and thus another name.

What is relevant for the purpose of identifying this woman is that the woman's behavior was so egregious that it would have made the "news headlines" of the day; it would have been discussed widely (and I expect that Simon the Pharisee made sure it was!). This aspect of the story provides us a link to another time and place.

Matthew, Mark, and John each record an account of a woman who anointed Jesus at a meal—but in Bethany. These three writers describe the same event, with nearly identical descriptions, but the event they describe is not the same as Luke's, which took place at an earlier point in Jesus' ministry in Galilee. Neither Matthew's (Mt 26:6-13) nor Mark's (Mk 14:3-9) account identify the woman or when this happened, but John informs us that the woman was Mary of Bethany and that this took place six days before Passover—just five days before Jesus was crucified. So we know that Luke's account was of a much earlier event. Here is the first part of John's account of the second anointing [my additions in brackets]:

> Jesus, therefore, six days before the Passover, came to Bethany where Lazarus was, whom Jesus had raised from the dead. So they made Him a supper there [Mt, Mk add: at the home of Simon the leper],[298] and Martha was serving;

---

[298] In Luke's account, the anointing also took place at the house of a Simon, but it was Simon the Pharisee from a city or town in Galilee. Simon was a very common name in the time of Jesus. No doubt Simon

but Lazarus was one of those reclining at the table with Him. Mary then took a pound of very costly perfume of pure nard, [Mt, Mk add: from an alabaster vial] and anointed the feet of Jesus and wiped His feet with her hair [Mt, Mk: and poured (the perfume) on His head]; and the house was filled with the fragrance of the perfume. (Jn 12:1-3)

What Mary of Bethany did was highly unusual, on par with the woman of Luke 7. First, Jesus was not a guest in Mary's home, but rather, a guest in Simon the leper's home—even though Lazarus, Martha, and Mary appear to have been assisting Simon in hosting the event. (Perhaps Simon had a larger dining room available, suitable for so famous a guest.) Without a doubt, Simon the leper—in contrast with Simon the Pharisee earlier— had already welcomed Jesus with a kiss and provided the other marks of hospitality: After all, how could one not properly honor a man who had both healed you of leprosy and raised a neighbor-friend from the dead? Therefore, what Mary did could easily have been received as an insult by Simon, as though she was trying to remedy a neglected courtesy by the host. Why *would* she have done this?

There are other aspects to Mary's actions that are even stranger. She anointed his feet (per John) and his head (per Matthew and Mark). These accounts are not in conflict; she simply did both. Oil or perfume was used to anoint a person's head, and water was used to wash a person's feet. But the normal application of these liquids would occur *before* a meal and usually by a servant. Why would Mary do this *during* a meal, and especially, if they had *already* been attended to by the host? Further, why would she have used perfume on his feet

---

the leper was a far more gracious host than Simon the Pharisee, for the leper must have been healed by Jesus for this event to have taken place. Leprosy was otherwise incurable at this time (except by divine miracle), and lepers were quarantined. Having thus been healed of leprosy, Simon in Bethany must have treated Jesus befittingly: like a king.

rather than water, as was customary? Further still, why would she have acted the part of foot-washing, when Jesus' feet were *already* clean?

Lastly, Mary of Bethany wiped Jesus' feet *with her hair*. To place this in context, for a married woman to have let down her hair in the presence of men would be grounds for divorce in the eyes of some rabbis.[299] It was an action that would have become the talk of the town. Could this really be the second time a woman had done this same outrageous thing?

There really is only one satisfactory explanation to this strange behavior on the part of Mary of Bethany, and that is to see that Mary of Bethany is the very same person as the unnamed woman in Luke's account of the "sinner woman," who likewise anointed Jesus' feet with perfume in Galilee. The second anointing in Bethany was a repetition of a shared memory between Jesus and Mary of what had transpired in Galilee, and it would have been understood as such by the disciples. By these actions, Mary asserted that she considered any opportunity to express her love to Jesus as being of greater value than the opinions of those who would reproach her for ignoring social etiquette. As in the earlier anointing, the other dinner guests may have thought it scandalous, but she didn't care.

It is interesting to note that Bethany and Magdala are not close in proximity. How did Mary of Bethany end up in Magdala and earn the name Magdalene? We can imagine a complete story: A young, impulsive woman who was bored with life in the small town of Bethany, and not interested in the circumscribed religious life of Jerusalem, chose to move to the beautiful and exciting seaside town of Magdala. Once there, she fell into an immoral lifestyle, perhaps beginning with promiscuity and

---

[299] Wenham, *Easter Enigma* (Wipf & Stock Publishers, 1992), 142, note 7.

The point is equally valid whether or not Mary of Bethany was married. Her marital status is not given by the biblical text, although it would be natural to assume that she was unmarried as she lived with her siblings.

leading to prostitution. Fortunately for her, Jesus traveled by and transformed her life from darkness and shame to peace and joy. Shortly after this transformation, she was drawn to the home of Simon the Pharisee to express her heartfelt thanks. But at Simon the Pharisee's house in Galilee, as recorded by Luke, she never completed the task she had started to do, which was to anoint his head.

And so, when Jesus arrived in Bethany sometime later, Mary saw the opportunity to complete the task she first had attempted to do in Galilee, which was to anoint Jesus' head with perfume oil—which she then does, according to Matthew and Mark. This, by itself, was unusual enough—she was not the host. But exceeding that, out of the memory of that shared moment with Jesus at the dinner in Galilee, she dropped to her knees and anointed his *feet* (!) with her long *hair* (!), thus re-enacting the earlier scene. It was an extraordinary way to say to the world, "Think what you will; I will not be ashamed to express my love to this man who set me free!" Jesus was clearly touched by this, as he declared, "Truly I say to you, wherever the gospel is preached in the whole world, what this woman has done will also be spoken of in memory of her."[300] And so it has.

The honor bestowed on Mary of Bethany goes beyond an eternal remembrance of her loving foot-wiping. When we see that Mary of Bethany, the redeemed sinner woman of Luke's story, is the same as Mary Magdalene, we appreciate that she was honored by God above all other women—even above all twelve disciples—by being the first person to meet the risen Jesus.

And so, after Mary had been healed and restored by Jesus in Galilee, she must have returned to her family (brother Lazarus and sister Martha) in Bethany, while still following Jesus as she was able and financially supporting his itinerant band.[301] As an aside, it is interesting to think of the close parallels of this event—where Mary returned from prostitution and ignominy to

---

[300] Mt 26:13; Mk 14:9
[301] Lk 8:1-3

be reunited with her family—to the story of the prodigal son.[302] Perhaps Mary's return to her family served as the template for Jesus' parable. Mary's feelings upon returning to her family would have paralleled those described for the prodigal son.[303] And, Martha's frustration with Mary as she prepared a meal[304] seems to imitate the older brother's reaction in Jesus' parable.

Does Mary of Bethany exhibit the same types of reactions and personality as Mary Magdalene (earlier identified with the sinner of Luke 7)? Indeed, she does. When Jesus was in town on another occasion, Mary of Bethany ignored the convention of catering to guests and simply sat at Jesus' feet, listening to him (to Martha's aforementioned dismay).[305] This is consistent with a woman who was deeply devoted to Jesus and disregarded customs. And when her brother Lazarus had died (Jn 11:1-44), Mary fell at Jesus' feet, weeping (sobbing, Gr. *klaíō*),[306] which is completely consistent with descriptions of Mary Magdalene and the unnamed woman in Luke 7. In contrast, John does not mention Martha as having wept or fallen at Jesus' feet on the same occasion.

Finally, and most convincingly, John firmly connects Mary of Bethany with the unnamed sinner of Luke 7. John wrote:

Now a certain man was sick, Lazarus of Bethany, the village

---

[302] Lk 15:11ff

[303] "And the son said to him, 'Father, I have sinned against heaven and in your sight; I am no longer worthy to be called your son.'" (Lk 15:21)

[304] But Martha was distracted with all her preparations; and she came up to Him and said, "Lord, do You not care that my sister has left me to do all the serving alone? Then tell her to help me." (Lk 10:40)

[305] She had a sister called Mary, who was seated at the Lord's feet, listening to His word. (Lk 10:39)

[306] Therefore, when Mary came where Jesus was, she saw Him, and fell at His feet, saying to Him, "Lord, if You had been here, my brother would not have died." When Jesus therefore saw her weeping, and the Jews who came with her also weeping, He was deeply moved in spirit and was troubled... (Jn 11:32-33)

of Mary and her sister Martha. *It was the Mary who anointed the Lord with ointment, and wiped His feet with her hair,* whose brother Lazarus was sick. (John 11:1-2, emphasis added*)*

In the first sentence above, John tells us that Mary and Martha were sisters living in Bethany. In the second sentence, he tells us that Lazarus was their brother, but most importantly here, he tells us unequivocally that Mary of Bethany is *"the"* Mary who had anointed Jesus with ointment and wiped his feet with her hair. There could be no other: John was certain that anyone reading his account would know specifically which Mary he was referring to and that there would be no possible confusion. This particular Mary was infamous for this event, precisely because it was so outlandish, and it would forever serve as her unique identifier. What her society considered shameful abounded to her glory among the followers of Jesus.

John was speaking, of course, of the *first* anointing event, the one in Galilee at Simon the Pharisee's house, by the woman whom Luke did not directly identify. So the identification of Luke's unnamed woman is, without question, Mary of Bethany. John describes the second anointing (in Bethany) in the *subsequent* chapter, so he could only be referring here to the earlier anointing that Luke described, and for which Mary was known throughout the community to which John was writing.

A number of biblical scholars and commentators have argued against making the connections regarding Mary Magdalene, Mary of Bethany, and the unnamed woman in Luke 7 as I have here. The disinclination to make these connections is understandable: Mary of Bethany and Mary Magdalene are beloved figures, the first remembered foremost for sitting at Jesus' feet and listening attentively, and the second for carrying a love-offering of embalming oils to Jesus' grave. It seems incongruous to merge those images with one of a person who had previously been a demonized prostitute. And yet, is that not the very essence of Christ's work: to set free the oppressed; to heal the sick rather than the healthy; to call the sinner rather than the righteous; and to give sight to the blind, not the seeing? Mary Magdalene's redemption is the most poignant scriptural example of Jesus "seeking and saving the lost."

One may still wonder why, if Mary Magdalene and Mary of Bethany are the same person, the gospel writers chose to identify the woman who first saw the resurrected Jesus as the former rather than the latter. There is a very pragmatic reason for why that might have been done. Recall that the Jewish leaders had no trouble resorting to an illegal kangaroo court and trumped-up charges to execute Jesus. Following Jesus' resurrection the same Jewish leaders persecuted his followers, who were performing miracles and proclaiming that he was still alive.[307] They even sought to kill all the apostles but decided instead to flog them without a trial or conviction—violating their own laws.[308]

The disciples also knew that in the week before Jesus was crucified, the Jewish leaders had been seeking to kill Mary's brother Lazarus, as many Jews began believing in Jesus because of Lazarus' having been raised from the dead.[309] In the midst of this environment of persecution, "Mary of Bethany" would have been a target and within easy reach of the persecutors based in Jerusalem. "Mary Magdalene," on the other hand, would be just the fading memory of a woman who once lived a week's journey away in a region under different jurisdiction. In short, the writers were trying to protect Mary.

There is more evidence that the nascent church was protecting Mary and her family. Consider that the greatest miracle, by far, that Jesus performed during his ministry was the raising of

---

[307] But the high priest rose up, along with all his associates (that is the sect of the Sadducees), and they were filled with jealousy. They laid hands on the apostles and put them in a public jail. (Acts 5:17-18) Also see Acts 12:1-3.

[308] Acts 5:33-40

[309] But the chief priests planned to put Lazarus to death also; because on account of him many of the Jews were going away and were believing in Jesus. (Jn 12:10-11)

Lazarus. The other two persons Jesus raised from the dead[310] were raised very shortly after their demises. Jesus' detractors could easily have said (and probably did) that those individuals weren't really dead but simply comatose.[311] But Lazarus was dead for four days, a fact that is very hard to discount. In the other two raisings, Jesus used both touch and command. For Lazarus, Jesus simply spoke—thus demonstrating unequivocally that his word had absolute authority over death. It was such an extraordinary work that "many of the Jews who ... saw what He had done, believed in Him" (Jn 11:45). No other sign that Jesus performed provoked such a great response. And it was Lazarus' raising that was the immediate provocation for Jesus' murder (Jn 11:45-53; 12:9-11).

Incredibly, despite the multifaceted significance of Lazarus' miracle, Matthew, Mark, and Luke make no mention of it, or even of Lazarus! Matthew and Mark also make no mention of either Martha or Mary, and Luke only mentions the sisters in a way that would prevent them from being connected with Lazarus or Bethany.[312] So, our knowledge about Lazarus, his raising, and his connection to Mary and Martha comes entirely from John.

This is significant, because John wrote his gospel much later than the others. We can presume that Lazarus was deceased by

---

[310] These two were the widow of Nain's son (Lk 7:11-15) and Jairus' daughter. (Mt 9:18-19; 23-25; Mk 5:22-24, 35-43; Lk 8:41-42, 49-56)

[311] Just as Jesus' detractors today sometimes pull out the absurd "swoon theory" in an attempt to explain away his resurrection. It's absurd simply because the Romans were very competent executioners—and they speared Jesus' body to be certain he was dead.

[312] Luke relates a story (Lk 10:38-42) about a woman Martha and her sister Mary, but omits all personal identifiers such as the name of the "village" where they lived, or even that they had a brother. Mary was the most common name in Palestine at the time, and Martha was the fourth most common, so this story could have occurred anywhere. The greater context of Luke's story is only known because of John's revelations about the trio of siblings.

the time of John's writing, and Martha may have been also. But Mary was probably still alive, which would explain John's adherence to the "Magdalene" cover name.

As further evidence of Mary of Bethany being the same person as Mary Magdalene, the two women do not appear together in the resurrection accounts. In fact, they never appear together in the same scene anywhere in the New Testament. And *that* is difficult to explain.

Why so? Because Mary of Bethany understood and loved Jesus deeply. Mary demonstrated a depth of spiritual insight that seemed woefully lacking among most of Jesus' followers, even his closest ones. She was the one who had been seated at Jesus' feet, attentively drinking in his words, when there were other obligations calling for her attention. She was the one who, only a few weeks before the crucifixion, had watched Jesus raise her brother from the dead.

Mary of Bethany was the one who, with her siblings, had hosted Jesus and his disciples for several nights just preceding his arrest. She was the one who had, as just recounted, eschewed social propriety and dumped perfume *valued at a year's worth of wages* on Jesus' head. And she was the one who, in the dark of night, had received the breathless nine disciples and heard that the light of her life had been arrested.

Now, here's the nub: Mary of Bethany could have easily walked from her home to Jerusalem in about 45 minutes. Would she just have stayed in Bethany? With Jesus under arrest? That is an impossibility; hell itself could not have kept her away. She would have been at the cross; she would have been leading the women to the tomb. For it could *not* have happened that she wasn't there.

Indeed, she was at the cross; she saw where they laid him; she helped prepare the spices;[313] she was the first up to make the

---

[313] Therefore Jesus said, "Let her alone, so that she may keep it for *the day* of My burial." (Jn 12:7, emphasis added) Jesus' statement was, in fact, prophetic—and also suggests that Mary kept some spikenard in reserve for this purpose.

trip to pay her last respects—and she saw him first.

So it was, that Mary Magdalene—otherwise known as Mary of Bethany—was given the task of taking the greatest news of all time to a small group of fearful, disbelieving men. She was the apostle to the apostles. She is my hero.

The Women Who Came to the Tomb

How can we know that Mary Clopas is the same person as "the other Mary"? Or, how is it known that Peter and Simon are the same individual? And how can we make other such identifications?

For Peter/Simon, the task is an easy one. In Matthew 10:2, we are given a direct equivalence: "Now the names of the Twelve apostles are these: The first, Simon, who is called Peter." In fact, there are 29 verses where these two names are clearly connected to a single individual, so you could say that this connection is rock solid.

Of the resurrection story characters, most identities are never in question. Still, other identifications are more difficult to make, and some must be made tenuously. Those which especially warrant further examination are the five women at the tomb: Mary Clopas, Salome, Joanna, Susanna, and course, Mary Magdalene.

The tables below are helpful in visualizing the identification of the five women who arrived at the tomb early on resurrection Sunday. These tables include the descriptions of the women as given in the four gospel accounts, with the associated references immediately follow each table. The left column of each table provides the names consistently used for these women in Parts One and Two in this book. Table 1 lists the women at the crucifixion; Table 2 lists the women who were witnesses to the burial; Table 3 lists the women who bought and prepared spices to anoint the body; and Table 4 identifies the women who arrived at the tomb early on resurrection Sunday.

It might seem odd that some of these women went to buy spices, given that Nicodemus had used 100 Roman pounds worth of spices to wrap the body just prior to interment. Surely the women had observed and known this, because Mary Clopas and Mary Magdalene had watched this procedure taking place outside the tomb. However, preparing bodies for burial was women's work, and the women had also seen that Joseph of Arimathea and Nicodemus had failed to anoint the body or the wrappings with perfuming oil for lack of time. The spices they bought afterwards were for the purpose of preparing these oils— a laborious process—so they could finish the preparation process of Jesus' body that was begun by the two earnest men.

Table 1: Women at the Crucifixion

Name	Matthew	Mark	Luke[314]	John
Mother Mary	—	—	—	His mother
Mary Magdalene	Mary Magdalene	Mary Magdalene	"Women who had come with Him out of Galilee"	Mary Magdalene
Mary Clopas	Mary the mother of James and Joseph	Mary the mother of James the Younger and Joses	"Women who had come with Him out of Galilee"	Mary the wife of Clopas
Salome	The mother of the sons of Zebedee	Salome	"Women who had come with Him out of Galilee"	His mother's sister

References for Table 1:

Among them was Mary Magdalene, and Mary the mother of James and Joseph, and the mother of the sons of Zebedee. (Mt 27:56)

There were also some women looking on from a distance, among whom were Mary Magdalene, and Mary the mother of James the Less and Joses, and Salome. (Mk 15:40)

---

[314] From Luke we know the names of some women who had gained distinction among those following Jesus around Galilee. See the discussion of Luke 8:1-3 below.

And all His acquaintances and the women who accompanied Him from Galilee were standing at a distance, seeing these things...Now the women who had come with Him out of Galilee followed, and saw the tomb and how His body was laid. Then they returned and prepared spices and perfumes. And on the Sabbath they rested according to the commandment. (Lk 23:49, 55-56)

Therefore the soldiers did these things. But standing by the cross of Jesus were His mother, and His mother's sister, Mary the wife of Clopas, and Mary Magdalene. (Jn 19:25)

Table 2: Women Who Witnessed the Burial

Name	Matthew	Mark	Luke	John
Mary Magdalene	Mary Magdalene	Mary Magdalene	"Women who had come with Him out of Galilee"	—
Mary Clopas	The other Mary	Mary the mother of Joses	"Women who had come with Him out of Galilee"	—
Salome	—	—	"Women who had come with Him out of Galilee"	—
Joanna	—	—	"Women who had come with Him out of Galilee"	—
Susanna	—	—	"Women who had come with Him out of Galilee"	—

References for Table 2:

And Mary Magdalene was there, and the other Mary, sitting opposite the grave. (Mt 27:61)

Mary Magdalene and Mary the mother of Joses were looking on to see where He was laid. (Mk 15:47)

Now the women who had come with Him out of Galilee followed, and saw the tomb and how His body was laid. (Lk 23:55)

John tells us that Joseph of Arimathea and Nicodemus prepared the body of Jesus and placed it in the tomb, but John does not mention any bystanders.

Table 3: Women Who Bought / Prepared Spices[315]

Name	Matthew	Mark	Luke	John
Mary Magdalene	—	Mary Magdalene	"Women who had come with Him out of Galilee"	—
Mary Clopas	—	Mary the mother of James (i.e., the Younger)	"Women who had come with Him out of Galilee"	—
Salome	—	Salome	"Women who had come with Him out of Galilee"	—

---

[315] We can expect that all five women who came to the tomb on resurrection Sunday would have participated together in these tasks if possible. Because the text only describes three (Mk 16:1), it seems reasonable that Joanna and her friend Susanna were attending to obligations at Herod Antipas' palace that prevented them from joining the others.

Joanna	—	—	"Women who had come with Him out of Galilee"	—
Susanna	—	—	"Women who had come with Him out of Galilee"	—

References for Table 3:

When the Sabbath was over, Mary Magdalene, and Mary the mother of James, and Salome, bought spices, so that they might come and anoint Him. (Mk 16:1)

Now the women who had come with Him out of Galilee followed, and saw the tomb and how His body was laid. Then they returned and prepared spices and perfumes. And on the Sabbath they rested according to the commandment. (Lk 23:55-56)

Table 4: Women at the Empty Tomb, early Sunday

Name	Matthew	Mark	Luke	John
Mary Magdalene	Mary Magdalene	Mary Magdalene	Mary Magdalene	Mary Magdalene
Mary Clopas	The other Mary	Mary the mother of James (i.e., the Younger)	Mary the mother of James (i.e., the Younger)	—
Salome	—	Salome	(The other women with them)	—
Joanna	—	—	Joanna	—
Susanna	—	—	(The other women with them)	—

References for Table 4:

Now after the Sabbath, as it began to dawn toward the first day of the week, Mary Magdalene and the other Mary came to look at the grave. (Mt 28:1)

When the Sabbath was over, Mary Magdalene, and Mary the mother of James, and Salome, bought spices, so that they might come and anoint Him. Very early on the first day of the week, they came to the tomb when the sun had risen. (Mk 16:1-2)

But on the first day of the week, at early dawn, they came to the tomb bringing the spices which they had prepared...and returned from the tomb and reported all these things to the eleven and to all the rest. Now they were Mary Magdalene and Joanna and Mary the mother of James; also the other women with them were telling these things to the apostles. (Lk 24:1, 9-10)

Now on the first day of the week Mary Magdalene came early to the tomb, while it was still dark, and saw the stone already taken away from the tomb. (Jn 20:1)

Of the four accounts, John has the least to say about the women. He informs us of four women at the cross but then omits all further mention of their involvement until Mary Magdalene brings a report that "They have taken the Lord out of the tomb!" This is not surprising since John had just witnessed the public lynching of a man who was not only innocent but also John's cousin. Added to such profound grief were a justifiable fear of the chief priests, as well as the new responsibility he had to care for Jesus' mother. In light of his emotional burden, it is not remarkable that women preparing anointing oils and taking those to the tomb should hardly have registered with John.

Nevertheless, John makes an important connection for us with his list of women at the crucifixion (Table 1). From there we can see that Mary Clopas is the name of the woman who is mother to James the Younger (one of the twelve disciples) and Joses. From the other tables we can identify her also as "the other Mary."

Another key identification John provides is his description of one of the women at the cross as "his mother's sister" (that is, Mother Mary's sister). In comparing the lists in Table 1, we see that this same woman was described by Matthew as "the mother of the sons of Zebedee" and by Mark as "Salome." Thus, we know that Jesus' aunt Salome was present at the cross along with Jesus' mother, Mary. But even further, the gospels inform us that Salome was married to Zebedee, who we know was the father of disciples James and John.[316] And so, the disciples James and John are revealed to be first cousins of Jesus.

Now, knowing that "his (Jesus') mother's sister," Salome, is also therefore John's own mother, why did John not just say that? There are two good reasons. First, the gospel writers tended to downplay their own involvement in their accounts, as mentioned earlier in the description of Mark. The second and more cogent reason is that the presence of Salome is more relevant to the story when we know she is Mother Mary's sister rather than John's mother. And so we can anticipate that upon Jesus' death, Mother Mary's sister Salome and nephew John would have accompanied her back to Zebedee's home in Jerusalem to comfort and care for her.

Joanna is mentioned only by Luke, who tells us that she was at the tomb Sunday, at early dawn. We would know nothing else about her, but for a single other fortuitous mention, in Luke 8:

> Soon afterwards, He began going around from one city and village to another, proclaiming and preaching the kingdom of God. The Twelve were with Him, and also some women who had been healed of evil spirits and sicknesses: Mary who was called Magdalene, from whom seven demons had gone out, and Joanna the wife of Chuza, Herod's steward, and Susanna, and many others who were contributing to their support out of their private means. (Lk 8:1-3)

---

[316] Going on from there He saw two other brothers, James the son of Zebedee, and John his brother, in the boat with Zebedee their father, mending their nets; and He called them. (Mt 4:21)

Fortunately, this passage provides us with multiple connections:

1. All of this ministry was taking place in Galilee, and all of these women encountered Jesus in the Galilean region.

2. Their encounters were dramatic: Mary Magdalene was delivered of demons, and Joanna and Susanna were either healed of sicknesses or demonic spirits, or both.

3. As a result, these women became followers and financial supporters of Jesus.

4. Joanna was wife to the steward for the ruler (tetrarch) of Judea and Perea, Herod Antipas, son of King Herod I. This was a high societal standing and indicates that Joanna was wealthy.

5. These three women would have known each other well.

6. The particular close grouping of Joanna and Susanna may represent a long-standing relationship between them, and they both provided financial support to Jesus and his traveling band of disciples. Thus, it appears that Susanna was also of upper-class status.

Luke later refers to these women, when they were at the cross, as "the women who had come with him out of Galilee." There may have been unnamed others from Galilee at the cross as well, since Luke 8:3 refers to "many others" as Galilean supporters besides those named explicitly.

Comparison of the tables affirms that there were at least five women at the tomb on Sunday morning (perhaps more), and four of them are explicitly named: Mary Magdalene, Mary Clopas, Salome, and Joanna. Because of her connection to Joanna and the other women, the most obvious candidate for the fifth person is Susanna.

Relationships

One component to gaining a more comprehensive view of the people involved in the resurrection story is to examine the relationships between them, insofar as they can be determined from the gospel accounts and other sources. In some cases the relationships are clearly evident, while others may be deduced. They may be likely or possible based on various clues. These relationships, in turn, were influenced by the geographical and political realities of the time.

Jesus grew up and conducted most of his ministry in a part of the Roman Empire called the province of Galilee, but his death and resurrection took place in Jerusalem, a city about a week's travel (by foot) directly south of Galilee, in the separate Roman province of Judea. At the time, Herod Antipas governed Galilee, while Pontius Pilate ruled Judea.

Most of the cities of note in the province of Galilee were located along the western coastline of the Sea of Galilee. Only the western shoreline was part of the province of Galilee; the eastern shoreline was part of two other provinces[317] with very different cultures. The eastern coast of the Sea was predominantly Gentile, with Roman and Greek influences, while Galilee and the cities of the western shoreline were predominantly Jewish.

During his approximately three years of ministry, Jesus spent the majority of his time among the cities along the western coast of the Sea of Galilee, although he also made trips across the Sea and ministered among the Gentiles there, as well as visited the Mediterranean cities of Tyre and Sidon.

The Sea of Galilee (actually, the world's lowest freshwater lake) has a circumference of only 33 miles. To help you visualize

---

[317] For the curious, about one-half of the eastern coast of the Sea of Galilee (northern half) was known as Batanea and governed by Antipas' half-brother, Philip the Tetrarch, and the other (southern) half was part of a loose coalition of city-states known as the Decapolis.

the scale, the coastline along the western shore, where Jesus taught and ministered, could probably be walked in a single day. The cities in Galilee in the first century formed a loose network of people who had their own culture, distinctive speech,[318] and even calendar.

Nearly all of the settlements along the Sea of Galilee were quite small by today's standards, and the New Testament use of the word "city" *(Greek: polis)* needs to be understood in the context of the time. It might be an exaggeration to say that a village would be anywhere you had two adjacent houses, and a city where you had a dozen—but not by much. Even Nazareth, Jesus' original hometown, is described by Matthew as a city,[319] yet archeology shows that it consisted of about fifty houses within four acres.[320]

At the beginning of his public ministry, Jesus relocated to the larger city of Capernaum[321]; its population during that period has been estimated at around 1,500.[322] Thus, it is conceivable that an adult living there could have known every other adult in the community, or nearly so. The lone exception to this generalization of small city sizes was Tiberias, the largest city on the Sea of Galilee; it was also, despite being on the western side,

---

[318] A little later the bystanders came up and said to Peter, "Surely you too are one of them; for even the way you talk gives you away." (Mt 26:73)

[319] ...and came and lived in a city called Nazareth. This was to fulfill what was spoken through the prophets: "He shall be called a Nazarene." (Mt 2:23)

[320] "The dwelling and older discoveries of nearby tombs in burial caves suggest that Nazareth was an out-of-the-way hamlet of around 50 houses on a patch of about four acres (1.6 hectares)."
AP Television, Dec 21, 2009, accessed Apr 23, 2022,
http://www.aparchive.com/metadata/youtube/87363c36b8d9af9378 057b2c0705e2f6

[321] ...and leaving Nazareth, He came and settled in Capernaum, which is by the sea, in the region of Zebulun and Naphtali. (Mt 4:13)

[322] JL Reed, *Archaeology and the Galileen Jesus: A Reexamination of the Evidence* (Harrisburg: Trinity Press International, 2000), 166.

overwhelmingly non-Jewish.

In distinct contrast, the city of Jerusalem, located 85 miles south of Capernaum, was a true city in the first century. Although still small by today's standards, most population estimates for the city range from 20,000 to 75,000 people at that time.[323] Compared to Galilee, it was far more cosmopolitan, educated, wealthy, and divided by class. Its primary industry was religious tourism which was created by large influxes of Jews from around the Mediterranean. Its economy, culture, and heartbeat centered on the massive temple complex.

Religious travelers would flood the city of Jerusalem during the three annual pilgrimages[324] to bring sacrifices and offerings, and to engage in traditional observances. The historian Josephus records 256,500 sacrifices being offered during Passover, so consequently, the population of pilgrims in the city during those events would have eclipsed the number of native residents.[325]

Even though both regions—Jerusalem and Galilee—were soundly Jewish and shared many commonalities, they were distinctively different and geographically separated by the non-Jewish region of Samaria. To many Jerusalem citizens, a Galilean would have been regarded as rough, rural, and unrefined.[326]

---

[323] Hershel Shanks, "Ancient Jerusalem: The Village, the Town, the City," accessed Apr 23, 2022, https://www.biblicalarchaeology.org/daily/biblical-sites-places/jerusalem/ancient-jerusalem

[324] Pesach (Passover or Unleavened Bread), Shavuot (Weeks or Pentecost), and Sukkot (Tabernacles, Tents, or Booths). For reasons unknown to me, everything in Judaism seems to have a plurality of names.

[325] Josephus, *Wars of the Jews*, Book 6, Chapter 9, Section 3. Consider that each sacrifice would serve a domestic group of typically ten persons, often more.

[326] Now as they observed the confidence of Peter and John and understood that they were uneducated and untrained men, they were amazed, and began to recognize them as having been with Jesus. (Acts

Because Galilee consisted of small settlements and the average family size was larger than what is typical today, the interconnectedness of people within the region—through marriage, extended families, and trade—must have been far greater than people would experience in a geographical region of similar size in modern times. Unlike today, people traveled shorter distances, as the primary means of transportation was by foot and secondarily by donkey. "High-speed" transportation was accomplished by running.

And as would be expected in a region of sparse but rooted population, where everyone would seem to be known or related to everyone else, we see considerable interconnectedness among Jesus and his followers. Consequently, it shouldn't be entirely surprising that at the beginning of his ministry, Jesus was baptized in the Jordan River by a relative—John the Baptist. Their mothers were related.[327]

The connectedness of Jesus and his twelve disciples is illustrated in the following table. Table 5 illustrates that among the twelve disciples there were at least two pairs of brothers, and perhaps even three.[328] The disciple Andrew had formerly

---

4:13)

[327] "And behold, even your [Mother Mary's] relative Elizabeth has also conceived a son in her old age; and she who was called barren is now in her sixth month." (Lk 1:36)

Note that in the KJV this verse uses "cousin" in place of "relative," but the Greek signifies a blood-relative or kinswoman, and so it is translated by the overwhelming number of English translations. The exact relationship between Jesus and John the Baptist cannot be determined from the text, but they were extended family.

[328] Alfred Edersheim, *The Life and Times of Jesus the Messiah*, (Hendrickson Publ. 1993), 360-361. Edersheim argues that three of the disciples—James the Younger (literally, The Less), Thaddeus (or Jude), and Simon the Zealot were all brothers and sons of Clopas. Accurate or not, this assertion has no effect on the conclusions in this book, although it would support the main points of this section.

followed John the Baptist and, when not with the Baptist, had
fished for a living from Bethsaida on the northern shore of the
Sea of Galilee. Andrew fished with his brother Peter (Simon at
the time), whom Andrew introduced to Jesus.

Table 5: The Twelve Disciples

Disciple	Hometown	Family / Friend	Other Connection
Peter (Simon/Cephas)	Bethsaida and Capernaum	Andrew's brother	Fishing partner
Andrew	Bethsaida and Capernaum	Peter's brother (Philip's friend?)	Fishing partner, John the Baptist
James	Capernaum	John's brother	Fishing partner, cousin to Jesus
John	Capernaum	James' brother	Fishing partner, cousin to Jesus
Philip	Bethsaida	Nathanael's friend (Andrew also?)	John the Baptist
Nathanael (Bartholomew)	Cana	Philip's friend	John the Baptist
Thomas (the Twin)	Galilee	Unknown	Unknown
Matthew (Levi; of Alphaeus)	Capernaum	Brother to James of Alphaeus?*	Taxed Capernaum disciples
James of Alphaeus (the Younger)	Galilee	Brother to Matthew?*	Cousin to Jesus
Judas of James (Jude/Thaddeus)	Galilee	Unknown	Unknown
Simon the Zealot	Galilee	Unknown	Unknown
Judas Iscariot	Kerioth in Judea	Unknown	Unknown

* Even though both are described as "of Alphaeus," this connection is
considered unlikely since the gospels do not describe them as brothers.

The two fishermen-brothers Andrew and Peter were partners

in the fishing business with two brothers from another family, James and John. These two pairs of brothers were obviously very close; perhaps for this reason they are always listed as the first four of the twelve disciples in all four gospel lists.[329]

Andrew and Philip undoubtedly knew each other before following Jesus, surely as fellow residents of the small village of Bethsaida, possibly also as fellow disciples of John the Baptist.[330] And when some Greeks approached Philip, requesting to see Jesus, Philip first brought them to Andrew (Jn 12:20-22). Likewise, Philip and Nathanael shared a prior connection, either as personal friends, relatives, or fellow disciples of the Baptist.[331] Because Philip (of Bethsaida) and Nathanael (of Cana) came from towns about 20 miles apart—a significant distance in those circumstances—it is quite possible that they also became acquainted through John the Baptist.

Remarkably, the Baptist, who is often only thought to have prepared Jesus' way by calling the nation to repentance, also had a major but little-appreciated role in pre-gathering disciples for Jesus. It may be that all of Jesus' disciples had been baptized by John, seeing that it was a stated prerequisite for selecting a

---

[329] Mt 10:2-4; Mk 3:16-19; Lk 6:13-16; Acts 1:13.

[330] Jesus was far from Galilee when He was baptized, and where He met Andrew: "These things took place in Bethany beyond the Jordan, where John was baptizing." (Jn 1:28)

"Bethany beyond the Jordan" (different from Bethany near Jerusalem) was near Jericho but on the eastern side of the river. So, when we read a few verses later: "The next day He purposed to go into Galilee, and He found Philip. And Jesus said to him, 'Follow Me.'" (Jn 1:43), Philip was in that same (desolate) vicinity, which he only would have been if he was there for the Baptist, either as a follower or perhaps simply to receive baptism.

[331] Note how Philip eagerly sought out Nathanael to tell him the exciting news: "Philip found Nathanael and said to him, 'We have found Him of whom Moses in the Law and also the Prophets wrote— Jesus of Nazareth, the son of Joseph.'" (Jn 1:45)

replacement for Judas Iscariot.[332]

We know very little about three of the twelve disciples: Matthew, Thaddeus, and Simon the Zealot. Nevertheless, eleven disciples—including these three—were likely all from Galilee. Given the connections we do know about, I suspect that each of the eleven disciples had some connection to either Jesus or another disciple prior to being called as an apostle. The one prominent outlier was Judas Iscariot, who by his name probably hailed from Kerioth, a city in the south of Judea. He was an outsider in more than one sense.

However, the relationships between some of them involved deeper familial and business connections than depicted in Table 5.

As previously mentioned, Mother Mary was sister to Salome, the wife of Zebedee. Salome and her husband Zebedee had (at least) two sons, James and John, who were therefore first cousins to Jesus and among the twelve disciples.

James bar Zebedee and John, prior to being called by Jesus, were fishermen. Their business involved their father Zebedee and some servants,[333] but unfortunately, we have no surviving organizational charts to know the business structure. My conjecture is that the elder Zebedee was the most prominent figure in the business (he had the servants, after all), employing his sons James and John, with a joint-venture or subcontract type of relationship to Peter and Andrew. Zebedee probably had long-standing business relationships with fish dealers in the city of Jerusalem, as Jerusalem was the destination for most of the

---

[332] "Therefore it is necessary that of the men who have accompanied us all the time that the Lord Jesus went in and out among us—*beginning with the baptism of John* until the day that He was taken up from us—one of these must become a witness with us of His resurrection." (Acts 1:21-22, emphasis added)

[333] Immediately He called them; and they left their father Zebedee in the boat with the hired servants, and went away to follow Him. (Mk 1:20)

fish harvested from the Sea of Galilee.

Clopas and his wife, Mary Clopas, were also related to Jesus. As explained in the description of Clopas, he was the brother of Jesus' father, Joseph. Thus, Clopas and his wife, Mary, were uncle and aunt to Jesus, and their children, James the Younger, Joseph/Joses, and Simeon, were Jesus' first cousins.

Clopas and Mary's son Simeon is not known from the New Testament. Instead, the historian Eusebius informs us that Simeon later became the second bishop of the church of Jerusalem after the martyrdom of James the Just (Jesus' brother).[334] Family connections are always important, and in the first century Jerusalem church, they were plainly so.

Clopas and Mary's son, James the Younger, was probably the same as the "James of Alphaeus" listed among the twelve disciples. His designation "the Younger" is literally "the Less" *(Greek: mikron)*—meaning less in age, stature, or status. Because "less" in stature or status could be a demeaning usage and therefore unlikely, I assume this to mean less in age—that is, younger. But in comparison to whom? Certainly to another man named James.

When we consider that there were two Jameses among the disciples, it becomes a possibility that Clopas' son was the younger of the two disciples by that name. The other James— that is, James bar Zebedee, John's brother—was certainly the elder to John, as he is listed first almost everywhere the two brothers' names occur together. This increases the likelihood that James bar Zebedee was also older than James of Alphaeus, making the latter the younger of the two Jameses. This fits with the description "James the Younger." It also matches the trend of Jesus choosing disciples with whom he had some connection, or who knew each other.

Some scholars contend that Clopas/Cleopas and Alphaeus are two versions (transliterations) of the Aramaic name

---

[334] Eusebius, *Church History,* III 11; cf. IV 22. It is from Eusebius that we learn about Simeon. And we know that James the Younger and Joses (or Joseph) were sons of Clopas and Mary from Mark 15:40.

"Chalphai."[335] This is controversial, but if true, it would strengthen the identification of the disciple "James of Alphaeus" as the son of Clopas, and as "James the Younger." In any case, they are presumed to be the same person in this book, as I believe the identification to be reasonable even though not indisputable. See Appendix F for more detail.

Other connections among the disciples that have been suggested by various commentators seem largely speculative. Nevertheless, if more was known about these men, the discovery of additional connections between them would not be surprising.

The known family connections of Jesus in his final week are shown in Figure 1. (Zacharias and Elizabeth were likely deceased, as they were "advanced in years" when Jesus was born.)[336] One point to appreciate here is that the merry messiah-band that followed Jesus from Galilee was a closely connected group. When Mother Mary stood watching her son die on the cross, her sister (Salome), her sister-in-law (Mary Clopas), her nephew (John), and possibly other family or friends (the women who traveled with him from Galilee, per Luke) accompanied her in grief. And when Salome, Zebedee, Clopas, and Mary Clopas were grieving over Jesus in Zebedee's home in Jerusalem, they shared the added concern for their own sons, members of the twelve disciples, who were hiding in fear.

The most vital point to appreciate from Figure 1 is that all of these people were related to Jesus and each other by blood or marriage. It was one very close, extended family—a fact that deeply influences the emotional tone of everything connected with the death, burial, and resurrection of Jesus Christ.

In spirit and in fact, these were *his* people.

---

[335] Wenham, *Easter Enigma*, 37.
[336] Lk 1:7 and context

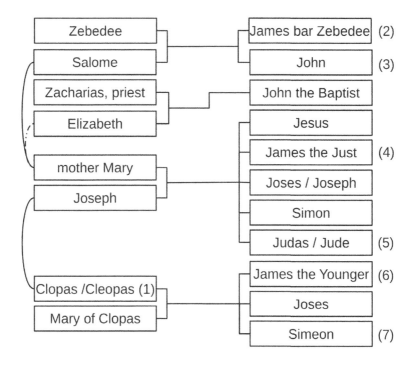

Figure 1. Familial relationships. The first column is the first generation; the second column is the second generation. Connecting lines on the left sides of boxes reflect sibling or cousin relationships, and connectors on the right sides of boxes represent marriage relationships.

Notes to Figure 1: (1) Clopas is arguably the same as Alphaeus; (2,3) James bar Zebedee and John belonged to the Twelve; (4) James the Just became the first bishop of the church of Jerusalem, is traditionally regarded as being the author of the book of James, and was martyred; (5) Jude is traditionally regarded as author of the book of Jude; (6) James the Younger is the same as James of Alphaeus, one of the Twelve; (7) Simeon became the second bishop of the church of Jerusalem and was martyred. Of the eleven names in the right column, at least six died for their beliefs.

Important Locations

The Mediterranean World

In Jesus' time, the greatest political power on earth was that of Rome, which ruled an expansive empire covering all the lands around the Great (or Mediterranean) Sea, including much of Europe, northern Africa, Asia Minor, and the Near East. (See map of Roman Empire.)

The city of Rome was located roughly central to its vast empire, and it exercised control over its vassal states and regions by provincial administration. The rule of each province was administered by a Roman governor appointed by Rome. The governors were obligated to levy taxes, suppress uprisings, and otherwise enforce the laws and dictates of Rome.

And certainly, uprisings were an ongoing problem for the empire, even though its vassal states experienced material benefits of being subservient to Rome, such as greater trade opportunities, a common language, and the Pax Romana.[337] Those benefits came at a price, however: Taxes were extreme and provincial autonomy was limited.

Palestine

In the far east of this empire was a relatively small but economically important province named Judea, governed by the Roman Pontius Pilate. (See map of Palestine.) It contained the city of Jerusalem, the largest in the province and the center of Judaism. Just north of Judea was a more obscure and rural jurisdiction named Galilee, governed by Herod Antipas.[338] The

---

[337] The Pax Romana was a period of time, usually given as 27 BC to AD 180, in which the Empire enjoyed relative peace, principally because its major external competitors had been defeated.

[338] Antipas carried the title of "tetrarch (ruler of one-fourth)," which

distance from Capernaum in Galilee to Jerusalem was about eighty-five miles, or five to six days' travel time by foot. Between the resurrection and ascension (forty days), the disciples made a round trip between these two locations.

It happened in Judea, in an insignificant town named Bethlehem, to an insignificant young couple, that Jesus was born. However, his life was spent from childhood upward in Galilee, including the majority of his ministry time. His last days were completed in the land of his birth, and he died only six miles north of his birthplace.

Two other towns near Jerusalem are connected to the resurrection story. The first is Bethany, home of Lazarus, Martha, and Mary. It was located about one and a half miles east of the city, or about a forty-five-minute walk. Although close, it was more than twice a Sabbath-day's journey and therefore unreachable from Jerusalem on Sabbaths, and vice versa. The other town of note is Emmaus, located about seven miles from Jerusalem. Several places near Jerusalem have been proposed as the site for Emmaus, but recent archaeological excavations have raised the merit of the village of Abu Ghosh as the best candidate. This town is described in Appendix G, along with the spiritual/prophetic implications.

Ten centuries earlier, both Galilee and Judea had been part of the sovereign nation of Israel, ruled by the famous King Solomon. But in the millennium since Solomon's time, the region had frequently suffered political division, repeated invasions, wars, and servitude to assorted empires and kingdoms, with only occasional or limited autonomy.

From 332 BC to the time of Jesus, Judea and Galilee had been continuously controlled by foreigners, with Romans being the most recent. Under General Pompey, in 63 BC, Rome had taken complete control of the eastern Mediterranean region. For the

---

came from the division of his father's (King Herod I) dominion, and he was referred to locally as "King Herod" (Mk 6:14), despite not being a sovereign but rather a client-ruler subservient to Rome. Antipas also governed Perea.

religious Jews of Judea and Galilee, who believed God had given them the land and told them "to set no foreigner over them,"[339] this was a long-endured but vexing situation. It led to great resentment, simmering violence, and a longing for the appearance of the Messiah—that is, the Deliverer promised through their prophets.

Jerusalem

Jesus' trial took place within Jerusalem, and his death and resurrection occurred just beyond the walls of the city, so it's important when comparing the gospel records to consider the geographical features and layout of the city at that time. Jerusalem was a major city and ranked among the top ten cities by population in the Roman world of the first century.

Turning now to the map of Jerusalem, the city was about a half mile east to west, and a mile north to south. It had a massive stone wall defining its periphery, and various named gates. The terrain of the city was uneven and hilly, with a general slope downward from west to east.

The largest structure in the city was the temple mount, in the northeast corner. It was a high, approximately rectangular, quarried-stone platform built upon Mount Moriah with monumental stone walls all around it; the eastern and northern walls of the mount served also as part of the city wall. The walls of the mount encompassed a large courtyard containing the largest building in the city, the temple. The temple faced eastward, and in front of the temple stood the altar on which daily and special sacrifices were performed.

Attached to the northwest corner of the temple mount, but external to it, was the Antonia Fortress. It was a rectangular citadel with four large towers at its corners, originally built by Herod I to protect the temple. In the time of Jesus, it housed a portion of the Roman garrison of Jerusalem, more for the purpose of monitoring the temple area for incipient civil unrest than for protecting it.

---

[339] Dt 17:15

The second-largest structure in the city was Herod's palace, also built by Herod I, which shared the city wall on the western side of the city opposite the temple mount. It contained the Praetorium where Jesus was tried and tortured, and served as Pilate's temporary residence during Jewish feasts. While in the city, Roman governors, as would be expected, took residence in this magnificent fortified palace rather than in the spartan barracks of the Antonia Fortress.[340]

Pilate's usual primary residence and administrative headquarters were in Caesarea, a port city on the Great (or Mediterranean) Sea. His reason for being in Jerusalem during the feasts was to assess the crowds for unrest and avert potential uprisings.

The third largest building in the city was Herod Antipas' palace (also called the Hasmonean Palace). This was the palace where Herod Antipas resided with his court when visiting Jerusalem, and it was here that Herod interrogated Jesus in-between trials before Pilate. Jerusalem was outside Antipas' jurisdiction, but the annual Jewish feasts in the city were the most important social and political events in Palestine at the time. Joanna and her husband Chuza, Antipas' steward, would have been staying there as members of the court, presumably with support staff and perhaps a few close connections.

Excluding the prominent thirty-six-acre temple mount, the city was divided by interior walls and major streets into four quarters. Directly northwest of the temple mount was the Second Quarter; it was the newest extension of the city and in the process of development and growth. The poorest area of the city was the Lower City in the southeast.[341] In the southwest was the Essene Quarter, which could be described as upper-middle class.

---

[340] As affirmation, historian Josephus reported that another governor of Judea, Florus (who ruled Judea AD 64 to 66), lodged at Herod's palace (Josephus, *Wars of the Jews*, Book II, 14.8).

[341] The original Jerusalem, or City of David, occupied about one-third of the lower city.

The Upper City (also called the Herodian Quarter) was the area where the elites (particularly, chief priests) and wealthy lived. It included the two palaces where Pilate and Antipas stayed when in town, a large theater of Greek style, and the upscale shopping market called the Agora. Archaeological excavations in the Upper City have uncovered the ruins of stunning homes exhibiting great wealth and artistic adornments. The extreme wealth differential between the rich and poor in Jerusalem contributed to social unrest and the civil war that preceded the destruction of the city in AD 70.

The strong outer walls of Jerusalem were punctuated by gates that could be closed if needed for defense. The two most important gates in the resurrection story are the Gennath Gate proximal to Herod's palace and the Essene Gate in the southwest corner of the city.

Outside the City Walls

Outside the city walls were (and are today) two large valleys, one that ran roughly parallel to the southern wall (the Hinnom) and another that ran roughly parallel to the eastern wall (the Kidron). The valleys met near the southeast corner of the city and then continued southward to the Salt (or Dead) Sea.

Like a wall to the east of the city is a mountain ridge called the Mount of Olives (also called "Mount Olivet" or simply "Olivet"), running 2.2 miles north to south. The Kidron valley separates the ridge and the city. The ridge contains three peaks, of which the central one is also (confusingly) called the Mount of Olives. It rises to an elevation of 2,684 feet, which is more than 300 feet above the temple mount, offering a panoramic view of the temple mount and the city.

A traveler leaving the city for Bethany would have descended into the Kidron valley and then begun ascending the Mount of Olives eastward on a curved path that passed the garden of Gethsemane (where Jesus was arrested) on the right. The path crossed the ridge near the central peak and then took a longer, slower descent to Bethany. Bethany was a little more than one and a half miles beyond the wall of the city, a distance about three times the width of the city.

On the western side of Jerusalem, near Herod's Palace, was the Gennath Gate. A path led northward from the Gennath Gate, between the city wall (on the exterior) and the Tower Pool. A short distance beyond the Tower Pool was a small rise, which is the traditional site of the crucifixion (identified as Golgotha in the gospel accounts), very close to which is the traditional site of Jesus' tomb. Today the Church of the Holy Sepulchre stands over both sites.

There is good reason to believe that the traditional sites for Golgotha and the tomb beneath the Church of the Holy Sepulchre are the authentic sites. The church has stood on its present location since it was dedicated in AD 335. Emperor Constantine had previously commissioned his mother Helena to locate Christian holy sites in Palestine. He ordered the construction of the church to be built at the site of Jesus' resurrection and was present for its dedication.

Archaeological excavations beneath the church have revealed an ancient quarry and tomb within it, and a prominent rock that was once part of a larger outcrop adjacent to the quarry's edge. All this corresponds well with the gospel accounts, and there are no other sites that fit so closely or have such long traditions.[342] For this book, the traditional sites are taken as the true locations of the death, burial, and resurrection of Jesus.

The Tomb

For centuries, Jews in Jerusalem buried their dead outside city walls, for reason of ritual purity. Jerusalem is surrounded by soft limestone rock that is easily worked, and tombs were cut into the rock. Poor people might be buried in shallow graves, but families that could afford it were buried in excavated caves, closed by a blocking stone. The golel, or blocking stone, could be

---

[342] For further reading, see Edward J. Schnabel, *Jesus in Jerusalem* (Grand Rapids, MI: William B. Eerdmans Publishing Co., 2018), 132-137.

rectangular with a tapered end to plug the opening like a cork in a bottle, or a round disk to be rolled in front of the opening. The round-disk type of stone was rare, judging from archaeology,[343] and has only been seen in tombs of the wealthy.

But indeed, Jesus' tomb was owned by Joseph of Arimathea, and Scripture records that he was rich and a leading member of the Sanhedrin.[344] Therefore, Joseph had all the means necessary to have an exceptional tomb cut for his family. The gospels confirm that a round golel stone was covering the opening, as the stone was "rolled."[345] And frankly, square rocks don't roll, especially extremely large ones.[346]

Just how large was a large golel? Perhaps four feet in diameter, considering other tombs incorporating such stones. That may not seem extremely large, until you do the math: Medium-density limestone weighs about 135 pounds/cubic foot, so a stone one foot thick of that diameter would weigh about 1,700 pounds! Plainly, even though the stone was round, the women would have needed assistance.

The golel stone covered an opening that was (obviously) smaller, probably somewhere between three and three and a half feet in height. This explains why John had to stoop to look into it (Jn 20:5). Tombs in this period typically opened into a small

---

[343] Only four of more than 900 tombs found in the Jerusalem area are known to have used round stones. Oddly, Kloner concludes that Jesus' golel must have been square, on the grounds that round stones were rare and only for the wealthy. It's not a convincing argument, as I explain. Amos Kloner, "Did a Rolling Stone Close Jesus' Tomb?" accessed February 3, 2022, https://www.baslibrary.org/biblical-archaeology-review/25/5/1.

[344] When it was evening, there came a rich man from Arimathea, named Joseph... (Mt 27:57a).
Joseph of Arimathea came, a prominent member of the Council, who himself was waiting for the kingdom of God (Mk 15:43a).

[345] Mt 27:60; Mk 16:4; Lk 24:2

[346] Looking up, they saw that the stone had been rolled away, although it was *extremely large*. (Mk 16:4, emphasis added)

room, tall enough to stand in, with carved stone benches along the walls. Many had recesses into which bodies were placed perpendicular to the walls (called loculi); these loculi might have openings a foot and a half square and continue six feet deep into the wall.

However, Jesus' body was placed on a stone bench along a wall, regardless of whether or not his tomb contained empty loculi. For John informs us that Mary "saw two angels in white sitting, one at the head and one at the feet, where the body of Jesus had been lying" (Jn 20:12), which would not have been possible if he had been placed in a loculus.

Also, Mark's gospel adds the detail that the stone bench, upon which the angels were sitting, was along the right side of the tomb. As Mark records, the women (less Mary) "saw a young man [an angel] sitting at *the right*, wearing a white robe..." (Mk 16:5).

Important Residences

Three residences in the southwest area of Jerusalem are of particular relevance to any reconstruction of events.

The Upper Room House

Jesus had at least one well-to-do supporter in Jerusalem. We know that the "large upper room" of the Last Supper could host 13 or more people. And only forty days after resurrection Sunday, the disciples returned to a "large upper room" after the ascension (undoubtedly the same location as the Last Supper) to wait for the day of Pentecost. By the day of Pentecost, there were 120 people gathered there to pray and wait, so the house must have truly been substantial.

> Then they returned to Jerusalem from the mount called Olivet, which is near Jerusalem, a Sabbath day's journey away. When they had entered the city, they went up to the upper room *where they were staying*; that is, Peter and John and James and Andrew, Philip and Thomas,

Bartholomew and Matthew, James the son of Alphaeus, and Simon the Zealot, and Judas the son of James. These all with one mind were continually devoting themselves to prayer, along with the women, and Mary the mother of Jesus, and with His brothers. At this time Peter stood up in the midst of the brethren (*a gathering of about one hundred and twenty persons was there together*)... (Acts 1:12-15, emphasis added)

There is every reason to believe these two "upper room" locations were the same place. Consider this: At the time of his final week, Jesus was considerably more famous among the leaders (chief priests and Sanhedrin) than among the masses in the city during the feast, the majority of whom were visiting pilgrims from outside the area.[347] This was partly because Jesus conducted most of his ministry in the Galilean region, visiting Jerusalem only occasionally and provoking the elites. His name was almost universally vilified in Jerusalem among the chief priests and Sanhedrin; Joseph of Arimathea and Nicodemus, both secretive followers, were two remarkable exceptions.

In this hostile environment, to have even one family of affluence who would risk wealth and standing to provide a base of operations for Jesus and his band is noteworthy, and it certainly appears to have been Mark's family. At the time of the Last Supper, Mark's father was alive,[348] but by the time of Peter's release from prison, it seems he was deceased.[349]

---

[347] When Jesus entered the city on a donkey in his final week, many of the people did not know who he was (see Mt 21:10).

[348] "And you shall say to the *owner* of the house, 'The Teacher says to you, "Where is the guest room in which I may eat the Passover with My disciples?"' "And *he* will show you a large, furnished upper room; prepare it there." (Lk 22:11-12, emphasis added to indicate masculine forms)

[349] ...he went to the *house of Mary*, the mother of John who was also called Mark, where many were gathered together and were praying. (Acts 12:12b, emphasis added)

Although speculative, it's certainly possible that the death of Mark's father may have occurred from the persecution under Saul/Paul, before Saul's conversion.[350] Saul was the chief instigator of "a great persecution" that began with the first martyr (Stephen) and was sufficiently severe to cause the church (except for the apostles) to abandon Jerusalem for a period (Acts 8:1).

An additional possibility is that Mark's family may have owned the garden of Gethsemane on the Mount of Olives. Being so near the city, it would have been a valuable piece of property, and to obtain any olive harvest, must have been walled and gated. Certainly this garden was owned by an affluent supporter of Jesus, as Jesus had "often met there with his disciples" (Jn 18:2).

This could provide another explanation for Mark's presence there when Jesus was arrested (see Mark's entry under "A Closer Look at the Characters"), as Mark could have been responsible for unlocking the gate for Jesus and his company.

The identification of the upper room with Mark's family is made in Acts 12, which records what happened when Peter escaped from prison, about fourteen years after the resurrection:

> When Peter came to himself, he said, "Now I know for sure that the Lord has sent forth His angel and rescued me from the hand of Herod and from all that the Jewish people were expecting." And when he realized this, he went to the house of Mary, the mother of John who was also called Mark, where many were gathered together and were praying (Acts 12:11-12)[351]

---

[350] But Saul began ravaging the church, entering house after house, and dragging off men and women, he would put them in prison (Acts 8:3). If Mark's father died under Paul's persecutions, then Mark's later working with Paul would represent an extraordinary example of forgiveness (2 Tim 4:11).

[351] This took place just prior to King Agrippa's death, which occurred in

This was a large home in Jerusalem where Christians gathered to pray. The home was gated and the family had at least one servant, so the owner, Mark's mother, had some wealth. That Peter, preeminent leader of the church, would choose to flee to this residence first, during a time of intense persecution, testifies to this home serving as a landmark and an asset to the early church. Further, all of these connections add weight to the picture of Mark and his home being closely connected to the disciples in numerous behind-the-scenes ways—from the Last Supper onward into the growth of the early church.

The most plausible connection is that Mark's home is the same as the house of the upper room. This was undoubtedly the same room where the disciples returned to Sunday evening after the resurrection; it was the same room the disciples were in one week later with Thomas; and it was known to Clopas/Cleopas and his traveling companion.[352]

It's fair to assume that Peter, following his denial of Jesus, sought asylum from the Jewish leadership and his own self-loathing at the upper room house of Mark. This location would have been a) already familiar to Peter, b) close to Zebedee's house where John would be, and c) a place where he could be alone. For Peter this home was a refuge.

Zebedee's Jerusalem House

There are good reasons to believe that Zebedee had a second home in Jerusalem and that it was neither very large nor very small. First, we know that Zebedee had a fishing business that employed at least six others besides himself.[353] The product of that business, dried fish, was in brisk demand in the city of Jerusalem.

AD 44.

[352] And they [Clopas and his companion] got up that very hour and returned to Jerusalem, and found gathered together the eleven and those who were with them. (Lk 24:33)

[353] Zebedee's employees: his sons James and John, Peter and Andrew (as partners to his sons), and at least two hired servants.

Secondly, the family knew Caiaphas, which could be explained through Zebedee's business in the city or owning a home near Caiaphas in Jerusalem. Given Caiaphas' position and temperament, the fact that Zebedee and his family were on speaking terms with the high priest, even if only at arms-length, says something about Zebedee's standing and relationship to the city. Caiaphas would not have concerned himself with undistinguished commoners.

Thirdly, and most persuasively, there is a long tradition that the Church of the Dormition in Jerusalem stands where Mother Mary eventually passed away, that is, in John's house, which John would have inherited from Zebedee. (John's older brother James was the first apostle to be martyred (Acts 12:2), so John would have inherited his father's estate.) It's located in an area called the Essene Quarter in the southwest of the city, an area that was affluent but not extremely wealthy.

Lastly, because Zebedee was Jesus' uncle, Jesus and his disciples would likely have taken their Passover meal at Zebedee's house if there was adequate room. Perhaps in previous years they did. The Scripture informs us that, before the final Passover, the disciples didn't know of the upper room house—meaning that in previous visits to Jerusalem they stayed at an alternative lodging location. Their first choice for lodging would have been with family if possible. Perhaps Jesus chose the upper room because Zebedee's house was unable to accommodate all of the guests in that final year.[354] It's doubtful that Zebedee's house had a room equal in size to the upper room, which could accommodate 120 persons.

Caiaphas' House

The residence of Caiaphas cannot be pinpointed with certainty, even though some possible sites have been

---

[354] It's also possible that he chose the upper room to establish a base of operations for the early church, or to avoid arrest until the time of his choosing. The reason for his choice is not recorded.

suggested.[355] Without question, his residence must have been in the Upper City, as he was wealthy.[356] However, his wealth was certainly dwarfed by that of his father-in-law Annas and others who lived in the northern third of the Upper City, along a line from Herod's palace to the southern end of the temple mount. It seems best, therefore, to tentatively place Caiaphas' residence in the lower half of the Upper City, as some early traditions suggest. Locating it north of Zebedee's house, but not far from it, is reasonable and could explain the relationship between the two families.

---

[355] Schnabel, *Jesus in Jerusalem*, 124-125.

[356] Wealth was conjoined inseparably with the upper layers of the priesthood. Caiaphas' affluence is evidenced by his elaborately carved ossuary, found in a tomb discovered in 1990.

The Order of Appearances

Beginning from resurrection Sunday, Jesus appeared to his disciples on multiple occasions over a span of forty days.

> To these [his disciples] He also presented Himself alive... appearing to them over a period of forty days and speaking of the things concerning the kingdom of God (Acts 1:3, partial, brackets added)

On the fortieth day he ascended to heaven. To whom did Jesus appear, and in what order? Paul gives us a starting point. In the book of First Corinthians, chapter 15, Paul provided a partial, chronological list of the appearances of Jesus after his resurrection:

> For I delivered to you as of first importance what I also received, that Christ died for our sins according to the Scriptures, and that He was buried, and that He was raised on the third day according to the Scriptures, and that He appeared to Cephas, then to the Twelve. After that He appeared to more than five hundred brethren at one time, most of whom remain until now, but some have fallen asleep; then He appeared to James, then to all the apostles; and last of all, as to one untimely born, He appeared to me also (1 Co 15:3-8)

Summarized as an ordered list, these appearances were to:

- Cephas (that is, Peter)
- The Twelve (disciples; actually, ten of the twelve disciples on the evening following the resurrection; Thomas was absent, and Matthias had not yet been chosen to replace Judas)
- More than five hundred brothers

- James (Jesus' brother)
- All of the apostles[357]
- Paul

Clearly, Paul was not endeavoring to be exhaustive. He omits other appearances to:

- Mary Magdalene
- The other women who visited the tomb
- Clopas/Cleopas and his traveling companion on the road to Emmaus
- The second meeting in Jerusalem with the Twelve, at which Thomas was present

He furthermore does not mention that in the first meeting with the Twelve (on resurrection Sunday evening), others were present (Lk 24:33). If we compare Paul's list with the four gospel accounts, it appears that Paul may have chosen to include only those people who were commissioned and sent forth to spread the good news.

Regardless of Paul's criteria for his list, if we put together all of the appearances from the New Testament, we would have the following ordered list (with references):

1. Mary Magdalene, in the early morning of resurrection Sunday (Jn 20:1-18)

2. The other women (Mary Clopas, Salome, and at least two

---

[357] Paul probably meant the eleven surviving members of the Twelve, as Matthias hadn't been selected and Paul had not met Jesus at the time of that appearance. It also was not meant to include the seventy, or the five hundred, or the eleven others listed as apostles in the New Testament. And although Jesus had appeared to his brother James by this time, James does not appear in the list of apostles who were staying in the upper room (Acts 1:13). Paul may also have been combining more than one meeting with "all the apostles" near the time of the ascension.

others) who accompanied Mary Magdalene to the tomb, after Mary had separated from them to report the stolen body: The appearance occurred after their encounter with the angels in the tomb (Mt 28:5-9)

3. Peter (Cephas): After Clopas had left the company of believers in Jerusalem, in the late morning to early afternoon of resurrection Sunday (1 Co 15:5, Lk 24:21-24)
   (Note in the latter reference that Clopas and his companion made no mention of the appearance to Peter. Therefore, they must have left the disciples in Jerusalem before they had learned of Peter seeing Jesus.)

4. Clopas and his unnamed traveling companion, during the later part of the afternoon of resurrection Sunday (Lk 24:13-35)

5. "The Twelve" (actually ten apostles, as Judas had fallen away and Thomas was absent), along with Clopas, his traveling companion, and an unknown number of other followers with them, in the evening of resurrection Sunday (Lk 24:29, 33, 36-43 and Jn 20:19-24). Although it was still resurrection Sunday, it may have been Nisan 19 because the Jewish calendar date changed at twilight. The meeting may have begun before twilight (Nisan 18), but it's very possible that Clopas and his companion made it back to Jerusalem from Emmaus at dusk. After their meeting with Jesus in Emmaus, when "the day was declining," they needed to travel approximately seven miles again. That would have taken the men about two and a half hours at a good pace.

6. The eleven disciples (including Thomas), on the Sunday following resurrection Sunday (Jn 20:26-29): Verse 26 says it occurred "after eight days," which could lead to some confusion regarding the day of the week. If the text is understood to have meant "after Jesus' first appearance," we (in the twenty-first century) would naturally end up with Monday. However, if we were to count days inclusively from the first meeting of the Twelve, we would end up with Sunday.
   Although counting inclusively seems odd today, there are

historical examples that this was done at times. For instance, Luke 9:28 has "after eight days" (counted inclusively), and Matthew 17:1 has "after six days" (counted exclusively), for the same interval prior to the Transfiguration. In Coffman's Commentaries on the Bible,[358] the author says that Matthew counted only complete days. According to other commentaries (Abbott, Dr. Constable, Carson), "after eight days" is a Greek expression meaning "a week later."

The consistent consensus among biblical commentators is that the appearance to Thomas occurred on the Sunday after resurrection Sunday. John did not specify the time of day.

7. The seven disciples who went fishing in Galilee (Peter, James, John, Nathaniel, Thomas, and two unnamed others), at least a week after the previous recorded meeting (Jn 21:1-11): It would have taken about a week to walk from Jerusalem to Capernaum, which must have been their destination in Galilee, as Jesus had a home in that city (as did Zebedee). The disciples were probably in Capernaum at least a few days before this fishing expedition.

8. More than five hundred brothers in Galilee (1 Co 15:6): Note that Paul calls these witnesses "brothers,"[359] implying that the crowd was almost exclusively followers of Jesus, with few of the idly curious. Where did they come from, and what caused them to gather? Since the upper estimate of Capernaum's population of that time is about 1,500 (of all ages), this group of five hundred brothers must have come from multiple towns and cities of Galilee.

Previously, Jesus had directed the Twelve to proceed to a

---

[358] James Burton Coffman, "*Matthew (Coffman New Testament Commentaries, Vol. 1),*" (Abilene, TX: Abilene Christian University Press, 1974).

[359] About half of English translations (including NASB) use "brethren," but the two words are identical. In this culture and time, the term only meant adult males, hence the total crowd size was much larger.

certain mountain in Galilee (Mt 28:16). The purpose of selecting a mountain for a venue was surely in anticipation of the crowd of "more than five hundred." Certainly Jesus could have appeared to these five-hundred-plus individually, or in smaller groups, but I think not. There is a discernible pattern in the period between the resurrection and ascension wherein Jesus and the angels gave commands to "go and tell," "go and take word," "go and preach," etc. This strongly suggests that Jesus must have sent out the Twelve to call these brothers to gather at a specific time on the designated mountain.

9. Jesus' brother James (1 Co 15:7): Paul's listing of James after the five hundred brothers suggests that this appearance occurred in Galilee.

10. All of the apostles—an appearance assumed to have occurred back in Jerusalem, to instruct them to go to the Mount of Olives (Lk 24:49-50, 1 Co 15:7, Acts 1:4): This is not recorded but is implied by the movements of the apostles.

11. All of the apostles (eleven of the Twelve), at the ascension (1 Co 15:7, Acts 1:9-13): Surely there were more persons present than just the Twelve. At this appearance, Joseph (also called Barsabbas or Justus) and Matthias were present, as Acts 1:21-23 tells us. We can expect that there were more.

12. Paul, at an untimely point, that is, a few years after the 40 days stated by Luke, probably in the mid-AD 30s (Acts 9:1-20, 1 Co 15:8): This is referred to as Paul's Damascus Road experience. The three descriptions in Acts of this dramatic event (Acts 9:3ff, 22:6ff, 26:13ff) would give the impression that Paul saw only a bright light, but other verses testify that Paul saw Jesus also (Acts 9:17, 1 Co 9:1).

In total, Jesus appeared to more than five hundred and twenty[360] of his own loyal followers after his resurrection

---

[360] By my count, no fewer than 526 people: "More than five hundred"

(perhaps more than double that number), but he ignored his cynics and detractors. Peter confirmed that Jesus was very selective in his appearances. In his message to Cornelius the centurion, Peter said, "God raised Him up on the third day and granted that He become visible, not to all the people, but to witnesses who were chosen beforehand by God, that is, to us who ate and drank with Him after He arose from the dead" (Acts 10:40-41). Paul also confirmed the selectivity of Jesus' appearances in his message to the synagogue congregation in Pisidian Antioch: "But God raised Him from the dead; and for many days He appeared to those who came up with Him from Galilee to Jerusalem, the very ones who are now His witnesses to the people" (Acts 13:30-31).

Yet, there was a notable exception to this principle of only appearing to his followers, when Jesus appeared to Paul—who at the time was named Saul and was a violent persecutor of the church. Paul's encounter occurred much later than those of the others, and he subsequently became the apostle to the Gentiles.

Another possible exception to Jesus' norm of appearing only

(logically, at least five hundred and one, in Galilee), plus at least five women at the tomb, eleven remaining members of the Twelve, Clopas and his companion, James bar Joseph, Justus and Matthias (Acts 1:22-23), three others called apostles (because seeing the resurrected Jesus was a requirement for apostleship)—Andronicus, Junias, and Barabbas (Rm 16:7, Acts 14:14) and Paul (years later). I did not count "those that were with them" (Lk 24:33), since this might double-count some of those already mentioned. This number is the absolute minimum based on the information in the New Testament.

However, the actual total was certainly much higher. Besides assorted others who may have been present in some of the smaller gatherings, the appearance to "more than five hundred brethren" (or brothers) is only accounting for the number of men. (Just as the numbers for Jesus' feeding of the multitudes counted only men.) The number of women and children present probably eclipsed the number of men, so the actual number of eyewitnesses must have been well north of 1,000.

to his loyalists was his appearance to his brother James (number nine above). We are told by John that at the time of an earlier feast (about half a year before the crucifixion), "not even His brothers were believing in Him" (Jn 7:5). The next mention of Jesus' brothers is in connection with the day of Pentecost.

> These all with one mind were continually devoting themselves to prayer, along with the women, and Mary the mother of Jesus, and with His brothers (Acts 1:14).

By this time James and the other brothers had become followers of Jesus and were waiting for the promise of the Holy Spirit.

But, did James believe in Jesus as the Messiah *before* Jesus personally appeared to him following the resurrection? That is a question that cannot be definitely answered from the New Testament. My leaning is to think that he did not, for a few reasons. Jesus' ministry was between two and three years in length, and after more than two years of ministry, James had not seen anything to persuade him that his brother was messianic. So, there's no particular reason to think that Jesus' last half-year before the crucifixion would have changed his mind.

James also leaned towards Jewish legalism; you could almost say that he was Pharisaic in mindset and practice. This would have been an obstacle to his conversion. I make this assessment from the legalistic flavor of the book of James (which he wrote); his sensitivity to Jewish sensibilities as displayed in Acts 15:13-21; Peter's reaction to "men from James" (Gal 2:11ff); and his reputation later as "James the Just," a man noted for strict adherence to the laws of Moses.

Furthermore, James was not present at the crucifixion, and I presume he had fled Jerusalem upon hearing of Jesus' arrest, for fear of being associated with his brother. (The disciples, except for John, were likewise not at the cross, but they had a more substantial reason for fearing persecution than James would have.) And finally, Jesus entrusted his mother to John rather than James, the closer relation. Therefore, there is good reason to think that Jesus' appearance to James was necessary for his conversion, just as Jesus' appearance to Paul on the road to Damascus was necessary for Paul to see the light.

In any case, the important fact is that James was a believer and a follower of Jesus by the time of the ascension. James eventually became the leader of the church of Jerusalem and was martyred for his faith.

There is an object lesson for today's church in appearance number five. This is Jesus' first appearance to his inner circle, the Twelve. It may be surprising that Jesus didn't appear to them first. Instead, he had already appeared to a "nobody" (Mary Magdalene), a group of women, the one disciple who had denied knowing him, and two other "nobodies"—Clopas and his unnamed companion. Perhaps Jesus was underscoring his earlier teaching that his church was not to be contaminated by human political ambition, that is, the desire for prominence, place, and power:

> "But do not be called Rabbi; for One is your Teacher, and you are all brothers. ... But the greatest among you shall be your servant. Whoever exalts himself shall be humbled; and whoever humbles himself shall be exalted." (Mt 23:8, 11-12)

Further, in appearance number five, Jesus did not reveal himself to his ten disciples *alone;* there were others with them already, as Clopas and his companion had just joined the group. And why should this be surprising? Jesus' journeys throughout the countryside of Galilee had included not just the twelve disciples, as is often portrayed, but numerous other disciples as well (Lk 8:1-3; note particularly the "many others" of verse 3).

We should thus assume, and I have in this book, that appearances six, ten, and eleven also included disciples who were not members of the Twelve. Remember, the day of Pentecost found 120 believers gathered together (Acts 1:15). Jesus was emphatically establishing a spiritual family, not a clerical hierarchy.

There might have been additional appearances that were not

recorded, of course, but certainly the total number of appearances was not large. For John related, concerning an appearance in Galilee, that:

> This is now the *third time* that Jesus was manifested to the disciples [particularly, the Twelve], after He was raised from the dead. (Jn 21:14, emphasis and brackets added)

John was speaking of the appearance to the seven disciples who had gone fishing (appearance number seven above); the first two appearances to "the disciples" were numbers five and six. This occurred perhaps two to three weeks after resurrection Sunday. Why two to three weeks? That's because the first week after the resurrection, the disciples had stayed in Jerusalem until Thomas had seen Jesus. The subsequent trip back to Galilee took approximately another week.

Therefore, it's obvious that the majority of the forty-day period of resurrection appearances was spent waiting and wondering when and where Jesus would appear next. For the followers of Jesus, it had to be a time of extreme suspense, anticipation, and immeasurable joy.

The Day of First Fruits

Yom HaBikkurim (also called the Day of First Fruits, Waving of the Omer, or Waving of the Sheaf) refers to an offering made shortly after Passover. It involved harvesting a small amount of barley, processing it, and offering it up on the altar of burnt offering.

Interestingly, the Hebrew word for "first fruit" (bikkur) is closely related to the Hebrew word for "firstborn" (bekhor); they both derive from the same root and sound nearly identical.[361] Paul makes the symbolic connection between Jesus' resurrection and this offering ceremony when he wrote "Christ has been raised from the dead, the first fruits of those who are asleep" (1Co 15:20).

The observance of Yom HaBikkurim was established in the Old Testament book of Leviticus, chapter 23, verses 5-16. Verse 11 specifies *when* it should be offered:

> He [the priest] shall wave the sheaf before the LORD for you to be accepted; *on the day after the sabbath* the priest shall wave it. (Lev 23:11, brackets and emphasis added)

Before and during the time of Christ, the meaning of the "day after the sabbath" was interpreted two different ways, resulting in a dispute between the Pharisees and a sect of the Sadducees over which day was meant. The Pharisees understood *the sabbath* as referring to the Passover sabbath (Nisan 15), meaning that the offering should occur annually on Nisan 16. The Sadducees, however, understood *the sabbath* as being the first Saturday after Passover, meaning that the first fruits should be offered on a Sunday (not a fixed calendar date).[362] These two

---

[361] Thanks to Rabbi Art Weiner for discussion related to the Day of First Fruits.

[362] *Encylopedia Judaica*, Second Edition, Volume 15, 419-420.

interpretations are still debated today.

Joshua 5:10-12 has been cited as support for the interpretation of the Pharisees. It describes the actions of the ancient Israelites shortly after crossing the Jordan River into Canaan:

> While the sons of Israel camped at Gilgal, they observed the Passover on the evening of the fourteenth day of the month on the desert plains of Jericho. *On the day after the Passover, on that very day, they ate some of the produce of the land, unleavened cakes and parched grain.* The manna ceased on the day after they had eaten some of the produce of the land, so that the sons of Israel no longer had manna, but they ate some of the yield of the land of Canaan during that year. (Jos 5:10-12, emphasis added)

However, these verses do not provide strong support for the Pharisee's view. They do not say that a grain offering was made; rather, they simply record that the Israelites ate some of the produce of the land upon entering it. Even if there was a "first fruits" offering (an assumption), Nisan 16 could have been a Sunday that year, satisfying either interpretation.

Josephus (c. 30 - c. 100, a historian living in Rome) and Philo (c. 20 - c. 50, a philosopher living in Alexandria) were both Pharisees, and they both wrote that Nisan 16 was the date for the offering of first fruits. However, both were Pharisees and could be expected to be promoting that sect's viewpoint. Josephus' chapter in which he provides his information is curiously titled, "Concerning the Festivals, and How Each Day of Such Festival Is to Be Observed," rather than "...Is Observed," perhaps reflecting his own desire of how it should be done.[363]

Strong support for the interpretation of the Sadducees is found in verses 15 and 16 of Leviticus 23:

You shall also count for yourselves from the day after the

---

[363] Flavius Josephus, *Antiquities of the Jews*, Book III, Chapter 10.

sabbath, from the day when you brought in the sheaf of the wave offering; there shall be seven complete sabbaths. You shall count fifty days *to the day after the seventh sabbath*; then you shall present a new grain offering to the LORD. (Lev 23:15-16, emphasis added)

In order to count (inclusively) fifty days and finish on a Sunday (*the day after the seventh sabbath*) you must begin on a Sunday. This makes the meaning of Leviticus 23:11 (above) very plain, and the Sadducees had the correct interpretation.

The important question then becomes: Who was the high priest at the time of Jesus' resurrection? And was that person a Pharisee or a Sadducee? The answer is Caiaphas, a Sadducee:

But the high priest rose up, along with all his associates (that is the sect of the Sadducees), and they were filled with jealousy. (Acts 5:17)

Caiaphas, who remained high priest until AD 36, was still high priest at the time of this event in Acts. Sadducees had occupied the high priesthood for decades by the time of Jesus, and had complete control of the temple practices. For scriptural, political, and prophetic reasons, the weight of evidence points to resurrection Sunday as the day when the omer was waved before God.

Jesus' resurrection fulfilled perfectly, and on the very same day, the symbolism of the first fruits offering.

Epilogue

The subtitle to this book is: "A Complete Account of the Most Important Day in Human History."

The Most Important Day: really? Yes. There is no other day that remotely comes close.

Before that day, the human race was devoid of any real hope. People lacked answers to basic questions, such as, "How did I get here?" and "Where do I go after I die?" All people-groups had some concept of a god, but he was distant, remote, and impersonal. Life on earth for most people was very hard and regularly brutal. The turmoil in human souls spilled over into violence between friends, neighbors, and nations—not unlike the condition of much of the world today. By and large, people had no hope and were without God in the world.

The root cause of the majority of human troubles, then and now, is that self-centered and dark, rebellious and arrogant "something" in each one of us. Before Jesus' resurrection, there was no solution for it. Each human being remained imprisoned in the darkness of their own heart and mind. Most people, in their efforts to just survive, probably gave this root cause problem little or no thought. Philosophers occasionally touched on it. Some religions, especially Judaism, recognized the problem, but the best answer they provided, before Jesus, was to kill an animal as a sacrifice to attempt to correct or redeem a moral wrong.

But sacrifices never removed the tendency to do wrong, so it was a constant cycle of wrongdoing followed by sacrifice. No human actions provided lasting freedom from actual guilt or the guilty feelings associated with it. Sacrifices and psychological repression were mere bandages over the festering infection.

And there was little reason to believe that there was any existence after death, despite the fanciful, bizarre, and conflicting scenarios envisioned by a few ancient cultures.

Therefore, many people of antiquity adopted an early materialistic worldview, including the chief priests of Judaism, as most of them were drawn from the Sadducee party, which did not believe in a resurrection of the body.[364]

Then came Jesus.

He was the first one who knew where he was from, and where he was going: "I proceeded forth and have come from God,"[365] and "I go to Him who sent Me."[366]

He told the world where we came from, and where we were going: "You are from below,"[367] and "Where I am going, you cannot come."[368]

He defined the primary problem of humanity and said he had an answer for it: "From the heart of men proceed the evil thoughts,"[369] and "If the Son makes you free, you will be free indeed."[370]

Jesus said he spoke for God, and he presented God as a loving Father: "I speak just as the Father has told Me,"[371] and "The Father Himself loves you."[372]

And Jesus said much more than this, as recorded in the four gospel records. But, how can we know if Jesus was speaking truth, and not just lofty sentiments from the mind of a common man? How can we know he was not a false prophet, like many others of his time or ours?

Well, there were the miracles. The blind were given sight, the deaf were healed, and the paralyzed walked. Even a few dead

---

[364] Mt 22:23; Acts 23:8

[365] Jn 8:42

[366] Jn 7:33

[367] Jn 8:23. "From below" means from the earth. Cf. Jn 3:31.

[368] Jn 8:21. Jesus said that he was going to the Father. Thus, he meant here that we would not enjoy the company of him or his father if we fail to change course.

[369] Mk 7:21

[370] Jn 8:36

[371] Jn 12:50

[372] Jn 16:27

people were brought back to life. And then there were the demonstrations of his power over nature (or "physics," if you will): He walked on water, stilled the storm with a word, and fed multitudes from a few scraps of food. There were those.

Yet the most mind-blowing, extraordinary thing that Jesus did was to predict his death by tortuous execution and to further say that he would rise from the dead three days later. He said this both to his followers and publicly.[373] It was the most audacious claim anyone could possibly make. No one else in history has ever made such a claim. Jesus didn't just make the claim; he fulfilled it!

The world changed for all humankind on that incredible morning when his followers discovered that Jesus had mastery over death. Everything of personal and existential importance changed at that very moment:

- It meant that Jesus' claim to divinity was true and nobody, before or since, possessed the knowledge of and relationship to God the Father that Jesus demonstrated—therefore, his words are the gold standard for knowing anything about God.[374]

- It meant that Jesus' statement about the depravity of man was accurate—and there will be no hiding of it.[375]

- It meant that Jesus' statement about a future accountability for our personal actions is a fair warning—and there will be no excuses.[376]

- It meant that Jesus' teaching about the purpose of his death—that it will serve as the complete atonement for

---

[373] To his followers: Mk 8:31; 10:34. Publicly: Mt 27:63.

[374] For I did not speak on My own initiative, but the Father Himself who sent Me has given Me a commandment as to what to say and what to speak. (Jn 12:49)

[375] For nothing is hidden, except to be revealed; nor has anything been secret, but that it would come to light. (Mk 4:22)

[376] And He will say, "I tell you, I do not know where you are from; depart from Me, all you evildoers." (Lk 13:27)

our transgressions if we believe in him—is the best news ever and a call to personal change.[377]

- And it meant that the materialistic view that this life "is all there is" is badly mistaken, and we will end up either in God's glorious presence or forever banished from it— it's our choice.[378]

Many have said that Jesus started the Christian religion, but that can be misleading. Jesus gave no commands to build buildings, create liturgies, organize worship bands, or fund seminaries and a professional clergy class.[379] Those religious additions are man-made augmentation to the paramount, life-altering message that Jesus is alive. Jesus' statements were not, in the conventional sense, religiously inclined; his teachings focused primarily on the relationship between an individual and God, and secondarily on the relationships between individuals. His death was the means that God ordained to repair the relationship between God and every person.

Before Jesus, there was no hope for anyone. Since the dawn of resurrection Sunday, the resurrection stands as *the* door to a relationship with God. For the believer, it's the guarantee. For those that don't yet believe, it is the best invitation they will ever receive. The resurrection is the only exit off the highway to hell.

That one day has made all the difference—the difference between a stone cold tomb, and just a cave.

---

[377] For God so loved the world, that He gave His only begotten Son, that whoever believes in Him shall not perish, but have eternal life. (Jn 3:16)

[378] For the gate is small and the way is narrow that leads to life, and there are few who find it. (Mt 7:14)

[379] He also never called his followers "Christians," although there is nothing wrong with that appellation.

If you have reached this point in the book without believing that Jesus came out of a tomb three days after suffering a horrific death by Roman crucifixion, then you are following in the venerable footsteps of the early disciples. They also found the idea too incredible to accept.

Stubborn Unbelief

The eleven remaining members of the Twelve—those prayerfully handpicked disciples of Jesus—were intransigent in their unbelief of the resurrection. In striking contrast, the women at the tomb believed immediately on the report of two angels whom they had never seen before. The difference is remarkable.

The men did not believe:

1. Mary's report of theft of the body (Jn 20:9)

2. The women's report of the angels' announcement (Lk 24:4-11, 22, 23)

3. Mary's report of seeing Jesus (Mk 16:10-11)

4. The women's report of seeing Jesus (Mt 28:9-10)

5. Peter's report of seeing Jesus (Lk 24:34)[380]

6. Clopas and his companion's report of seeing Jesus (Mk 16:12-13)

7. Their own eyes, when they saw Jesus (Lk 24:41)

8. And for Thomas, he also didn't believe when the other

---

[380] Verse 34 is interesting. It's often interpreted to be the words of the travelers to the disciples, but the travelers had no knowledge of the appearance of Jesus to Simon (Peter). Rather, the verse describes the disciples sharing Peter's report of his personal visitation from the resurrected Christ. In the following verse, the travelers corroborate that they had seen Jesus also. Yet amazingly, even after the testimonies of Mary, the other women, Peter, and the travelers, verse 37 testifies that they still were not believing.

disciples told him they had seen Jesus (Jn 20:24-25).

Perhaps it's not surprising; people die every day, but resurrections are rare indeed. And human nature finds exceptionally good news difficult to trust.

But these men finally did believe. They became so convinced that they devoted the remainder of their lives to sharing the good news that Jesus is still alive. They all suffered greatly for their belief, but they could not be dissuaded from what they knew to be true. Early tradition says that all of them except John were martyred.

Peter said it plainly: "For we did not follow cleverly devised tales when we made known to you the power and coming of our Lord Jesus Christ, but we were eyewitnesses of His majesty" (2Pt 1:16). The resurrection is not some "cleverly devised tale." It is true. It is past, present, and future: Jesus was alive, Jesus is alive today, and he always will be.

This leaves you, Dear Reader, with a three-way fork in the road.

1. You can choose to not believe that Jesus is alive, and continue your life along its present trajectory. Good luck with that.

2. You can believe that Jesus is alive but choose to ignore the implications. The result is that you will miss out on the purpose for life, which is to have a relationship with God.

3. You can believe that Jesus is alive and let that knowledge change your life. It means that you ask Jesus to forgive you for your past wrongdoings and to guide the remainder of your life on earth. That's the first and most important step to knowing Jesus.[381]

---

[381] It's only the beginning step, however. Visit graceonly.com/dawn for more.

Peter summed it up well: "And we have the prophetic word more fully confirmed, to which you will do well to pay attention as to a lamp shining in a dark place, until the day dawns and the morning star[382] rises in your hearts" (2Pt 1:19).

May the Dawn of the Resurrection fully illuminate your heart!

---

[382] The "morning star" is a biblical name for Jesus. (Rev 22:16)

It is finished.
John 19:30

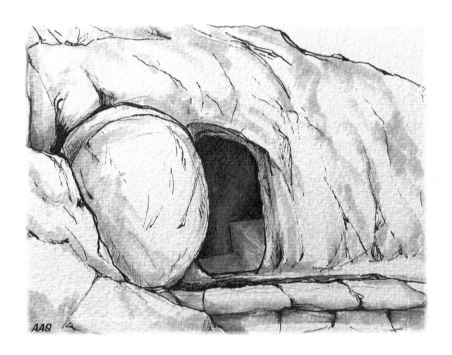

And death is no longer
master over Him.
Romans 6:9

Appendices

Appendix A: Calendar Notes

Then God said, "Let there be lights in the expanse of the heavens to separate the day from the night, and let them be *for signs and for seasons and for days and years.*" (Gen 1:14, emphasis added)

Since before recorded history, people have recognized the movements of heavenly bodies and used them for markers of time. The most obvious was the (apparent) motion of the sun, created by the earth's rotation about its axis, giving us the period of a day. Different cultures have used different starting points for the day; for example, the Romans' civil day began at midnight while the Jews' day began at dusk. This is discussed in more detail in Appendix C.

The second most obvious time marker is the visible phases of the moon, caused by the orbiting of the moon about the earth, giving us the period of a month.

The third, but less obvious movement is that made by the sun over the course of a year. The sun will rise (and set) at different points on the horizon depending on the day of the year. The Egyptians recognized this early in their history, perhaps because they had a flat horizon. Other observable yearly variations include the seasons and the length of daylight.[383] These yearly changes are due to two factors: the orbit of the earth about the sun and the inclination of the earth's spin axis to the plane of its orbit.

The relationship between these three time markers—the day, month, and year—are not nice and tidy; they are not integer multiples. There are not exactly thirty days in a month, nor 365

---

[383] Except for those persons on the equator, where daylight is always twelve hours.

days in a year. The reason for the untidiness is that the causes behind these time markers, namely, the rotation of the earth, the orbit of the moon, and the orbit of the earth (combined with its tilted axis)—are completely independent of one another.[384] This bothered some of the ancients from a theological perspective, as they expected that a perfect God would use simple numerical relationships between these time units, but they might have also considered that God seems to handle fractions pretty well.

The time period of a week is completely arbitrary but very useful for practical purposes. The Jews used a seven-day week, and the Romans used an eight-day week in the first century. Other cultures have had four- to ten-day weeks, but all "weeks" are unrelated to astronomical observations.

In the creation of a calendar, the non-integer relationships between days, months, and years can create problems. If you were to make all years equal to 365 days, for example, the year would be about one-quarter day short of the time for the earth to orbit the sun.[385] This would create a problem in that the seasons, and their associated planting and harvesting dates, would gradually drift later and later on the calendar. If each year had 366 or more days, the seasons would consequently shift earlier on the calendar.

The Julian calendar adopted by the Romans in 45 BC (and used by Romans in the time of Jesus) had years of 365 days, but it added the improvement of an additional "leap day" to every fourth year, giving an average of 365.25 days per year.[386] These

---

[384] Or very, very nearly so. The slight gravitational interactions between these movements are interesting but practically irrelevant.

[385] On average, a solar year is about 365.242 days. This value varies slightly year-to-year, due to the gravitational effects of Venus and the moon, and other factors of interest mainly to astronomers.

[386] This worked well for hundreds of years, but being slightly longer than a solar year, seasons very slowly shifted earlier on the Julian calendar. The Gregorian calendar, adopted in the sixteenth century, improved on this accuracy by omitting one leap day in certain centuries.

familiar leap days are examples of *intercalations*—that is, insertions to keep the calendar in closer synchronization with the solar year.

The Jewish calendar in the first century was *lunisolar*; that is, it was based on the monthly phases of the moon with periodic adjustments to maintain rough synchronization with the yearly cycle of the sun. In Jerusalem, the Sanhedrin was responsible for calendrical matters, and it used a council of three men to determine when months began.[387]

The beginning of Jewish months was determined when at least two of the three delegated observers testified to seeing the first sliver of a new moon appear in the evening in Jerusalem. After the head of the Sanhedrin declared that a new month had begun, a trumpet was blown and heralds sent out with the news.

Sometimes it wasn't possible to observe the new moon because of weather conditions. In such cases, knowing that the moon's phases repeat approximately every 29.5 days, the Jews would announce the month so that the months would alternate between 29 and 30 days. By post-Talmudic times (after AD 500), the Jewish calendar's months simply alternated between 29 and 30 days, beginning with Nisan having 30 days.

In the time of Jesus, however, the Jews followed a visual determination of each month's commencement, and especially for the first month (Nisan) and seventh month (Tishri), which occurred near the equinoxes.[388] So important were the observations on these two days that the official observers were allowed to exceed the travel distance limit of 2,000 cubits on the Sabbath, if necessary, to bring their reports.

Periodically, intercalations were necessary to the Jewish

---

[387] Jack Finegan, *Handbook of Biblical Chronology* (Peabody, MA: Hendrickson Publishers, 1998), 35-39.

[388] The equinoxes are the two days of the year when the daylight and nighttime periods are most nearly equal. These are the vernal (or spring) equinox and the autumnal (or fall) equinox. They occur around March 21st and September 22nd, respectively, on our modern calendar.

calendar because twelve months averaging 29.5 days yields a calendar year of only 354 days, which is a little more than eleven days short of the solar year. Rather than adding eleven days to every year, the Jews allowed the calendar slippage to reach about thirty days, more or less, before inserting an entire month.

The procedure used by the Sanhedrin to determine when to add an intercalary (leap) month is interesting. An example of a decision to add an intercalary month is in a letter from Simeon, son of Gamaliel and head of the Sanhedrin in the two decades before the destruction of the temple (AD 70), which reads, "We beg to inform you that the doves are still tender and the lambs still young, and the grain has not yet ripened. I have considered the matter and thought it advisable to add thirty days to the year."[389] The length of the added month was either twenty-nine or thirty days, at the discretion of the council. It is crucial to notice that all of the criteria are based on signs of spring observed at a certain point in the lunar cycle, and the intercalary month would be added if spring was late in arriving.

Centuries later in the Talmud, the rabbis taught that a year would be extended by an intercalary month if two of three criteria were observed:

1. The barley crop was premature.

2. The fruit trees were premature.

3. The vernal equinox was late.

Notice that the rabbi's criteria were different (though similar) from those listed by Simeon; the primary difference is that the rabbis referenced the equinox. However, the Jews in the first century did not use the equinox as a criterion to determine whether to add an extra month to the calendar, and therefore, Passover (Nisan 14) could occur before or after the equinox. Historically, there is clear evidence that this was the case.[390]

---

[389] Finegan, *Handbook of Biblical Chronology*, 38.

[390] Roger T. Beckwith, "Cautionary Notes on the Use of Calendars and Astronomy to Determine the Chronology of the Passion," *Chronos,*

Very importantly, we have no way of knowing which years were intercalated and which were not. The intercalations of Jesus' time were based entirely upon whether the signs of spring came early or late.

Several attempts have been made to apply our modern astronomical understanding towards determining the date of the crucifixion, but they have been hampered by two errors: firstly, assuming that it took place on a Friday, and secondly, that it occurred after the vernal equinox.[391]

In the year AD 30, the fourteenth day of the lunar month *after* the equinox would have been Friday, April 7th. Because this was a Friday, this date has been accepted by many as the date of Jesus' crucifixion. However, the fourteenth day of the lunar month *before* the equinox would have been Wednesday, March 8th.

Wednesday, March 8th, AD 30. At the beginning of the year in which Jesus died, there was no need to attach a thirteenth month to extend the outgoing year of AD 29. For the doves and lambs were mature enough to be used for sacrifice, and the barley was ripe enough to be ready for the Omer offering to be made on Nisan 18. The weather had been good.

Spring came early that year.

Kairos, Christos: Nativity and Chronological Studies Presented to Jack Finegan, edited by J. Vardaman and E. Yamauchi, (Winona Lake: Eisenbrauns, 1989), 189-193.

[391] Example: Colin J. Humphreys and W. G. Waddington, "Astronomy and the Date of the Crucifixion," *Chronos, Kairos, Christos: Nativity and Chronological Studies Presented to Jack Finegan*, edited by J. Vardaman and E. Yamauchi, (Winona Lake: Eisenbrauns, 1989), 165-181.

Appendix B: Was the Last Supper a Passover Meal?

There is confusion over Jesus' Last Supper meal—that is, whether it was a true Passover celebration or not, and on which exact day it took place. Some of the confusion exists due to different meanings assumed for Passover. The word "Passover" has meant different things in different contexts and different times, so clarification of the term and its usage is needed.

Another point of confusion arises when we read John's account of the moment when the chief priests and co-conspirators led Jesus to Pilate for trial:

> Then they [the chief priests and their co-conspirators] led Jesus from Caiaphas into the Praetorium, and it was early; and they themselves did not enter into the Praetorium so that they would not be defiled, but *might eat the Passover.* (Jn 18:28, emphasis added)

This means that the day of the crucifixion was Nisan 14—the day on which Passover sacrifices were made at the temple and consumed after twilight. The obvious question is: If the priests hadn't eaten Passover yet, how could Jesus and his disciples have eaten Passover the previous evening? Let's address this question first.

The Practice of Passover

Originally, Passover was not a feast but a sacrificed animal:

> Then Moses called for all the elders of Israel and said to them, "Go and take for yourselves lambs according to your families, and slay the Passover [lamb]." (Ex 12:21; brackets represent a translator's addition; see also Ex 12:11, 27)

There are a few important things to notice about this very first

Passover, which delivered the ancient Israelites from slavery, and which was commanded by God to be celebrated annually:

1. It (the lamb) was to be "kept until the fourteenth day of the same month [Nisan 14]," then killed at twilight (Ex 12:6). The word typically translated as "twilight" is actually a phrase, "between the two evenings." This means that the lamb was to be killed as Nisan 13 was transitioning to Nisan 14, or between the time that the sun first went below the horizon (early twilight), and late twilight (in later years, this was defined as when the first three stars had appeared)—in short, at the very beginning of Nisan 14. Recall that Jewish days changed at sundown, so the first Passover sacrifice occurred as Nisan 13 was changing to Nisan 14.

2. The original Passover was to be eaten in individual homes, and the blood smeared on the lintel (the beam above the door) and doorposts (Ex 12:3-7). (Strikingly, this forms the sign of the cross.) It was the only sacrifice that God ordained to be performed by laypeople, and it originated prior to the establishment of the priesthood.

3. The Feast of Unleavened Bread was to immediately follow the day that the Passover lamb was sacrificed and eaten, and it was to last for seven days, Nisan 15 through 21 (Lev 23:5-8). No work was to be done on the first (15th) or last (21st) day.

Between the days of the Exodus, when the Jews sacrificed the first Passover, and the time of Jesus, the meaning and practice of Passover changed.

During the period of the separate kingdoms of Israel and Judah, which began about 930 BC after the death of King Solomon, the two kingdoms fell into apostasy and idolatry by following the practices of the nations around them.[392] Even the Mosaic law, observance of Passover, and the temple sacrifices were largely forgotten; it was a spiritually dark time for the

---

[392] Idolatry in these instances involved worshiping, praying, and sacrificing to statues of "gods" made from wood, metal, or stone.

descendants of Israel.

Fortunately, in this dark period of history, two kings arose in Judah that instituted reforms: Hezekiah, and three generations later, his great-grandson Josiah. When Hezekiah called the people to return to the long-neglected celebration of Passover, he called them to celebrate the Passover at the temple in Jerusalem, and the Levites sacrificed animals for the people.[393]

Perhaps the well-meaning kings wanted the Passover celebration to be centralized, so that they could insure the people's compliance, but regardless of their reasons, this change departed from God's original directive in three aspects. Sacrifices now occurred at the temple, rather than in individual homes among family and neighbors; the slaughter of the lambs (and young goats) was performed by priests or Levites rather than by heads of households; and the application of blood to the lintels and doorposts was replaced by the pouring out of the sacrificial blood upon the side of the temple altar. These changes effected a centralizing of religious practice and a formalization of what was previously an intimate, family-centered observance.

Josiah's enlightened reign was followed by that of his son Jehoiakim, a corrupt and idolatrous king. During Jehoiakim's sorry reign, Jerusalem fell to invaders, and a large segment of the population of the nation of Judah was exiled to Babylon. At the beginning of the exile, the Passover and Unleavened Bread celebrations were combined into one.[394] As a result, Passover lambs were now sacrificed late on Nisan 14, just before the start of Unleavened Bread—another departure from the original practice.

In AD 38, very close to the time of Jesus, the Jewish writer Philo explained that Passover sacrifices were being offered both at the temple by the priests and *also* by individuals either at the temple, or "at home" according to the original ordinance from Moses:

---

[393] 2 Chr 30:13-27; 35:1-19.
[394] *Encyclopedia Judaica*, Second Edition, Vol. 15, 680.

Accordingly, in this month, about the fourteenth day of the month, when the orb of the moon is usually about to become full, the public universal feast of the Passover is celebrated, which in the Chaldaic language is called Pascha; at which festival not only do private individuals bring victims to the altar and the priests sacrifice them, but also, by a particular ordinance of this law, the whole nation is consecrated and officiates in offering sacrifice; every separate individual on this occasion bringing forward and offering up with his own hands the sacrifice due on his own behalf.[395]

This is important to know because, if Passover animals were only being sacrificed at the temple, there would be a sharp limitation on the number that could be handled. The size of the temple area limited the number of animals that could be sacrificed; furthermore, only three batches of animals were sacrificed in the afternoon of Nisan 14. Joachim Jeremias has offered a detailed estimate of how many animals could have been processed within those constraints, arriving at the number of 18,000.[396] As mentioned before, the historian Josephus records that about 256,500 animals were sacrificed in Jerusalem during Passover for some 2.7 million participants, and this works out closely to the expected ratio of one sacrifice for every ten participants.

Jeremias' number of 18,000 animals would only account for seven percent of Josephus' estimate, which raises questions about the accuracy of Josephus' number. However, the number of people in Jerusalem—native residents and visiting pilgrims— could easily have been large enough to support a number like Josephus', *if the Passover animals were not all slaughtered at the temple*. When the Roman General Titus surrounded Jerusalem in AD 70 during Passover, about 1.2 million persons were trapped inside the city, according to Josephus.

---

[395] Philo, *On the Life of Moses*, Book II, XLI:224-225.
[396] Joachim Jeremias, *Jerusalem in the Time of Jesus*, (Peabody, MA: Hendrickson Publishers, 1969), 82.

Additionally, many more pilgrims, encamped outside the walls in an extended tent city, must have fled when they saw the Romans approaching. Given the enormous population during the Passover, the temple was incapable of handling all of the slaughtering.

Obviously, therefore, the Passover sacrifices at the temple represented only a small portion of the total number of animals sacrificed. The majority were sacrificed in domestic gatherings all over the city (and the surrounding area), on both the evening of Nisan 13—in keeping with the instructions from Moses—and on Nisan 14 also, as a matter of practical logistics. Jesus, and many others in the city of Jerusalem, celebrated Passover as Moses had instituted, eating the meal at the beginning of Nisan 14 rather than Nisan 15.

On Nisan 13, Jesus instructed his disciples Peter and John to "go and prepare the Passover for us, so that we may eat it" (Lk 22:8). Peter and John understood "prepare the Passover" as "sacrifice the Passover lamb and roast it," and they did precisely that. (They would have prepared the other parts of the meal as well, but it seems the procurement of the meal components had already been made by others.) The twelve disciples ate the Passover with Jesus during the early night of Tuesday the 14th, just after Nisan 13 had ended. Jesus died in the afternoon of Wednesday the 14th, as the priests began sacrificing Passover animals in the temple.[397]

None of the gospel writers make mention of a Passover lamb being eaten at the Last Supper. That's certainly interesting, but it's no reason to discount the meal as a true Passover meal. The other traditional elements of such a meal were surely present, yet only two are mentioned: bread and wine. Jesus chose to make bread and wine the symbols for his sacrifice of body and blood, as the gospels highlight. The essential Passover lamb was not the one butchered by Peter and John but rather the one who

---

[397] Recall that in Jewish days, night precedes daylight. But days of the week here are figured according to the modern convention and change at midnight.

broke the bread and shared it around the table.

The Various Meanings of "Passover" and "Unleavened Bread"

Between the time of Moses and that of Jesus, the term "Passover" had expanded to include the *day* of the sacrifice, Nisan 14, and also the whole eight-day period that included the Feast of Unleavened Bread, Nisan 14 to 21. And, sometimes that same eight-day period was simply called "Unleavened Bread." We see these multiple meanings used in the New Testament.

1. In Mark 14:12, Passover means the lamb.[398]

2. In Mark 14:1, it means the day of the sacrifice.[399]

3. And in Luke 22:1 it refers to the eight-day period including the Feast of Unleavened Bread.[400]

Since the two feasts, Passover and Unleavened Bread, are back-to-back and therefore continuous in observance, this fluidity of meanings is not surprising at all. Further, leaven (*chametz*) had to be removed from houses *prior to* the evening of the Passover meal, so in a very real sense, "Unleavened Bread" would start on Nisan 13 and continue through the end of Nisan 21. Peter and John would have searched the upper room on the 13th to verify that all leaven had been removed, as part of their Passover preparations. Added to the indefinite usage of the terms, Passover sacrifices were being made both on the 13th (domestically) and 14th (traditionally, in the temple) of

---

[398] On the first day of Unleavened Bread, when the Passover lamb was being sacrificed, His disciples said to Him, "Where do You want us to go and prepare for You to eat the Passover?" (Mk 14:12)
[399] Now the Passover and Unleavened Bread were two days away; and the chief priests and the scribes were seeking how to seize Him by stealth and kill Him. (Mk 14:1)
[400] Now the Feast of Unleavened Bread, which is called the Passover, was approaching. (Lk 22:1)

Nisan.[401]

With all of the above as background, we can make sense of the timestamps in the following puzzling verses (emphases added; brackets are translators' additions).

1. *Now on the first day of Unleavened Bread* the disciples came to Jesus and asked, "Where do You want us to prepare for You to eat the Passover?" (Mt 26:17)

2. *On the first day of Unleavened Bread, when the Passover lamb was being sacrificed,* His disciples said to Him, "Where do You want us to go and prepare for You to eat the Passover?" (Mk 14:12)

3. *Then came the first day of Unleavened Bread on which the Passover lamb had to be sacrificed.* And Jesus sent Peter and John, saying, "Go and prepare the Passover for us, so that we may eat it." (Lk 22:7-8)

Each of these verses is referring to Nisan 13: the day when Peter and John were sent to prepare the most consequential meal in history. Nisan 13 is the definitive date because it was the day before the traditional temple observance of Passover and the day of the crucifixion. All three writers understood the meaning of the expressions that they wrote and the exact date that they were referencing. Therefore, it is obligatory to interpret the timestamps in light of the known date, rather than try to assign another date, or imagine a conflict, because of a *presumed* understanding of the timestamps.

---

[401] Although it is known that Passover sacrifices at the temple occurred in the afternoon of Nisan 14, rather than a bit later (at dusk), the gospels do not say if the lamb for the Last Supper was slaughtered in the afternoon of the 13th or at dusk between the 13th and 14th. If the latter, then the meal could not have been eaten until about midnight because of the time needed to prepare and roast the whole animal. The same situation was true for the first Passover, and it is meaningful that the Israelites were consuming the Passover lamb at the very moment that God was bringing judgment on Egypt (Ex 12).

Therefore, to these three historians, the common understanding in that day of the phrase "Unleavened Bread" had to include the entire feast from Nisan 13 to Nisan 21. Furthermore, these verses clearly communicate that Jesus and his disciples believed the legitimate time to eat the Passover was at the start of Nisan 14. Moses would have agreed.

It was a real Passover meal, with Jesus as the true Passover lamb "who takes away the sin of the world" (Jn 1:29).

Appendix C: At What Hour Was Jesus Crucified?

As described in the "When Was Jesus Crucified?" section of Part Three, the Jewish daylight period—sunrise to sunset—was divided into twelve equal hours, and those hours varied in length over the course of the seasons. If sunrise was at 5:00 a.m. (modern time) and sunset was at 7:30 p.m., then each hour would be 72.5 minutes in length. Therefore, the "first hour of the day" would be from 5:00 a.m. to 6:12 (and 30 seconds) a.m. (to be precise) and so on. That's how a modern Jew would calculate time for religious purposes, but recognize that in the common usage of Jesus' time, the starting and ending points of each hour had no such precision.

In Jesus' final week, which took place in the springtime near the vernal equinox, those hours would have been approximately sixty minutes in length. So, for an easy, approximate conversion, we can assume sunrise took place at 6:00 a.m. and sunset at 6:00 p.m. As such, the "first hour of the day" would be anytime between 6:00 a.m. and 7:00 a.m.; the "second hour" would be from 7:00 a.m. to 8:00 a.m., and so forth. In most commentaries and study Bibles, the number six is usually added to the Jewish time; for example, the "third hour" is usually interpreted as 9:00 a.m. However, that can lead to some misunderstanding, as the third hour is much better expressed as 8:00 a.m. to 9:00 a.m.; therefore, the conversions expressed in these resources are actually giving the *ending* times of those one-hour periods. To avoid being tedious, I will sometimes use the same convention below, but keep in mind that a single modern timestamp represents the end point of the hour.

For the discussions below, the hours of greatest interest to us are the third and sixth hours of the day. The third hour of the day would be approximately 8:00 a.m. to 9:00 a.m., and the sixth hour would be approximately 11:00 a.m. to noon.

In the section "When Was Jesus Crucified," it was mentioned that Mark and John seem to give different times of the day for when the crucifixion of Jesus began. Mark wrote: "It was the *third hour* [that is, about 8 a.m. to 9 a.m.] when they crucified Him" (Mk 15:25). On the other hand, John wrote: "Now it was the day of preparation for the Passover; it was about the *sixth hour* [that is, about 11:00 a.m. to noon]. ... So he [Pilate] then handed Him over to them to be crucified" (Jn 19:14). Several potential solutions have been put forth to reconcile these verses,[402] which will now be described together with my comments regarding the strengths and weaknesses of each.

Was John's Time a Rough Approximation?

Mark appears to give the time accurately, while John does not, since John wrote, "about the sixth hour."

This observation, while true, is not very satisfying as a complete explanation. If John intended to give the best precision he could, adding the adjective "about" would seem to allow, in my estimation, an additional variation of perhaps an hour to either side of the stated time. (Had he intended a wider window, he simply could have said, "midday.") This allowance (plus-or-minus one hour) would widen the time window to be 10:00 a.m. to 1:00 p.m., as the "sixth hour" would ordinarily mean 11:00 a.m. to 12 noon as stated above. However, even with this greater allowance, it would still not accommodate Mark's time window of 8:00 a.m. to 9:00 a.m.

Was John Using Roman Civil Time?

In Roman timekeeping, there was a distinction between civil days and natural days. Civil days ran from midnight to midnight, as most of the world reckons today. Natural days, in contrast, divided the daylight period of the day into twelve parts, describing them in the same way as the Jews: "The first hour of

---

[402] Albert Barnes, "Barnes' Notes on the Whole Bible," accessed at https://www.studylight.org/commentaries/eng/bnb/mark-15.html.

the day" meant the same to both Jew and Roman, namely, the first hour after sunrise. It has been proposed by Coffman[403] and others that because this was an official Roman event, John used Roman civil time, meaning that "about the sixth hour" in John 19:14 meant about 6:00 a.m. (end point of the hour). However, Dr. Thomas Constable,[404] quoting Leon Morris, wrote that "apparently this Roman system of reckoning time was not common. The only documentary evidence that the Romans used it appears in a few legal documents."

Although Dr. Constable thinks this to be the best explanation, I disagree. Throughout Palestine, the normative method for timekeeping appears to have been twelve-hour divisions of the daylight period. Moreover, John himself uses the Jewish method of timekeeping elsewhere in his gospel. For example, in John 1:39, Jesus invited two of John the Baptist's disciples to stay with him at the tenth hour (presumably because it was getting late). It would not have been at 10:00 a.m. (too early) or 10:00 p.m. (too late). It could only have been the tenth hour of the Jewish day, or about 4:00 p.m., as we would say.

A second episode in John's gospel was also given in Jewish time. In chapter four, Jesus stopped at Jacob's well, "wearied from His journey" at "about the sixth hour" (Jn 4:6). He would not have been weary at 6:00 a.m.; and neither would his disciples have gone into the village to buy food at 6:00 p.m., when shops would have been closed. The best interpretation is Jewish time, in which the sixth hour is about noon.

Another problem presents itself if we take the (Roman civil) time of the crucifixion to be 6 a.m. It means that all of the events of the morning, leading up to the cross, would have to be greatly compressed—to a degree that strains credibility. For these

[403] James Burton Coffman, "Coffman's Commentaries on the Bible," accessed at https://www.studylight.org/commentaries/eng/bcc/john-19.html

[404] Dr. Thomas Constable, "Dr. Constable's Expository Notes," accessed at https://www.studylight.org/commentaries/eng/dcc/john-19.html.

reasons, I think the theory that John was using Roman civil time is not tenable.

Was Either Mark or John Referring to the Time of Sentencing?

Perhaps one of the two writers (Mark or John) was describing the time of *sentencing*—when Jesus was released to be crucified—and the other meant the time when he was actually suspended on the cross.

To assess this view, let's assume first that John ("about the sixth hour") meant when Jesus was hung from the cross, perhaps as early as ("about") 10:30 a.m. or so.[405] That certainly is a possible interpretation when reading only John, as the stated time occurs in the middle of Pilate's sitting on the judgment seat, Gabbatha. This final exchange between Pilate and the chief priests seems to immediately precede Jesus being "handed over" to be taken to the cross. If so, then John's time is appropriate to a near-noon literal crucifixion. However, it is very difficult to read Mark in any way that would suggest that Jesus was *sentenced* at "the third hour," that is, 9:00 a.m. Mark's time record occurs after Jesus is brought to Golgotha, is offered myrrh, and is crucified, with the soldiers dividing his clothing. To view Mark's time as representing Jesus' sentencing is not a straightforward reading of the text.

Let's try the reverse: Perhaps John was referring to the time of Jesus' sentencing. In order for that to be credible, we first have to accept that John was using Roman civil time and meant "about 5:00 a.m. to 6:00 a.m.," which has already been shown to be unlikely. Even if all of the events of the morning could be compressed into the word "about," that is, in the first hour or so of the morning, John's context doesn't permit such a reading: John makes note of the "sixth hour" time *after* describing Jesus' scourging and mocking, and just prior to his release to the cross. Since the cross was only about 400 yards away from the

---

[405] The sixth hour begins at 11:00 a.m., and I'm allowing for John's approximation ("about") to begin an hour earlier, 10:00 a.m., followed by half an hour for Jesus to move the 400 yards to the cross.

Praetorium, the time to cover that distance would not have taken several hours, even with Jesus' weakened condition; the soldiers would not have been patient. Therefore, the accounts presented in Mark and John cannot be convincingly reconciled by this theory.

Were Mark and John using Quarter-Day Time Divisions?

In the first century, the technology of timepieces was limited primarily to hourglasses and sundials, neither of which would have been in the possession of the eyewitnesses of these events. Daylight times were visually estimated by the position of the sun. Because of the very approximate nature of such estimations, the Jews often divided both the night and the day into four equal parts of three hours each. Consequently, the first division of the morning would be (to use our modern frame of reference) from 6:00 a.m. to 9:00 a.m., and so forth. The four divisions of daylight would then be "the first hour," or early morning; "the third hour," or late morning; "the sixth hour," or early afternoon; and "the ninth hour," or late afternoon. So, if Jesus had been crucified at 11:00 a.m. (modern time), for example, then both Mark and John would have been accurate within the chronological tolerance of their day—especially when we recall that John wrote "about the sixth hour" to communicate a rough estimate.

This explanation could certainly be valid. In the gospels of Matthew, Mark, and Luke, all of the times given for events (excluding parables) are in three-hour blocks (third, sixth, and ninth hours). However, it's also noteworthy that John records two events at other hours: the healing of a royal official's son at the seventh hour (Jn 4:52) and the invitation from Jesus to two of John the Baptist's disciples at the tenth hour (Jn 1:39), so John didn't limit himself to quarter-day time divisions. On the other hand, at the time of Jesus' crucifixion, John was surely not preoccupied with precise time recording.

Could John's Time Be the Result of an Early Copyist's Error?

In ancient writing, the Greeks (and others) often used letters as substitutes for the words for numbers. They did not have a separate set of numerals. So the first letter of their alphabet (the letter alpha) meant one, the second letter (beta) meant two, etc. The third letter (gamma, or Γ) meant three, and the letter digamma, or F, meant six. (Digamma was originally the sixth letter of the Greek alphabet, but it was generally obsolete by the first century except for use as a numeral.) Therefore, because of the visual similarity of Γ and F, representing three (or third) and six (or sixth), respectively, a mistake between these two "numerals" could easily have been made. Thus, an error of this kind in an early manuscript could subsequently be widely dispersed through descendent copies. According to Barnes, there is an example of just such a historical error in the "Chronicon" of Paschal, where Otho is said to have reigned for six months, yet it is known that he reigned for only three months. There is also patristic evidence and a minor amount of manuscript evidence for the view that the original text of John 19:14 read "third." This view is attributed to the early Christian writer Ammonius (AD 200-300) and was echoed by Eusebius (early AD 300s), Epiphanius of Salamis (late 300s), and Jerome. Epiphanius indicated that Clement of Alexandria and Origen also endorsed this view.[406] Peter of Alexandria wrote, in a manuscript fragment concerning the Passover, "It was the preparation of the Passover, and about the 'third' hour, as," he adds, "the most accurate copies of the Bible have it; and this was the handwriting of the evangelist (John), which is kept, by the grace of God, in his most holy church at Ephesus."[407] Further, manuscripts Codex L, Codex Delta, and Miniscule 72 read "third."[408] Therefore, John's gospel may well have originally

---

[406] James Snapp, Jr., "Lecture 15 - Introduction to NT Textual Criticism - Numerals," YouTube, September 14, 2020, presentation, 0:27:10, https://www.youtube.com/watch?v=g3GRDIMAXZw.

[407] Barnes, "Barnes' Notes on the Whole Bible", v.25.

[408] Snapp, Jr., "Lecture 15 - Introduction to NT Textual Criticism -

been written as "third hour," thus agreeing with Mark's account.

This is, I think, the most reasonable explanation for how the discrepancy between the gospels of Mark and John could have arisen. I believe that Mark's reading is correct and the "sixth" hour in most manuscripts of John 19:14 is a copyist's manual version of a "typo" that occurred early in the chain of transmission. Moreover, Mark's time allows for all of the trials and scourging of Jesus before the crucifixion, and it makes room for the other events that occurred while Jesus was on the cross, before the sky grew dark around noon.

Numerals."

Appendix D: Clopas' "Third Day"

On their journey to Emmaus,[409] Clopas and his companion spoke to Jesus after his resurrection, a conversation that occurred on a Sunday. One of them gave an indication of the time that had passed between the crucifixion and that day (the day of the resurrection).[410]

> One of them, named Cleopas [or Clopas], answered and said to Him, "Are You the only one visiting Jerusalem and unaware of the things which have happened here in these days?" And He said to them, "What things?" And *they* said to Him, "The things about Jesus the Nazarene, who was a prophet mighty in deed and word in the sight of God and all the people, and how the chief priests and our rulers delivered Him to the sentence of death, and crucified Him. But we were hoping that it was He who was going to redeem Israel. Indeed, besides all this, *it is the third day since these things happened.* But also some women among us amazed us. When they were at the tomb early in the morning, and did not find His body, they came, saying that they had also seen a vision of angels who said that He was alive." (Lk 24:18-23, emphasis and brackets added)

What did the speaker mean when he said "it is the third day since these things happened"?

It could have been a reference to Jesus' earlier statements that he would rise on the third day (Mt 20:19; Mk 10:34; Lk 18:33).[411] In other words, the meaning could perhaps be

---

[409] Mk 16:12-13; Lk 24:13-35

[410] As noted earlier in the book, if Jesus was resurrected prior to midnight, it would have been the same Jewish day, but today we would call it Saturday evening.

[411] Note that the wording of Matthew and Luke could be construed to

expressed as, "The time period referred to by Jesus has elapsed, but we haven't seen him," in which case it should be viewed as an approximation, or minimum, rather than a precise accounting of elapsed time.

On the other hand, if "third" is counted as we do today (excluding the starting day but including the ending day), beginning from the day of Jesus' crucifixion, then the crucifixion happened on a Thursday.

However, because Jesus was laid in the tomb just as the day was transitioning to the Sabbath of Passover, it is possible that the speaker was counting from that specific Sabbath. Clopas likely heard of Jesus' death and burial from Mary, his wife (who witnessed both events), after dark (at the start of Nisan 15), making this plausible. Counting the days from when the story thus reached Clopas means that the crucifixion happened on a Wednesday.

Regardless, Friday seems to be excluded from consideration if we take Luke 24:21 at face value, and interpret "third" as we do today. (If we also were to consider inclusive and exclusive counting as possibilities, this passage becomes even more indefinite as a time anchor.)[412]

Furthermore, we have better indications of the day of the week of Jesus' crucifixion than from this offhand comment by one of the travelers, which is, in fact, a Greek idiom that Marvin Vincent has said, "cannot be neatly rendered."[413] My opinion is that its meaning is subject to various interpretations and it would be a mistake to give it too much weight.

---

mean two to three days later, because "on" could mean at the beginning or end of the third day. Mark's wording, however, seems to mean after three days have elapsed.

[412] See "The Order of Appearances," Appearance Number Six, for a longer comment about inclusive/exclusive counting of days.

[413] Marvin Vincent, *Word Studies in the New Testament* (1887), on Luke 24:21.

Appendix E: The Year of the Resurrection

Scholars have long attempted to determine the specific years of Jesus' birth and death—and thus, resurrection. There are differences of opinion among them for the dating of these events. It can be said unequivocally that the year of Jesus' last week cannot be pinpointed with total certainty. However, that year can be confidently narrowed to a small window of time, and some of the years within that window are more likely than others. The subject is quite interesting and, I believe, worth the commentary provided here, although this short appendix cannot do justice to the voluminous material that has been written on the subject. What follows is a brief overview of the major evidence for various viewpoints.

Calculating from Jesus' Birth

One approach to reckoning the year of the resurrection is to begin with the birth of Jesus. The earliest church sources are fairly consistent in giving the year of his birth as 3/2 BC.[414] If Jesus was born in that year and began his ministry at age thirty, his ministry would have commenced in the year AD 28/29.

Unfortunately, we don't know Jesus' exact age at the commencement of his ministry. We only know, from Luke, that Jesus was "about thirty years of age" (Lk 3:23). The qualifier "about" must add a tolerance of at least a year to either side of that approximation—thus, we should presume an age range of twenty-nine to thirty-one years (or wider), which would give us a ministry commencement of AD 27 to AD 30.

How long was Jesus' ministry? Many commentators think

---

[414] Jack Finegan, *Handbook of Biblical Chronology* (Peabody: Hendricksen Publishers, 1998), Table 139. Other years for the Nativity have been proposed; these dates and the reasons for them are well covered by Finegan.

three to three and a half years because John mentions three Passovers.[415] This oft-repeated ministry length overlooks two considerations: first, that the distance between the first and third Passovers is two years, and second, that Jesus died on the third Passover. It isn't known how long before the first Passover (Jn 2:13) his ministry began, so with these considerations, his ministry lasted between just over two years and just under three years (unless, for some reason, John did not mention all of the Passovers).

There are suggestions from Luke and John that Jesus' first visit to Jerusalem for Passover was not long after his baptism, making his ministry closer to two years in length. Directly on the heels of his baptism, Jesus began his forty-day fast in the wilderness (Lk 4:1ff). Upon returning to the Jordan, he then began collecting disciples, several of whom were former disciples of the Baptist (Jn 1:29-51). Only three days later, Jesus turned water into wine, revealing his miraculous power for the first time publicly (Jn 2:1-11).

"After this," Jesus and his family and disciples stayed a few days in Capernaum (Jn 2:12). The "after this" time is not specified, but the sense is not long afterwards. The very next verse reads, "The Passover of the Jews was near, and Jesus went up to Jerusalem" (Jn 2:13). So, the apostle John gives the impression that Jesus' first Passover during his ministry period occurred close to his baptism. Luke gives a similar impression—after Jesus performed some healings in Capernaum, he then traveled to Judea (Lk 4:40-44)—which was probably the occasion of the first Passover visit. It's possible that Jesus could have begun his ministry about two months before the Passover of John 2:13. It's also possible that it was closer to three years. Nevertheless, elsewhere in this book I have generally referred to Jesus' ministry as "three years" to avoid being cumbersome.

Putting these numbers together, if Jesus began his ministry between AD 27 and AD 30, and it lasted for two years, his

---

[415] Jn 2:13; 6:4; 13:1. Some scholars believe a fourth Passover can be read from John; this is discussed later in this Appendix.

crucifixion occurred between AD 29 and AD 32. (This bracket would be wider if we assume a greater tolerance for Luke's estimate of Jesus' age, and a year higher on the maximum side if we assume that his ministry lasted closer to three years.)

Many estimates for Jesus' birth year have been influenced by reliance upon a presumed date for Herod the Great's death as 5/4 BC. King Herod was the ruler of Palestine at the time of Jesus' birth and was infamous for his slaughtering of all the infants of Bethlehem and its vicinity, who were two years old and under, in an attempt to destroy Jesus (Mt 2:16). If Herod died in 4 BC and he killed infants up to age two, then Jesus must have been born no later than 5 BC.[416]

However, there is considerable evidence to show the death of Herod as having occurred in 1 BC. Among the evidence is Josephus' testimony that Herod's death was preceded by an eclipse of the moon and followed by a Passover not long after—both of which agree better with 1 BC than the alternatives.[417] Among the years considered to be reasonable candidates for Jesus' birth, only in 1 BC was there a total eclipse of the moon. This fits well with a 3/2 BC birth year for Jesus.

Tiberius' Reign

As mentioned previously in Part Three, John the Baptist's ministry, and Jesus' ministry following right after, began in "the fifteenth year of Tiberius" (Lk 3:1). In Rome, Tiberius began a co-regency with Augustus (his predecessor) in AD 12; this co-regency was of the provinces that included Judea. His first full year of co-regency would have been AD 13. In the autumn of AD 14, Augustus died and Tiberius was named head of state. The first full year of the sole regency of Tiberius was thus AD 15. So, we have four years to choose from, for the beginning of Tiberius' reign, before we need to add fifteen years to arrive at the year when John began to baptize. All of these years can be argued

---

[416] This presumes that Herod issued the order near his own death and that he used an extra year as a cushion to avoid missing his target.
[417] Finegan, *Handbook of Biblical Chronology*, 291-301.

for—and have been. It seems to me that Luke would have counted using the first full year that Tiberius reigned in the provinces, using the Syrian calendar—where Luke was from, according to tradition. This would establish the start of John's ministry as somewhere between October 1, AD 27, and September 30, AD 28. Thus, Jesus' last three Passovers would have been in AD 28 to 30 (if Jesus' ministry started within five months of John's), or AD 29 to 31 (if Jesus' ministry started more than five months after John's).

The Age of the Temple

Also mentioned in Part Three of this book, the construction time of the temple given by some Jewish critics of Jesus ("It took forty-six years to build this temple") in John 2:20 can be used to establish a precise year for Jesus' resurrection, and it calculates to AD 30. It has been noted that the word for "temple" (*Greek: naos*) used here means the temple sanctuary, consisting of the Holy place and the Holy of Holies—in contrast to the word for "the entire consecrated temple area" (*Greek: hieron*).[418] In fact, the sanctuary only took a year and a half to construct, but the entire temple area was still under construction at the time of this exchange, so why did the Jews use the term for the sanctuary? The answer to that lies in the dialogue itself and in the following verse: "But He was speaking of the temple of His body" (Jn 2:21). Jesus had begun the conversation by referring to his own physical body as a temple (*naos*), but the Jews had no idea that he was speaking metaphorically. In response, the Jews countered using the same term, but obviously meaning the greater temple area, perhaps to buttress their argument— specifically, that Jesus was talking about an impossibility. Conceivably, *naos* may have been used colloquially to reference the entire complex at times.

In any case, the long period of forty-six years, the grammatical structure of the Jews' statement, the approximate period in which the statement was made, together with the fact that the

---

[418] Finegan, 346-349.

temple complex was still under construction, cannot be understood to mean anything other than a period from when Herod first began construction to that present moment. It's interesting that this offhand, scoffing remark gives us the most precise milepost for the year of the crucifixion and resurrection. Sometimes, critics do us a real service.

Early Christian Historians

The Christian historian Julius Africanus lived much of his life in Palestine from about AD 170 to about AD 240. He wrote five books titled *Chronographies* that were, according to Eusebius, "a work accurately and laboriously prepared."[419] Africanus' work has been lost as a whole, but much has been retained through excerpts and quotations by other ancient writers, including Eusebius. Fortunately, we have his chronology of the life of Jesus, in which Africanus gives a birth year for Jesus as the second year of the 194th Olympiad (3/2 BC), and a date for his death and resurrection as the first year of the 202nd Olympiad (AD 29/30). This evidence deserves particular attention because of the earliness of Africanus' work, his location in Palestine, and his reputation as one of the greatest scholars of his age.

The historian Eusebius lived about a century after Africanus and composed two works of relevance here, *Chronology* and *Church History*. Eusebius assigns the birth of Jesus to 2 BC; the fifteenth year of Tiberius (and beginning of John the Baptist's ministry) to AD 28; and the death and resurrection of Jesus to AD 31.[420]

Pseudo-Chronological Markers

There are historical and scriptural passages that may appear initially to provide utility for dating purposes but fail the task under scrutiny. Some commentators have read more into these passages than seems credible. Here are several.

---

[419] Eusebius, *Church History*, VI, XXXI, 2.
[420] Finegan, *Handbook of Biblical Chronology*, Table 96.

1. In John 8:57, the Jews said to Jesus, "You are not yet fifty years old, and have you seen Abraham?" (Abraham lived centuries before Jesus.) This may seem to suggest that Jesus was in his forties at the time. However, fifty was the age in Judaism beyond which Levites no longer participated in the temple service (Num 8:25), so the statement made to Jesus could be paraphrased, "You're a young man! That's impossible!" It does not have any usefulness as a time marker, even though Irenaeus, the early Greek bishop, interpreted this statement as an observational comment on Jesus' apparent age.[421]

2. In John 4:35, Jesus said, "Do you not say, 'There are yet four months, and then comes the harvest'? Behold, I say to you, lift up your eyes and look on the fields, that they are white for harvest." Jesus was simply using an idiom as a metaphor to teach his disciples that people were generally ready for evangelical outreach, and he did it by *contrast*—in essence, saying "the time is now" rather than "there's plenty of time to wait," as the idiom expresses on its face. He said this immediately after revealing to the woman at the well that he was the Messiah—an evangelical encounter. While this idiom is not known from other sources, the leading phrase "Do you not say?" identifies it as an idiom, an adage. It's difficult to imagine the disciples having any concern about harvests, particularly after having seen Jesus multiply loaves. Yet, some scholars believe this verse indicates the time of year when it was spoken.[422] From this verse, it has been suggested that Jesus' ministry spanned four Passovers, but I don't believe this verse provides justification for that view.[423] Such a view would require Jesus to have been in Judea for eight months prior to this statement—an improbable situation in view of the hostility of the Judean authorities towards him. Jesus frequently taught using metaphors, and they

---

[421] Finegan, 346.

[422] Harold W. Hoehner, *Chronological Aspects of the Life of Christ* (Grand Rapids: Zondervan Corp., 1977), 56-58.

[423] Finegan, *Handbook of Biblical Chronology*, 352, Table 173.

should be understood for the pedagogic value intended by the rabbi.

3. In Revelation 1:14, the apostle John records a vision in which Jesus appears with white hair, and this has been suggested as evidence that Jesus was much older than thirty to thirty-five at the time of his death.[424] This is quite the overreach. First of all, tradition tells us that John had this vision near the end of his own long life. Secondly, it is a *vision*, and the entire vision is of a *glorified* Jesus. And lastly, John's vision is a profound parallel of "the Ancient of Days" seen by Daniel (Dan 7:9).

4. Jews valued the wisdom of the aged and learned rabbis. Therefore, it "will be difficult to convince [someone who knows the culture] that a man of thirty could have been accepted as a teacher of authority."[425] The same point could be made about someone who had not studied under the great teachers of Jerusalem, as Paul had learned under Gamaliel (Acts 22:3). Yet both points are false. Jesus healed all manner of diseases and raised three dead people. He regularly put the "smartest men in the room" to silence by the simple, powerful wisdom of his replies to their hostile interrogations (Mt 22:46, Mk 12:34, Lk 13:17, 14:6, 20:40, Jn 8:7-9).

What Jesus said and did would have garnered him attention, whether he was nine years of age or ninety.[426] Finally, I must remark that Jesus was *not* accepted as a

---

[424] Nikos Kokkinos, "Crucifixion in AD 36," *Chronos, Kairos, Christos: Nativity and Chronological Studies Presented to Jack Finegan*, edited by J. Vardaman and E. Yamauchi (Winona Lake: Eisenbrauns, 1989), 156.

[425] A quote from A. T. Olmstead in Kokkinos, "Crucifixion in AD 36," 156.

[426] As an aside, I think Jesus' statement to Nicodemus, "Are you the teacher of Israel, and do not understand these things?" (Jn 3:10) suggests a younger man instructing an elder. Notice also, in that same exchange, that the reason Nicodemus came to Jesus was because of the miraculous power evident in his works (Jn 3:2).

"teacher of authority" by the political, religious, financial, and educational elites of his day (with only a few exceptions); they were precisely the ones who murdered him. Nor is he so accepted today! He finds his place and acceptance, then and now, among those like Mary Magdalene, those who are broken and outcast, those with leprosy. Only the humble can see his majesty.

5. Jesus died prior to the other two men crucified with him, suggesting that he was an older man. There are three counterpoints to this idea: one based on human nature, one scriptural, and one spiritual. Jesus was first put on trial as the "King of the Jews" and later had the same inscription placed above his head on the cross. The Roman soldiers who flogged Jesus were aware of this charge, and it would have intensified the flogging they administered because of their animosity toward the Jews. (The Roman occupiers were hated by the Jews— and vice versa—and Romans were occasionally murdered by Jewish assassins called Sicarii.) A close examination of the Shroud of Turin shows that Jesus' lacerations from the flogging covered all visible areas, head to foot. That would have, from a physical viewpoint, accelerated his death. Scripturally, the only direct statement we have for Jesus' age is "about thirty" for the start of his ministry (provided by Luke), and we should regard that information with the highest weight.

Lastly, Jesus' death was supernatural, in that he died with a loud cry, "Father, into your hands I commit my Spirit" (Lk 23:46), which is not how crucified people expire; rather, they die of asphyxiation and are therefore unable to utter a strong exclamation at the end. So unusual was Jesus' point of death that the centurion on duty declared that he was the Son of God (Mk 15:39). Jesus' manner and moment of passing from this life was evidently at his own choosing, as he had prophesied earlier: "I have authority to lay it [his life] down, and I have authority to take it up again" (Jn 10:18). From this perspective, his death was age-irrelevant.

6. The death of Sejanus on October 18th, AD 31—Lucius Sejanus was an ambitious equestrian who had risen in

Rome to become the prefect of the Praetorian Guard. By AD 26 or 27, when Tiberius retired to the island of Capri, Sejanus essentially controlled the Roman government and maneuvered to take Tiberius' place. Eventually, Tiberius became convinced of Sejanus' usurpation and had him executed in the autumn of AD 31.

The potential impact on the chronology of the resurrection relates to the attitude of Sejanus toward the Jews. The historian Philo wrote that Sejanus hated and had hostile designs against the Jewish nation.[427] It could be expected that Pilate would act with greater apparent anti-Semitism while Sejanus was in power than after his death. Therefore, because Pilate acquiesced to the Jewish authorities at the trial of Jesus, it could indicate that he was acting more flexibly toward the Jews in general, and thus, Sejanus must have already been executed, meaning that the trial took place in AD 32 or later.

This is a very interesting theory, but it hangs on the question of whether Pilate was, during Jesus' trial, showing deference or hostility toward the Jews or not. In the case of Jesus, Pilate did, after all, condemn an innocent *Jewish* man. While Pilate probably wasn't fond of the Jews because they were especially difficult to govern, it cannot be convincingly argued that he hated them either. Judea was a valuable territory to Rome because of its tax revenues, so Pilate had incentive for avoiding major provocations. Certainly, it is true that he had been heavy-handed at times, but that was not extraordinary for Roman rule—or for that matter, for any imperialistic empire.

Was Pilate really acting deferentially toward the Jews, in the trial of Jesus? That's a difficult case to make. Consider that the trial was a very politically complex one for Pilate. He was trying a man who was not from his jurisdiction (Lk 23:7). The trial was taking place in the midst of potentially the most volatile time of the year— Passover, when the city was packed with Jews from all over the empire (Mt 27:20). Any riot at such a time could be especially difficult to quell. The man (Jesus) was

---

[427] Philo, *Flaccus*, I (1).

innocent, Pilate concluded, and he could have followers who might riot if he was condemned. Caiaphas the high priest was a useful intermediary between the Romans and Jews, but he was forcing Pilate's hand out of envy (Mt 27:18). The chief priests had assembled enough of a mob that a riot was actually starting and could escalate if Pilate released Jesus (Mt 27:24). Moreover, the Jewish leaders insinuated that they would accuse Pilate (to Caesar) of releasing a man who was opposing Rome (Jn 19:12). If all of that wasn't enough, Pilate had been awakened by the inflamed mob at the break of day (Mk 15:1), and Pilate's wife had sent him a message to have nothing to do with Jesus (Mt 27:19).

In my opinion, every choice Pilate faced was a losing proposition, and I believe he was—speaking only of the politics— simply trying to reduce his losses in a bad predicament. History shows how awful his choice was. But, given the nature of Pilate's predicament and the considerations involved, Pilate may have made the same decision *whether or not Sejanus was in power*. It's hard to believe that if Sejanus had received a communication from Caiaphas that Pilate had released *a Galilean Jew who was conspiring against Rome (Jn 19:12), forbidding people to pay taxes (Lk 23:2), and threatening to destroy the temple (Mt 26:61)*, Sejanus would have been pleased about it. (While none of those charges were true, they were the accusations leveled against Jesus.) Therefore, Sejanus' death seems incapable of providing us with additional data for determining Jesus' final year on earth.

7. The historian Josephus wrote that the defeat of Herod Antipas (ruler of Galilee and Perea) in AD 36 by King Aretas was divine retribution for the beheading of John the Baptist. As backstory, John the Baptist was beheaded because he had criticized Antipas for getting rid of Antipas' first wife—who just happened to be Aretas' daughter—in order to marry the infamous Herodias. This, plus lingering boundary disputes between the two kings, prompted Aretas' move against Antipas. If Aretas acted immediately following the Baptist's death, then we might presume that he died in AD 35, and we know Jesus

died later than John—which could support a crucifixion date of AD 36. The weakness of this argument is that Josephus also stated that the divorce was just the beginning of hostilities, and we should expect that Aretas would have strategically waited until the most opportune time.[428]

Astronomical Considerations

Attempts to apply astronomical events and calculations to events surrounding Jesus' life have, in my opinion, mixed value. As mentioned above, the complete lunar eclipse of 1 BC seems to be strong evidence for fixing the date of King Herod's death. However, other attempts to apply modern astronomy to the chronology of Jesus' life lack persuasiveness.

Several writers have noted that Halley's Comet was visible in Palestine in 12 BC, and have dated Jesus' birth to that year on the assumption that this was the Nativity star seen by the magi (Mt 2:1-12). Not only does such a date create multiple problems with other chronological markers, but it also doesn't explain how a comet could lead the magi to the very house in which Jesus lived (Mt 2:9). Surely, some (perhaps most) scholars would reject a literal reading of Matthew 2:9, as it requires supernatural agency, but then, we are talking about an infant who later healed "all who came to him" and rose from the dead.

Other attempts have been made to date the crucifixion from the darkness that occurred from noon until 3:00 p.m. of that day (Mt 27:45, Mk 15:33 Lk 23:44). However, a naturalistic explanation of the darkness is impossible. Solar eclipses cannot occur near a full moon (which this day was), as the moon is on the opposite side of the earth from the sun and therefore cannot block the light from the sun. Moreover, solar eclipses only last minutes, not hours—the longest solar eclipse in the first century being six minutes and forty-seven seconds in length.[429]

---

[428] Hoehner, *Chronological Aspects of the Life of Christ*, 101-102.
[429] "Catalog of Solar Eclipses: 0001 to 0100," NASA (NASA), accessed April 10, 2022,

It has also been suggested that the gospel writers meant a *lunar* eclipse, but the testimony of the multiple witnesses makes this seem quite absurd. Another suggestion has been that Peter's quotation of Joel on the day of Pentecost that "the sun will be turned into darkness and the moon into blood" (Acts 2:20) was referring to a total lunar eclipse, which sometimes appears red-hued. This idea has a significant problem. The moon occasionally appears to have a reddish hue when it is near the horizon, even without an eclipse. This occurs due to particulate matter in the atmosphere and/or refraction. So, although Peter was probably referring to a reddish moon that had been noted by people in Jerusalem, it would not have required an eclipse and thus cannot be used for dating purposes.

Even so, there is one historical note about an "eclipse" that could possibly relate to the darkness of the crucifixion day. Phlegon, a secular chronologer of the second century AD, wrote of "the greatest eclipse of the sun" beginning at the sixth hour of the day [noon] in AD 32/33, accompanied by an earthquake in Bithynia and Nicaea (western Turkey today).[430] Of course, if the darkness Phlegon referred to was a natural eclipse, then it also could not have been the darkness of the crucifixion, for the reason given above. A check of astronomical calculations shows that the only (natural) eclipse seen in Asia Minor during the years AD 21 to 40 was in AD 29. Because that is the *only* total or annular eclipse seen in Bithynia during those twenty years, it is possible that Phlegon's date, recorded over a hundred years later, was in error. Furthermore, that eclipse missed Palestine. Unfortunately, Phlegon did not include several pieces of information that would have been very helpful in assessing whether his record was of a *supernatural* eclipse, such as the length of time of the darkness, and whether the darkness was seen and the earthquake felt in Judea also. His account is certainly intriguing, but it cannot be used to definitively date the

---

https://eclipse.gsfc.nasa.gov/SEcat5/SE0001-0100.html.

[430] Phlegon puts the date as year four of the 202nd Olympiad, or July 1, AD 32, to June 30, AD 33.

crucifixion and resurrection.

J. K. Fotheringham employed astronomy in a study attempting to narrow the potential years under consideration or even pinpoint the year by identifying which year(s) in the span AD 26 to 34 would have Nisan 14 falling on a Friday.[431] A more recent study was conducted by Humphreys and Waddington.[432] These studies begin on the wrong foot by assuming that the crucifixion happened on a Friday, whereas the New Testament text better supports a Wednesday, as explained earlier. They also generally assume that the beginning of Nisan always occurred after the spring equinox, and that is not the case.[433] And even for a year in which Nisan 14 could have occurred on a given weekday, we wouldn't know if that year had begun a day late because of poor visibility in Jerusalem. Therefore, astronomy cannot unequivocally determine the year of the crucifixion.

There is even some uncertainty, in this author's mind, whether our continuous seven-day cycle of weeks can be traced backward beyond Augustus for alignment with the Jewish weekdays of the first century, even though this is generally done unquestioningly in studies relying on astronomy. Recall that Romans in the first century used eight-day weeks. Even though the use of the eight-day week slowly declined in favor of the seven-day week, it wasn't until AD 321 that Constantine made the seven-day week official.

---

[431] J.K. Fotheringham, "The Evidence of Astronomy and Technical Chronology for the Date of the Crucifixion," *Journal of Theological Studies* 35 (1934): 146-162.

[432] Humphreys and Waddington, "Astronomy and the Date of the Crucifixion," *Chronos, Kairos, Christos: Nativity and Chronological Studies Presented to Jack Finegan*, edited by J. Vardaman and E. Yamauchi (Winona Lake: Eisenbrauns, 1989), 165-181.

[433] Roger T. Beckwith, "Cautionary Notes on the Use of Calendars and Astronomy to Determine the Chronology of the Passion," *Chronos, Kairos, Christos: Nativity and Chronological Studies Presented to Jack Finegan* (1989), 183-205.

Conclusions

1. The possible years for Jesus' crucifixion and resurrection can be bracketed with a fair degree of confidence to AD 29 to 33.

2. It is impossible to determine with complete confidence the exact year, but some years are much better candidates than others.

3. Any calculations beginning from Jesus' birth will never be exact because of Luke's imprecise statement that Jesus was "about" thirty years of age.

4. The best data for determining the year are, in my opinion, two starting points: 1) Luke 3:1 (that is, the beginning of John the Baptist's ministry) and 2) John 2:20 (concerning the age of the temple). To these we would add the length of Jesus' ministry estimated from John's mention of three Passovers.

5. When all of the data are examined, I believe AD 30 is the best candidate, but other years from AD 31 to AD 33 are also possible.

6. The determination of the particular year of these events has little significance for understanding what happened in that year or the harmonization of the gospel accounts.

7. Unquestionably, the greater matter is what actually *did* happen in that year.

Appendix F: Is Cleopas the Same as Alphaeus?

One of the lesser-known members of the twelve disciples is James of Alphaeus. This James is described in all four gospel listings exactly that way: "of Alphaeus." Other than this appendage, we know almost nothing about him. However, we do know that there was a married couple related to Jesus, Clopas and Mary, who had a son named James the Less, and as discussed earlier, there are some reasons for thinking James the Less and James of Alphaeus (i.e., son of Alphaeus) might have been the same person.

A stronger case for this equivalence would exist if we can show that Clopas and Alphaeus are two variations or alternatives of the same name. Among scholars and commentators, there are differences of opinion on whether they are.

The eminent and erstwhile scholar Alfred Edersheim states emphatically that they are the same:

> Alphaeus and Clopas are the same name. The first occurs in the Babylon Talmud as Ilphai, or Ilpha, as in R. HaSh. 17b, and often; the other in the Jerusalem Talmud as Chilphai, as for example in Jer. B. Kama 7a.[434]

John Wenham explains how Alphaeus and Clopas could be two versions of the same Aramaic name transliterated Chalphai. He says that in the Aramaic, the first letter of Chalphai is a gutteral, so it could be transliterated into Greek as a k, giving Clopas, or as an h (known as "rough breathing" and signified with a small sign similar to a comma). The rough breathing mark was often omitted both in speaking and writing, resulting in either Halphaios or Alphaios. The latter would be Latinized as

---

[434] The references are to Talmudic tractates, or essays. These are ancient rabbinical writings. Edersheim, *"The Life and Times of Jesus the Messiah,"* 889, note 59.

Alphaeus.[435]

On the other hand, modern scholar Eckhard Schnabel dissents, writing that this connection is implausible for several reasons:

- it would be surprising for a person to be known by such different Greek forms of his name
- the various Greek forms of Alpheus all lack the long first vowel of Klopas
- the Semitic original of the name Klopas is distinct from the Semitic name from which Alphaeus is derived.[436]

Schnabel's first reason is not persuasive to me. In English—as an example, but in other languages as well—we have various short-form variations of names that differ significantly from the long forms, such as Jack for John, Chuck for Charles, Hank for Henry, Daisy for Margaret, and Buffy for Elizabeth. (Even "Nancy" as a short form for Ann!) His second reason is more compelling, but again, in English we have Daisy with two long vowels substituting for Margaret with none. His third reason does not seem to address Wenham's explanation for how Chalphai could possibly transliterate into Clopas or Alphaeus. In my estimation, Chalphai does seem somewhat intermediate between the two (arguably) descended forms.

Given the differences of opinion on the matter, it is evident that the equation Clopas=Alphaeus is presently speculative and apt to remain so unless other ancient records are discovered. Nevertheless, the connection is interesting, possible, and one to which I lean, albeit slightly. I have no investment in the controversy and would prefer that it could be settled definitely, either way.

My opinion remains, however, that James the Less and James of Alphaeus are the same individual. My principal reason is that

---

[435] Wenham, *"Easter Enigma,"* 37.
[436] Schnabel, *"Jesus in Jerusalem,"* 423, note 173.

I think Peter, speaking through Mark's gospel,[437] would not have referred to Mary's son as "James the Less" unless he had a comparison in mind: that is, a comparison between the two Jameses that figure most prominently into the gospel account—the members of the Twelve—and particularly when Peter was narrating events surrounding the resurrection (Mk 15:40).

If Mary's son James had been a person without connection to Peter's narrative, Peter would have had no reason to add the identifier of "the Less," and would not have even needed to add James' name to identify which Mary of whom he was speaking, just as he indeed omitted James only seven verses later (Mk 15:47).

As mentioned before, these identifications, if *incorrect*, would have very little impact on the story. They would have no effect on Part Two, The Unified Account. In Part One, Mary of Clopas would continue to have great interest in going to Bethany, as she would have wanted to remain by the side of her very close friend Mary Magdalene.

---

[437] See "Writers" chapter for the relationship between Mark and Peter.

Appendix G: The Significance of Emmaus

One of the most heartwarming elements connected to the resurrection story is that of the two travelers who meet the risen Jesus on the road to Emmaus (Lk 24:13-35). It contains suspense and mystery, wrapped with grief, surprise, and great joy. We are told that these travelers were walking from Jerusalem to Emmaus, which was "about seven miles from Jerusalem." The exact location of the village of Emmaus is not known with certainty today, but there is one town that outshines the rest of the candidates for the title to the biblical place where Clopas and his companion traveled with Jesus.

There are a number of sites that have been proposed as the location of Emmaus. The leading candidates include Mozah, Abu Ghosh, Al-Qubeiba, Bethel/Baytin, and Nicopolis/Imwas. Several of these are unlikely because of their distances from Jerusalem. Nicopolis/Imwas was about 18.6 miles from Jerusalem, which is farther than Luke's description of the location. Bethel is also farther, about ten miles away. Mozah is about 3.5 miles from Jerusalem, which is too close. However, Abu Ghosh and Al-Qubeiba both fit the distance of "about seven miles" well.

Al-Qubeiba lacks the history to be a viable candidate for Emmaus. It seems to have little history prior to the Crusader period, and was only gradually adopted by the Franciscan custodians of holy sites in Palestine as the location for Emmaus in the thirteenth century. Abu Ghosh, however, has been settled since Neolithic times. The early Crusaders believed it to be the site of Emmaus; they built a church there in 1140 that still stands today, though much of it has been reconstructed.

In September 2019, the Jerusalem newspaper *Haaretz* reported that archaeologists in Israel had discovered a massive stone fortification adjacent to the small village of Abu Ghosh in a site known as Kiriath Yearim (Kiriath-jearim in English Bible translations). The fortification exhibits three phases of construction. The first phase of construction was during the Hellenistic (pre-Roman) period. The second phase was during a later Hellenistic period, and the last phase was Roman, in the first century AD.[438]

Both the historian Josephus[439] and the author of 1 Maccabees[440] knew of a place, west of the city of Jerusalem, on the road to Jaffa and the Great Sea, which was known as Emmaus and had fortifications. The recent discovery of fortifications at Abu Ghosh/Kiriath-jearim lends support to identifying this site as the Emmaus of Luke 24.

To summarize, Abu Ghosh/Kiriath-jearim:

* matches Luke's description for distance

* was a size fitting the description of a "village"

* had fortifications that matched the description of Emmaus by Josephus and the author of 1 Maccabees as a military camp

* has the earliest-known historical claim as the location of Emmaus

I think it should be accepted as the authentic site, unless future discoveries should provide sufficient evidence otherwise.

Furthermore, Abu Ghosh has a historical and spiritual heritage that has relevance to the person of Jesus. Many events in the life of Jesus were specifically intended to fulfill some prophetic passage from the writings of Moses, the prophets, or the history of Israel. What possible connection could the small village of Abu Ghosh have to Jesus' life and ministry?

---

[438] Ariel David, "Israeli Archaeologists May Have Found Emmaus, Where Jesus Appeared After Crucifixion," Sept. 3, 2019, https://www.haaretz.com/israel-news/.premium.MAGAZINE-israeli-archaeologists-may-have-found-emmaus-where-jesus-appeared-after-crucifixion-1.7774167.

[439] Josephus, *The Jewish War*, Book 5, ch. 1, sect. 6.

[440] 1 Mc 4:1-4; 3:40, 9:50.

The interesting connection is found in the time of Samuel the prophet and David the king of Israel. Prior to Samuel, the ark of the covenant[441] and the temple had been located at Shiloh, and Eli had been the officiating priest.[442] Because of the sin in Eli's household, God permitted the Philistines to capture the ark in battle (1 Sm 4:11). The temple of Shiloh was later destroyed, perhaps by the Philistines also. It's recorded that not long after, the priestly family of Eli had moved from Shiloh to Nob, thus indicating that the temple in Shiloh was gone at that point (1 Sm 21:1ff).

The Philistines discovered that having possession of the ark brought them misfortune, so they returned it to Israel. First it went to the town of Beth-shemesh, where some of the inhabitants looked into it (not treating it as holy) and many of them died. In response, the inhabitants of Beth-shemesh sent messengers to Kiriath-jearim and requested that they come and take possession of the ark. (Unsurprisingly, the messengers made no mention of the misfortune that had fallen upon their town because of the ark!) And so, the ark came into Kiriath-jearim (that is, Emmaus):

> And the men of Kiriath-jearim came and took the ark of the LORD and brought it into the house of Abinadab on the hill, and consecrated Eleazar his son to keep the ark of the LORD. From the day that the ark remained at Kiriath-jearim, the time was long, for it was twenty years; and all the house of Israel lamented after the LORD. (1 Sm 7:1-2)

---

[441] The term "covenant" here means the agreement between God and Israel. The ark was a wooden box (about 27" wide and high, and 45" long) with a lid, all overlaid with gold and carried with two long poles.

[442] Originally, the tabernacle (religious tent) that the Israelites carried through their wilderness journey was installed in Shiloh, but eventually it was either transformed into a more permanent structure, or else (more likely) a separate structure for a temple was built. It was called a temple in 1 Samuel 3:3, and it had rigid doors and doorposts (1 Sm 3:15, 1:9).

During that twenty-year period, the people of Kiriath-jearim experienced blessing and the rest of Israel lamented because the ark was not in the temple and the sacrificial system was probably suspended. The news about Kiriath-jearim's blessings reached the ears of King David, so he moved the ark to the capital city of Jerusalem. When the ark finally reached Jerusalem, there was great rejoicing:

> So David and all the house of Israel were bringing up the ark of the LORD with shouting and the sound of the trumpet. (2 Sm 6:15)

The ark has always represented the presence of God among his people. While the ark was in Kiriath-jearim, the people of that town experienced special blessings of having God's presence near. Of course, it was not the temple that sanctified the ark; it was the ark that sanctified the temple, and that's why the people lamented its absence.

It was the sin of the priesthood under Eli that caused the ark to be removed from Shiloh, the holy city, to Kiriath-jearim; it was the sin of the priesthood under Caiaphas that caused Jesus to be removed from Jerusalem, the holy city, to the same place— Emmaus. The destruction of the temple at Shiloh occurred soon after the ark left Shiloh; similarly, the temple at Jerusalem was destroyed soon after Jesus' crucifixion.[443] The presence of the ark blessed the inhabitants of Kiriath-jearim, and the presence of Jesus at the same place was an extraordinary blessing to the two travelers from Jerusalem.

When Jesus broke bread in Emmaus for Clopas and his companion, it was the first time in history that Communion was ministered to humanity. At the Last Supper, Jesus had broken bread as part of Passover and told his disciples to remember him by it.

However, the broken bread at Emmaus/Kiriath-jearim was

---

[443] Titus' troops surrounded Jerusalem forty years, to the very day, from Jesus' crucifixion.

the *fulfillment* of Passover; it was Communion in all of its power. Figuratively speaking, the blood was now on the mercy seat and the ark had returned to Kiriath-jearim.

The venerated ark of the covenant contained sacred items: a golden jar holding manna, Aaron's rod (which budded), and the tablets of the covenant. The manna in the ark was a sample of the miraculous food that God provided the Israelites as they wandered in the wilderness (Ex 16:4, 14-16, 33). The manna was also a symbol of a better bread to come in the person of Christ. Jesus himself made this connection:

> "I am the bread of life. Your fathers ate the manna in the wilderness, and they died." (Jn 6:48-49)

The rod of Aaron was an almond branch that had miraculously sprouted and borne blossoms and ripe almonds in a single night (Num 17:1-11). It represented the authority of the priesthood. By his resurrection, Jesus demonstrated that he was a priest superior to the existing priesthood:

> But Jesus, on the other hand, because He continues forever, holds His priesthood permanently.... For the Law appoints men as high priests who are weak, but the word of the oath, which came after the Law, appoints a Son, made perfect forever. (Heb 7:24, 28)

The tablets of the covenant were two stone slabs on which were written the Ten Commandments. In the history of the world, no one had ever completely kept those commandments. Until Jesus did. He was the perfect fulfillment of the law represented by those two inscribed stone tablets.

When Jesus sat with Clopas and his companion in Emmaus, he sat as the fulfillment of everything the ark represented:

- He was the fulfillment of all righteousness, symbolized by the stone tablets.

- He was (and is) the final high priest, as represented by Aaron's rod.

- He was (and is) the bread of life, symbolized by the jar of manna.

Jesus had fulfilled every detail of his commission from God the Father. He had broken the powers of sin, death, and darkness. He had set free those who would believe in him from their "slavery in Egypt."

Clopas and his friend were the first to celebrate the feast with the One who did it all.

Appendix H: Two Earthquakes, Multiple Resurrections, and Debated Text

A few of the resurrection-related verses in the gospels deserve some explanation for how they were viewed and handled in this book. Matthew records two earthquakes, one at the death of Jesus (Mt 27:51) and one at his resurrection (Mt 28:2). He also records a most curious detail in proximity to the first earthquake: namely, the "resurrection of the saints" (Mt 27:52-53). And in the gospel of Mark, the authenticity of the last twelve verses has long been debated. Let's take a closer look at these verses.

Two Earthquakes and Multiple Resurrections

Matthew 27:52-53 mentions a very unusual event. It occurs within the general context of Jesus' trial before Pilate and his crucifixion and burial. Here is what Matthew wrote in these interesting verses (*in italics*), together with the two preceding verses for context:

> 50 And Jesus cried out again with a loud voice, and yielded up His spirit. 51 And behold, the veil of the temple was torn in two from top to bottom; and the earth shook and the rocks were split. 52 *The tombs were opened, and many bodies of the saints who had fallen asleep were raised; 53 and coming out of the tombs after His resurrection they entered the holy city and appeared to many.* (Mt 27:50–53, emphasis added)

Now Matthew informs us of two earthquakes: one at Jesus' crucifixion (cited above), and another at his resurrection:

> And behold, a severe earthquake had occurred, for an angel of the Lord descended from heaven and came and rolled away the stone and sat upon it. (Mt 28:2)

Although the rocks (in verse 51) appear to have been split at the first earthquake, the events described in verses 52-53 are most reasonably connected with the second earthquake and should be therefore considered a parenthetical note of what happened three days after the crucifixion when the second earthquake took place.

It is plausible to associate the opening of these other tombs with Jesus' resurrection for two reasons. The first is that it seems quite unreasonable for the aforementioned saints to have been resurrected at Jesus' death and then to have delayed entering the city until after his resurrection. The second reason is that this event resembles the appearance of the heavenly host that heralded Jesus' birth,[444] by likewise providing heavenly attestation to a mighty work of God.

For these reasons, verses 52 and 53 have been chronologically placed together with the resurrection in the Unified Account (Part Two).

That much is straightforward. Unfortunately, Matthew tells us precious little of the details surrounding this "resurrection of the saints," and the other gospels say nothing about it. For example, we do not know:

1. who these "saints" were

2. whom they appeared to

3. what they may have said or done, beyond "appearing to many"

4. what sort of resurrection this was (bodily or spiritual)

5. what happened to these saints afterward.[445]

---

[444] And suddenly there appeared with the angel a multitude of the heavenly host praising God and saying, "Glory to God in the highest, And on earth peace among men with whom He is pleased." (Lk 2:13-14)

[445] If you wish to read a detailed, thoughtful analysis of this "resurrection of the saints," see *"The Six Miracles of Calvary"* by William R. Nicholson. There are newer versions of this book in which

Therefore, because Matthew provided so little detail, this event was simply omitted from "Dawn" (Part One). To include this event without elaboration would have raised these unanswerable questions, but including it with elaboration would have necessitated speculation about these details, for which there is insufficient basis. Though it would be nice to know more about this curious event, we simply do not.

Nonetheless, for completeness, these verses *are* included in Part Two, The Unified Account, as they are contained within Matthew's gospel.

The Debated Text of Mark's Ending

The last 12 verses of the Gospel of Mark, 16:9-20, are not included in some early manuscripts and are rejected by many contemporary scholars as being non-original material. Even some august scholars such as Dr. Robert Stein, N.T. Wright, and Craig Evans doubt or dismiss the authenticity of these verses. I disagree and have therefore included that passage throughout this book. My reasons for accepting these verses as genuine are the following.

First, there are about 1,650 ancient Greek manuscripts of the Gospel of Mark, and of these, only three end the text at 16:8. Of the three manuscripts that completely omit verses 9-20, two are early: Codex Vaticanus (B) and Codex Sinaiticus (Aleph)—and therefore deserve further commentary.[446]

Codex Vaticanus contains an entire blank column after Mark 16:8. This blank column tells us that the copyist of this manuscript was aware of the missing verses and left room for

---

Nicholson's archaic phrasing has been modernized, but I prefer the original. Copies can be easily found.

William R. Nicholson, *The Six Miracles of Calvary* (Chicago, IL: Moody Publishers, 2000).

[446] James Snapp, YouTube presentation, https://www.youtube.com/watch?v=ogk3PdaoZi8, 2:30-4:00, viewed Feb. 18, 2022.

them to be added. It was a technique used by ancient copyists to convey that they were aware of something missing from the source document(s) that they were transcribing.[447]

Codex Sinaiticus is a very interesting and unique case. The four pages that cover the verses from Mark 14:54b through Luke 1:76a were replacement pages, written by the proof-reader of the manuscript while it was in the production phase. The proof-reader clearly was aware of the existence of verses 9-20, but was opposed to including them, inasmuch as he stretched the spacing of his writing to avoid leaving a blank final column, and added an enlarged and embellished design element before the closing title to the book of Mark. The purpose of the elaborate design element, which is unique in the manuscript for its emphasis, and the stretched writing, was to emphatically communicate that "this chapter ends right here." This extra effort on the part of the proofreader shows that he was cognizant of at least one other version of Mark that did not end at verse 8.[448]

The book of Mark was probably authored in the mid-AD 50s; however, the oldest extant manuscripts are dated to the AD 300s. Yet the earliest evidence we have concerning the contested ending of Mark comes not from the manuscripts but from earlier Christian writers, who referred to the verses after Mark 16:8 either directly or obliquely in their writings.

One such early and well-known writer was the bishop Irenaeus, who wrote a large work titled *Against Heresies* in the period AD 174-189 while he was in Rome.[449] From what remains of this work, it is clear that Irenaeus accepted as authoritative Mark 16:19, which he quotes—thus indicating his acceptance of

---

[447] James Snapp, Jr., *Authentic: The Case for Mark 16:9-20* (Elwood, IN: Self-published, 2021), 6-7.

[448] Snapp, Jr., Authentic, 8-11.

[449] James Snapp, YouTube presentation, https://www.youtube.com/watch?v=ogk3PdaoZi8, 35:40ff, viewed Feb. 18, 2022.

the last twelve verses.[450]

Therefore, both the preponderance of textual evidence and the testimony of early church writers make it clear that the early church widely accepted these verses as authentic.

Lastly, it is inconceivable that Mark intended to end his gospel at verse 8 of chapter 16. At this point, the entire message of the book of Mark is incomplete, just as any book would read if its last chapter was removed.

So if Mark had no intention of ending at verse 8, why do we have two early manuscripts that do? Several explanations have been proposed. One explanation suggests that a scribe by the AD 300s had received a scroll of the gospel with a damaged end, and having only that available, made copies that began a chain of flawed transmission. That is certainly a possibility, and it would also explain why the copyists of the Vaticanus and Sinaiticus codices may have treated the ending of Mark as they did.

Another explanation, favored by those who reject the authenticity of the longer ending of Mark, is that Mark was interrupted after finishing verse 8, and then another writer later appended the final twelve verses. One reason for thinking Mark may have been interrupted is that the verses in question seem more compressed than the rest of the gospel. Indeed, they are. In just the last twelve verses, Mark covers the resurrection, the slowness of the disciples to believe, the appearance to Clopas and his companion, the Great Commission, and the ascension. That's compressed!

However, it's quite plausible that Mark completed the long ending of his gospel under circumstances of which we can only speculate, but which caused the last dozen verses to appear compressed. For example, he may have been hurried if he was forced to leave Rome quickly. Or, he may have been separated from Peter and so added the verses from his own recollection of discussions with Peter, without Peter available to narrate every word. Or, he may have been working from an outline and simply

---

[450] Irenaeus, *Against Heresies*, (Lyons, Gaul: Gallican church, ~AD 174) Book 1, XXX:14.

transcribed the outline for the last twelve verses to hasten publication for reasons unknown.

In any event, the evidence that the longer ending might have come from another hand (or is "non-Marcan," to use the language of the long-ending deniers) is surprisingly weak under scrutiny.

An alleged piece of evidence that has drawn much attention is the fact that the final twelve verses contain fourteen words that are not used anywhere else in the book of Mark. That sounds impressive at first. But the strength of this "evidence" vaporizes when we learn that there are fourteen different passages of twelve consecutive verses in Mark's gospel that contain *at least* fourteen words used only once in his entire book. Four of these passages contain more than *twenty* once-used words![451]

The debate over Mark 16:9-20 has a long history, and my comments above only convey the barest summary of the topic. While I felt it necessary to explain my reasons for including these verses (as the verses have been much maligned in my view), to dig any deeper into the subject is beyond the purpose of this book.

So, for the erudite and curious reader who may desire digging deeper into the weeds of this controversy, I would recommend starting with *The Last Twelve Verses of the Gospel According to S. Mark Vindicated Against Recent Critical Objectors and Established* by John William Burgon.[452] Burgon's publication was rebutted by F. J. A. Hort, and the two had a testy academic exchange over the evidence.

For a more current and readable treatise on Mark 16:9-20, I highly recommend the book cited earlier, namely, *Authentic: The Case for Mark 16:9-20* by James Snapp, Jr., which is 231

---

[451] Snapp, Jr., *Authentic*, 33-34.
[452] The original print edition was published in 1871.
Burgon, John William. *The Last Twelve Verses of the Gospel According to S. Mark Vindicated Against Recent Critical Objectors and Established*. (Grand Rapids, MI: Christian Classics Ethereal Library, 2005).

pages of very detailed analysis of the patristic, versional, lectionary and manuscript evidence in favor of these verses. It is well-written and, in my opinion, the final word on the subject. Any scholar today who rejects Mark 16:9-20 without digesting and responding to Snapp's work has not done their homework and should withhold comment until they do.

Unfortunately I cannot recommend any general biblical commentary on the subject of the ending of the gospel of Mark. Nearly all commentaries mention the controversy related to the last twelve verses, but regardless of which side of the debate they align with, those I've read do not appear to have explored the topic sufficiently.

Endnotes

A Mt 27:50; Mk 15:37; Lk 23:46; Jn 19:30
B Mt 27:51-52, 54; Mk 15:39; Lk 23:47
C Mt 27:51; Mk 15:38
D Mt 27:55-56; Mk 15:40-41; Lk 23:48-49
E Jn 19:31-37
F Mt 27:57-58; Mk 15:42-45; Lk 23:50-52; Jn 19:38
G Mt 27:59; Mk 15:46; Lk 23:54a; Jn 19:38-40
H Mt 27:60; Mk 15:46b; Lk 23:54a; Jn 15:41-42
I Mt 27:61; Mk 15:47; Lk 23:54b-55
J Mt 27:62-66
K Mk 16:1; Lk 23:56a
L Lk 23:56b
M Mt 28:2-4
N Mt 27:52-53
O Mk 16:3-4; Lk 24:1-2
P Mt 28:5; Mk 16:5-6; Lk 24:3-8; Jn 20:2
Q Mt 28:6-7; Mk 16:6-7; Lk 24:6
R Mt 28:8; Mk 16:8; Jn 20:2
S Jn 20:3-17
T Lk 24:9-11
U Mt 28:9-10
V Mt 28:11-15
W Mk 16:9-11; Jn 20:18
X Lk 24:11
Y 1Co 15:5
Z Mk 16:12; Lk 24:13-17
AA Lk 24:18-34
BB Mk 16:13-14; Lk 24:33b-38; Jn 20:19
CC Lk 24:39-48; Jn 20:20
DD Jn 20:21-23

^{EE} Jn 20:21-25

^{FF} Jn 20:26-29

^{GG} Mt 28:16

^{HH} Jn 21:1-25

^{II} Mt 28:16-17; 1Co 15:6

^{JJ} Mt 28:18-20

^{KK} 1Co 15:7

^{LL} Acts 1:4-8; Lk 24:49

^{MM} Mk 16:15-18; Lk 24:50

^{NN} Mk 16:19; Lk 24:50-51; Acts 1:9; Eph 1:20-21

^{OO} Lk 24:52; Acts 1:10-12

^{PP} Lk 24:53; Acts 1:13-14

^{QQ} Jn 20:30-31

Made in the USA
Middletown, DE
19 March 2023

27103133R00219